1971

COLLEGE ALGEBRA

A Blaisdell Book in Pure and Applied Mathematics

CONSULTING EDITOR
SEYMOUR SCHUSTER, *University of Minnesota*

College Algebra

MERLIN M. OHMER
The University of Southwestern Louisiana

CLAYTON V. AUCOIN
Clemson University

BLAISDELL PUBLISHING COMPANY
A Division of Ginn and Company
WALTHAM, MASSACHUSETTS · TORONTO · LONDON

Preface

PRIOR TO THE REVOLUTION in school mathematics, the typical college algebra textbook included all of the topics of high school algebra in addition to many topics not included in the standard high school curriculum. At that time the standard college algebra course was part of the curriculum of most entering college freshmen. This course provided a review of high school algebra and an introduction to additional topics which are desirable and useful in the study of analytic geometry and calculus.

Today, many students enter college with two years or more of high school algebra. These students usually omit the college algebra course and begin their college studies with analytic geometry and calculus. Those topics previously included in the college algebra text, which were not included in the high school algebra courses, are now included in the analytic geometry and calculus course. It would be inconsistent with the philosophy of the more up-to-date programs to include, in a college algebra course, all of the topics of high school algebra and, in addition, those additional topics which would have to be repeated in the analytic geometry and calculus course. Furthermore, in a one-semester college algebra course, it is impossible to cover adequately the two-year high school algebra course, at a higher level of abstraction than the typical high school course, if the additional topics are included. For this reason we have written this text as a high-level review of the standard two-year high school algebra course. We believe that the main purpose of a good college algebra course is to provide the student with an adequate foundation in those topics which are absolutely essential to a systematic study of analytic geometry and calculus; therefore, we have omitted some of the traditional topics of the traditional college algebra text.

College Algebra may be taught, in one semester, according to *any one* of the following outlines:

1. Chapters 1 through 7, or
2. Chapters 1 through 8, or
3. Chapters 1 through 9, or
4. Chapters 1 through 7, Chapters 10 and 11, or
5. Chapters 1 through 8, Chapters 10 and 11, or
6. Chapters 1 through 11.

The material has been taught in most of the above combinations at the University of Southwestern Louisiana and at Clemson University.

The end of the proof of each theorem is indicated by the symbol "◇." Although it is preferable to include the proofs, the instructor who wishes to omit them may do so without disrupting the continuity. As each theorem is motivated by examples preceding and following it, the text flows well without the proofs.

We are indebted to many persons, especially to our colleagues who urged us to write *College Algebra*. In particular, we express our gratitude to Dr. Seymour Schuster of the University of Minnesota for his valuable suggestions, comments, and criticisms. He followed and read the manuscript as it was developed and reread it after it was completed. We are grateful also to Dr. Z. L. Loflin, Chairman of the mathematics department at the University of Southwestern Louisiana, and to Miss Jessie May Hoag, also of the mathematics department, for their encouragement; to Mrs. Louise Fulmer of Clemson University for her valuable comments; and to Mr. M. J. Cortez of Allemand School, to Miss Diana Kay Regan, and Miss Mary Catherine Dugas for typing most of the manuscript and preparing the answers to the exercises.

Finally, we thank our wives and children for their patience, understanding, and encouragement during the preparation of the manuscript.

MERLIN M. OHMER
CLAYTON V. AUCOIN

Lafayette, Louisiana

Contents

CHAPTER 7. *The Complex Number System*

CHAPTER 8. *Exponents, Radicals, and the Binomial Theorem*

CHAPTER 9. *Theory of Polynomial Equations*

CHAPTER 10. *Finite Number Systems*

CHAPTER 11. *Algebraic Structures*

Table of Symbols

U	*the universal set*
$\varnothing$	*the empty, or null, set*
$\tilde{A}, U \smallsetminus A$	*the complement of A*
$A \subset B$	*A is a subset of B*
$A \not\subset B$	*A is not a subset of B*
$a \in A$	*a is an element of A*
$a \notin A$	*a is not an element of A*
$A \approx B$	*A is equivalent to B,*
	A is in one-to-one correspondence with B
$A \not\approx B$	*A is not equivalent to B*
	A is not in one-to-one correspondence with B
$A \cup B$	*A union B, the union of A and B*
$A \cap B$	*A intersection B, the intersection of A and B*
$A \times B$	*A cross B, the Cartesian product of A and B*
$a\ \mathsf{R}\ b$	*a is related to b*
$a\ \not{\mathsf{R}}\ b$	*a is not related to b*
C_0	*the set of counting numbers, $\{0, 1, 2, 3 \ldots\}$*
I^+	*the set of positive integers, $\{1, 2, 3, \ldots\}$*
I^-	*the set of negative integers, $\{^-1, ^-2, ^-3, \ldots\}$*
I	*the set of integers $\{\ldots, ^-3, ^-2, ^-1, 0, 1, 2, 3, \ldots\}$*
R_a	*the set of rational numbers*
R	*the set of real numbers*
C	*the set of complex numbers*
$(F, +, \times)$	*a field with binary operators $+$ and $\times$*
$(R_a, +, \times, <)$	*the rational number system with order relation $<$*
$(R, +, \times, <)$	*the real number system with order relation $<$*
$\sim p$	*not p (negation)*

$p \lor q$	*p or q (disjunction)*
$p \land q$	*p and q (conjunction)*
$p \to q$	*if p, then q (or p only if q) (conditional)*
$p \leftrightarrows q$	*p if and only if q (biconditional)*
$a < b$	*a is less than b*
$a \leq b$	*a is less than or equal to b*
$|a|$	*the absolute value of a*
$b|a$	*b divides a*
gcd	*the greatest common divisor*
lcm	*the least common multiple*
$\sqrt{a}, a^{\frac{1}{2}}$	*the principal (nonnegative) square root of the non-negative real number a*
$\sqrt[m]{a}, a^{\frac{1}{m}}$	*the principal mth root of a*
(a, b)	*the ordered pair whose first member is a and whose second member is b*
$f: A \to B$	*function from A to B*
$p(x)$	*polynomial in x*
i	*an imaginary number such that $i^2 = {}^-1$*
$a + bi$	*a complex number ($a \in R, b \in R$)*
$(G, \odot)$	*a group with binary operator $\odot$*
a'	*the inverse of the element a of a group*
$\begin{pmatrix} 123 \\ 312 \end{pmatrix}$	*a permutation on three symbols*

COLLEGE ALGEBRA

CHAPTER 1

Sets

1.1 Introduction

The purpose of this section is to present a brief introduction to some of the fundamental terminology in the subject of mathematics. In any discussion, we must *agree* on the definitions of the terms used, or else we must leave certain terms *undefined*. You have probably witnessed heated arguments between friends. Usually such an argument ends where it begins; each person leaves still convinced of his own point of view. Actually, the debaters may have been in almost complete argreement. This apparent paradox has a simple explanation – the two persons did not agree beforehand on the definitions of the words used. Each attached his own special meanings to the words. For example, a United States official may have a definition of the word *democracy* far different from that of a USSR official. Your experience tells you that the two officials probably cannot agree on an issue involving democracy. To avoid ambiguity and contradictions in mathematics, we must agree, in advance, on the definitions of all technical words used or else we must state which words are undefined. The reason for not defining certain mathematical words is that it is impossible to define all mathematical words without permitting our definitions to form circular chains. As simple as this fact may seem, many great mathematicians and philosophers of the past did not realize this. If you look up the definition of an unfamiliar word in a standard dictionary, you discover that this unfamiliar word is defined in terms of other words. If you look up these other words, you find that they are defined in terms of other words. Eventually one of the new words is the original word whose definition you were seeking. For example, we might find the following:

> set — group
> group — assemblage
> assemblage — collection
> collection — set

Once we have selected the relatively small number of undefined words in the mathematical system under investigation, we strive to have the definitions obey the following properties:

1. Any definition of a new word must be expressed in terms of the undefined words and/or the previously defined words and common nontechnical English words.
2. Any definition must be consistent with itself and with other definitions.
3. Any definition must be meaningful.
4. Any definition must be expressed in such a manner that it includes all desired cases and excludes all undesired cases.

Just as we begin with certain undefined words, we also begin with certain statements which we assume to be true. These assumed statements are called *postulates*. Other names for the assumed statements are *axioms* and *assumptions*. Among other things, the postulates describe the undefined words. For example, the words *point, line*, and *plane* are left undefined in Euclidean geometry. However, they are described in the postulates. Two of these postulates are: (1) two different points determine exactly one line; (2) three noncollinear points determine a unique plane.

Just as we define the new words in terms of the undefined words and/or the previously defined words, we prove new statements, called *theorems*, from the postulates, definitions, and previously proved theorems. The reasoning process which we employ in proving theorems is controlled by the laws of logic or rules of inference. The laws of logic control the combination of given sentences (called the *hypotheses*) into one or more new sentences (called the *conclusion*).

Since our use of the word *sentence* is different from the English usage, we begin with its definition.

DEFINITION 1. A *sentence* is any declarative statement which is either true or false, but not both true and false.

Thus we see that a sentence must be meaningful and unambiguous. The following are examples of sentences.

Example 1.   My mother has blue eyes.

Example 2.   All dogs are quadrupeds.

Example 3.   Some dogs are quadrupeds.

Example 4.   No dogs are quadrupeds.

Example 5.   Benjamin Franklin wore glasses.

Example 6. $14 + 2 = 16$.

Example 7. $6 + 3 = 3 + 6$.

Example 8.   5 is equal to 6.

Example 9.   All ninth grade algebra students study mathematics and some ninth grade students study English.

Example 10.   If John comes home, then his wife will cook dinner.

Although we could refuse to admit that Examples 1, 5, and 10 are sentences on the grounds that one cannot determine, for example, whether the sentence in Example 10 is true until he knows who *John* is, we prefer to agree that any name appearing in a sentence specifies a particular person, object, and so on. In everyday conversation when one of your acquaintances tells you that Jack Jones is ill, you know that he is referring to a particular Jack Jones, in spite of the fact that, in reality, there are numerous persons named *Jack Jones*. Actually, although one would ordinarily say that the sentence of Example 6 is true, it is similar to Examples 1, 5, and 10. When we write "$14 + 2 = 16$," we mean "fourteen plus two is equal to sixteen." The symbols "14," "2," and "16" are similar to the names *John, Ben*, et cetera. They symbolize or represent the numbers just as the name *John* symbolizes or represents the person. You probably have learned that the symbol "14" may represent some number other than fourteen.* However, when we write "$14 + 2 = 16$," you know that we are referring to particular numbers. Thus we agree to visualize a sentence as stated by a specific person at a specific time and place. In this way any possible ambiguities are clarified by the context.

The similar statement "$x + 2 = 16$" is *not* a sentence because the symbol x does not specify a particular number. Until we know that the symbol x specifies a particular number, we cannot determine whether "$x + 2 = 16$" is true or not. For example, if $x = 14$, we can say that

---

* For example, in base 5 the symbol "14" represents the number *nine*.

"$x + 2 = 16$" is true; whereas, if $x = 23$, we can say that "$x + 2 = 16$" is false. A nonspecific symbol (such as x, y, z, $\triangle$, $\square$, et cetera) for a number or person or object is called a *variable*. Since replacement of the variable x by a symbol for a specific number converts the statement "$x + 2 = 16$" into a sentence, we say that the statement "$x + 2 = 16$" is an *open sentence*. In a similar manner the open sentence "x wears glasses" can be converted to a sentence by the replacement of the variable x by the name of a particular or specific person. Later we give a more formal definition of *variable*. In the meantime, the intuitive concept of variable is sufficient.

DEFINITION 2. A statement which contains a variable is called an *open sentence* if and only if it is not a sentence but becomes a sentence upon replacement of the variable by a specific number, person, or object.

Notice that an open sentence may contain more than one variable. Throughout this chapter, the word *number* means *counting number*; that is, 0, 1, 2, 3, and so on.* The following are examples of open sentences.

Example 11. $x + 2 = 5 \times 7$

Example 12. $x + 7 = 7 + 2x$

Example 13. $4x = 4 + x$

Example 14. $x^2 + 3x + 2 = 0$

Example 15. $a + 2 = 2x$

Example 16. $6 + 3x = a + by$

Example 17. $ax^2 + bx + c = 0$

Some examples of nonsentences which are not open sentences are the following:

Example 18.   Study mathematics while you are young.

Example 19.   Why are you wearing sunglasses?

Example 20.   The tallest man in the class.

The replacement method is not the only method of converting an open sentence to a sentence. For example, we could assert that there is a num-

---

* Many texts consider 1, 2, 3, . . . as counting numbers and 0, 1, 2, 3, . . . as whole numbers. See page 42 for further discussion of counting numbers.

ber x such that $x + 2 = 7$. The assertion, "there is a number x such that $x + 2 = 7$," is a sentence; in fact, it is a true sentence. Similarly, the assertion, "for all numbers x, $x + 2 = 7$," is a sentence; but it is a false sentence. The open sentence $x + 3 = 3 + x$ becomes a sentence if we prefix the phrase "for all x." Thus "for all numbers x, $x + 3 = 3 + x$" is a sentence, and, in fact, is a true sentence. Note that "there is a number x such that $x + 3 = 3 + x$" is also a true sentence. Although "$x + 3 \neq x$" is not a sentence, the statement "for any number x, $x + 3 \neq x$" is a true sentence. You may notice that the latter sentence has the same meaning as the sentence, "there is no number x such that $x + 3 = x$."

Observe that we have converted an open sentence by prefixing the phrase "for all numbers x" or the phrase "there exists a number x such that." As both of these phrases convey the idea of quantity, the words *all* and *there exist* are called *quantifiers*. An alternate expression for the quantifier *there exists* is *some*. The third quantifier is *no* or *none*. The sentences "*all* dogs are quadrupeds," "*some* dogs are quadrupeds," and "*no* dogs are quadrupeds" illustrate the use of the quantifiers *all, some,* and *no*. Recall that the word *number* in this chapter means *counting number*. Thus the sentence "for some number x, $x + 3 = 1$" is false. If we included the negative numbers, the sentence, "for some number x, $x + 3 = 1$," would be true. Thus we realize that a quantifier refers to a specific collection of numbers, persons, or objects. The sentence, "the base angles of an isosceles triangle are equal," means "for all isosceles triangles t, the base angles of t are equal." Hence the quantifier here is *all* and refers to the collection of isosceles triangles. Whenever the quantifier is omitted by the writer and supplied by the reader, we say that the quantifier is *implied* rather than *expressed*. Thus, in the foregoing, the quantifier *all* is implied. If we supply a quantifier to an open sentence, we convert that open sentence to a sentence.

The quantifier *all* is called the *universal quantifier*, and the quantifier *some* (there exists) is called the *existential quantifier*. As the quantifier *no* (none) may be expressed in terms of the universal or existential quantifier, it is not given a special name. For example, the sentence "no odd number is divisible by two" may be expressed as either "there does not exist an odd number which is divisible by two" or "for all x, if x is an odd number, then x is not divisible by two."

In summary we list the two methods of converting an open sentence to a sentence.

1. Replace the variable by the name of a specific number, person, or object.
2. Quantify the variable.

A comment on the words *if and only if* used in the definitions may be in order. You are familiar with the definition of equilateral triangle; namely, triangle *ABC* is said to be *equilateral* if and only if the sides are of equal length. This definition is really a statement of *two* facts. First, any triangle whose sides are of equal length is an equilateral triangle. Second, the sides of any equilateral triangle are of equal length.

Exercise 1.1

I. Classify the following as *sentence, open sentence*, or *neither.*

    (1) Mary went to the movie.
    (2) All the students in this class did their homework.
    (3) $3 + 4 = 11 - 4$.
    (4) No men live forever.
    (5) $x - y = a + b$.
    (6) All men are mortal.
    (7) Adam dates a freshman.
    (8) $\frac{2}{3} + \frac{3}{5}$.
    (9) If x is less than 7.
    (10) There is a number y greater than 11 and less than 17.
    (11) If the sum of two numbers is zero, then both of the numbers are zero or neither is zero.
    (12) $100 - 4 + 13$.
    (13) 11 is greater than y.
    (14) $5 + 4 = 9$ and $3 + 4 = 8$.
    (15) $x - 2 = 7$.
    (16) $x + 5$ is larger than 8.
    (17) $2x - 3 = 2 + 3$.
    (18) $2x - 1 = 5$.
    (19) $\frac{x}{5} = 10$.
    (20) $\frac{x}{5} + \frac{3}{5}$ is larger than.
    (21) $\frac{x}{5} + \frac{3}{5}$.
    (22) $\frac{x}{5} + \frac{3}{5}$ is larger than $\frac{7}{5}$.
    (23) $a + 0 = a$.
    (24) $b \times 1 = b$.
    (25) How are you?
    (26) $24 + 4 = 14 + 10$.
    (27) Go away.
    (28) $\frac{0}{6} = 0$.

(29) $0 + a = 0$.

(30) $\frac{24}{3} = 9$.

II. Identify the quantifier or quantifiers in each of the following sentences, as *all, some (there exists)*, or *no (none)*.

(1) All birds fly.

(2) Some birds fly.

(3) Some students will become teachers.

(4) No reptiles can fly.

(5) Some numbers are odd.

(6) There is a smallest number.

(7) For every number, there is a larger one.

(8) There is no largest number.

(9) For all numbers x, $x + 5 = 8$.

(10) There exists a number x such that $x + 5 = 8$.

(11) Some birds fly and no monkeys fly.

(12) For all numbers x, if x is positive, then $x + 2$ is positive.

(13) For all numbers x, either x is even or x is odd.

(14) Any even number is divisible by two.

(15) There is a man x such that x has blue eyes.

III. State whether a quantifier is expressed or implied in each of the following.

(1) $4 + 3 = 9$.

(2) For all x, $x + 5 = 5 + x$.

(3) Men are mortal.

(4) There is no x such that $x = x + 1$.

(5) $5 + 4 = 4 + 5$.

(6) A rectangle has four sides.

(7) Socrates is mortal.

(8) A rose is a flower.

(9) 5 is a counting number.

(10) An equilateral triangle has equal angles.

IV. Identify the quantifier (expressed or implied) in each of the statements in Exercise III.

V. Classify each statement in Exercise III as a *sentence* or an *open sentence*.

VI. Quantify each of the following open sentences by use of each of the three quantifiers (*all, some, none*). Determine whether each of the resulting sentences is *true* or *false*.

(1) $x + x = 2x$
(2) $x + 3 = 7$
(3) $t + 5 = 5$
(4) $6 + y = 6$
(5) $7 + y = y$
(6) $t + 5 = t$
(7) $t + 6 = 6$
(8) $2t + 3t = 5t$
(9) $a + 7 = 3$
(10) $5 + b = 2$

1.2 Introduction to Sets

The idea of *set* is one of the most widely used concepts in mathematics. There are several reasons for making a systematic study of sets. First, the system of real numbers can be developed systematically and logically from the theory of sets. Second, the terminology of modern mathematics is laden with the language of sets. For these reasons the language of sets is being introduced into the elementary curriculum, in many instances in the first-grade texts. In this text the words *set, class, collection*, and *aggregate* will be considered synonymous. As you learned in Section 1.1, it is not possible to define every word used. However, sufficient description is given (usually in the postulates) of each mathematical concept or word used. In this text, the word *set* is taken as undefined, and the concept of set is described by the following examples.

Example 1.   All students in this room.

Example 2.   All chairs in this room.

Example 3.   All boys in this room.

Example 4.   All girls in this room.

Example 5.   All mathematics books in this room.

Example 6.   All books in this room.

Example 7.   All Latin books in this room.

Example 8.   The counting numbers from 1 to 10 (1, 2, 3, 4, 5, 6, 7, 8, 9, 10).

Example 9.   All teachers in this room.

Example 10.   The counting numbers greater than 5 and less than 8.

Example 11.   The counting numbers 1, 2, 3, . . . , 100.

Example 12.   The even counting numbers 0, 2, 4, ...

Example 13.   The golf clubs in Arnold Palmer's golf bag.

Example 14.   The set of dishes in your mother's cabinet.

The three dots, . . . , in Examples 11 and 12 indicate that we have not *written* all of the elements of the set and that the indicated pattern is followed throughout. This is the approximate meaning of *et cetera* (*etc.*) in English. Throughout this text, the set of counting numbers (the numbers 0, 1, 2, 3, . . .) will be denoted by C_0.

We see that a *set* consists of a collection of objects. These objects (or members) are called *elements* of the set. One necessary property of a *well-defined* set is that it be determinable whether a given element is a member of the set. It is easy to see that all of the examples above have this property. The set of interesting numbers and the set of pretty girls are not well-defined sets because there is no universal agreement on the meanings of interesting numbers and pretty girls. Hereafter in this text the word *set* shall mean *well-defined set*.

We say that the elements of a set *belong* to the set. In Example 8, 1 belongs to the set, 2 belongs to the set, . . . , and 10 belongs to the set. Every boy in this room belongs to the set described in Example 3.

We usually designate a set by a capital letter such as $A, B, C, . . .$ and the elements of a set by lower-case letters $a, b, c, ...$ The symbol $\in$ means *is an element of* or *is a member of*. For example, $a \in A$ means *a is an element of A*. We may describe a set by listing each of its elements exactly once in braces. Thus the sets A and B of Examples 8 and 12, respectively, may be described as follows:

$$A = \{1, 2, 3, . . . , 10\}$$
$$B = \{0, 2, 4, . . .\}.$$

The number 0 is an element of B; in the notation we write $0 \in B$. However, 0 is not an element of A; we write $0 \notin A$. Similarly, $3 \notin B$ but $3 \in A$.

Exercise 1.2

I. Use English sentences and give five examples of sets.

II. Use set notation and give five examples of sets.

III. Let $A = \{0, 2, 4, . . .\}$, $B = \{1, 3, 5, . . .\}$, $C = \{3, 6, 9, . . .\}$, $D = \{1, 5, 9, 13\}$, $E = \{8, 24\}$, $F = \{3, 9, 15\}$, $G = \{0, 5, 10, 15, 20\}$.

To what sets does each of the following belong? Write your answer in the form $a \in K$ or $a \notin K$; for example, $4 \in A$, $4 \notin B$, et cetera.

(1) 0
(2) 3
(3) 5
(4) 24
(5) 9
(6) 15
(7) $\frac{5}{2}$
(8) 999
(9) 24600000
(10) 1000.1

1.3 Subsets

Every element of $\{1, 3, 5\}$ is an element of $\{1, 2, 3, 4, 5\}$, but *not* every element of $\{1, 2, 3, 4, 5\}$ is an element of $\{1, 5, 3\}$. Every element of $\{1, 3, 5\}$ is an element of $\{5, 1, 3\}$, and every element of $\{5, 1, 3\}$ is an element of $\{1, 3, 5\}$.

DEFINITION 3.   The set A is said to be a *subset* of the set B (written $A \subset B$) if and only if each element of A is an element of B. The set A is said to be a *proper subset* of the set B if and only if $A \subset B$ and $B \not\subset A$.

Thus if $A = \{2, 3, 7\}$ and $B = \{2, 3, 5, 6, 7, 8, 9\}$, then A is a subset of B. We note that any set A is a subset of A. The notation $\subset$ means *is a subset of*, or *is contained in*, and the notation $\not\subset$ means *is not a subset of* or *is not contained in*. Thus in the example above $A \subset B$ but $B \not\subset A$. Hence A is a proper subset of B. However, $X \subset X$ for any set X. In particular, $A \subset A$ and $B \subset B$, but A is *not* a proper subset of A. If $S = \{1, 3, 5, 7\}$ and $T = \{1, 3, 5, 9\}$, then $S \not\subset T$ and $T \not\subset S$. Even though *some* elements of S belong to T, there is *one* element of S which does not belong to T. Which one? In order that $A \not\subset B$ there must be at least one element $a \in A$ such that $a \notin B$. Why does this follow from the definition of $A \subset B$?

It follows immediately that $A = B$ if and only if $A \subset B$ and $B \subset A$. From this we see that $A = A$ for any set A. If $C = \{1, 3, 5, 7\}$ and $D = \{1, 5, 7, 3\}$, then $C \subset D$ and $D \subset C$ and hence $C = D$. The order in which the elements are listed is unimportant.

You may have wondered if there is another way to describe a set without specifically *listing* each of its elements. If we wish to describe the set of all boys in this room, we may write $B = \{b : b$ is a boy in this room$\}$, which is read *B is the set of all b such that b is a boy in this room*. The colon (:) is read *such that*. If $E = \{x : x$ is an even counting number$\}$, then $E = \{0, 2, 4, 6, \ldots\}$. This same set E could have been written $E = \{y : y$ is an even counting number$\}$. The set $A = \{10, 12,$

14} is a subset of *E*. We could have written $A = \{x: x$ is an even count-ing number and x is greater than 8 and x is less than 16}. However, in this case it is simpler to write $A = \{10, 12, 14\}$. In some cases, the former notation is simpler.

Exercise 1.3

   I. Write three subsets of $\{10, 12, 14\}$.

  II. Write four subsets of {red, white, blue}.

 III. (1) Write five subsets of {Tom, Dick, Harry}.
      (2) Write 15 subsets of $\{1, 2, 3, 4\}$.

 IV. Write each of the following sets notationally in two ways.

      (1) The set of all counting numbers.
      (2) The set of all even counting numbers.
      (3) The set of all odd counting numbers.
      (4) The set of all multiples of 5 which are counting numbers.
      (5) The set of all counting numbers greater than 9 and less than 100.
      (6) The set of all counting numbers greater than 5.
      (7) The set of all counting numbers less than 10.
      (8) The set of all numbers equal to 15.
      (9) The set of all counting numbers between 15 and 16.

  V. Describe in words each of the following sets.

      (1) $\{x: x$ is a counting number and x is greater than 100}.
      (2) $\{101, 102, 103, \ldots\}$.
      (3) $\{x: 5x = 10\}$.
      (4) {Sunday, Monday, Tuesday, Wednesday, Thursday, Friday, Saturday}.
      (5) $\{11, 13, 15, \ldots\}$.

 VI. Let $A = \{1, 11, 21, \ldots\}$, $B = \{21, 22, 23, \ldots\}$, $C = \{0, 2, 4, \ldots\}$, $D = \{101, 111, 121, \ldots\}$, $E = \{1001, 1002\}$, and $F = \{1001, 1003, 1005\}$. Write $X \subset Y$ or $X \not\subset Y$ for $X = A, B, C, D, E, F$ and $Y = A, B, C, D, E, F$. (*Hint*. State whether $A \subset A$, $A \subset B$, $A \subset C$, $\ldots$, $A \subset F$, et cetera. There are 36 possible cases.)

1.4   Finite Sets, Infinite Sets, and One-to-One Correspondence

   You have probably noticed that some of the sets in Exercise 1.3 con-tained limited numbers of elements, whereas other sets contained un-limited numbers of elements. In order to distinguish between these two types of sets, we introduce the concepts of *finite* set and *infinite* set. Intuitively, which sets of Exercise 1.3 do you think are finite? Before we state actual definitions of *finite* set and *infinite* set, we first consider the problem of *pairing* or *matching* sets.

DEFINITION 4. The set A is said to be *in one-to-one correspondence with* (or *equivalent to*) the set B if and only if there is a correspondence between A and B such that each element of A corresponds to exactly one element of B, and each element of B corresponds to exactly one element of A.

We employ the notation $\approx$ to indicate that two sets are equivalent. Thus we write $A \approx B$ and say A *is equivalent to* B (or A *is in one-to-one correspondence with* B); for example, $\{1, 2, 3\} \approx \{a, b, c\}$ and $\{4, 1, 7, 9\} \approx \{2, 4, 9, 10\}$. Observe that two equivalent sets are not necessarily equal. The double-headed arrow $\leftrightarrow$ is employed in the actual paring of the elements, as illustrated in the following examples.

Example 1. $\{1, 2, 3\}$ and $\{11, 12, 13\}$ are in a one-to-one correspondence. To show the pairing process, we sometimes exemplify this by the following scheme.

$$
\begin{array}{lll}
1 \leftrightarrow 11 & 1 \leftrightarrow 13 & 1 \leftrightarrow 12 \\
2 \leftrightarrow 12 & 2 \leftrightarrow 12 & 2 \leftrightarrow 11 \\
3 \leftrightarrow 13 & 3 \leftrightarrow 11 & 3 \leftrightarrow 13
\end{array}
$$

Are there any other one-to-one correspondences between the given sets?

Example 2. $\{11, 12, 13\}$ is in one-to-one correspondence with $\{x, y, z\}$.

Example 3. The set of counting numbers $\{0, 1, 2, 3, \ldots\}$ is in one-to-one correspondence with the set of even counting numbers $\{0, 2, 4, 6, \ldots\}$. We can pair them as follows:

$$
\begin{array}{ccccccc}
0 & 1 & 2 & 3 & \cdots & n & \cdots \\
\updownarrow & \updownarrow & \updownarrow & \updownarrow & \cdots & \updownarrow & \cdots \\
0 & 2 & 4 & 6 & \cdots & 2n & \cdots
\end{array}
$$

What even counting number should be paired with the counting number 5, 25, 109?

Example 4. The sets $\{1, 2, 3, 4, 5, \ldots\}$ and $\{30, 31, 32, 33, 34, \ldots\}$ are in one-to-one correspondence.

$$
\begin{array}{cccccccc}
1 & 2 & 3 & 4 & 5 & \cdots & n & \cdots \\
\updownarrow & \updownarrow & \updownarrow & \updownarrow & \updownarrow & \cdots & \updownarrow & \cdots \\
30 & 31 & 32 & 33 & 34 & \cdots & n+29 & \cdots
\end{array}
$$

Example 5. The sets $A = \{0, 1, 2\}$ and $B = \{0, 2\}$ are not in one-to-one correspondence. To convince yourself of this fact, try to pair their elements. Is any proper subset of A in one-to-one correspondence with A?

DEFINITION 5. Any set A is said to be *infinite* if and only if there is a proper subset of A which can be put into one-to-one correspondence with A.

From Example 3 we see that the set of counting numbers is an infinite set, since the set of even counting numbers and the set of counting numbers are in one-to-one correspondence. Set A from Example 5 is *not* infinite since no proper subset of A can be put into one-to-one correspondence with A.

DEFINITION 6. Any set A is said to be a *finite* set if and only if it is not infinite.

Thus the sets in Examples 1, 2, and 5 are finite sets. It can be proved that the set $\{1, 2, 3, \ldots, k\}$ is finite.

More intuitive but less precise definitions of *finite* set and *infinite* set are the following. A *finite* set is one which can be counted such that the counting eventually terminates, whereas an *infinite* set is one in which the counting procedure never terminates.

This definition uses terms which have meaning in ordinary conversation but have not been defined mathematically. Notice that Definition 5 does not have this disadvantage. Precise definitions are pleasing and beautiful to mathematicians and eliminate the possibility for misconceptions. Definition 5 characterizes the essential properties of an infinite set, whereas the intuitive notion gives one only a feeling of the concept of infinite set. While these intuitive definitions could be made rigorous, we prefer not to develop the background necessary for this treatment.

Exercise 1.4

1. Put each of the following pairs of sets in one-to-one correspondence.

(1) $\{0, 5, 10, 15\}$ and $\{a, b, x, y\}$.
(2) $\{a, \#, t, \%\}$ and $\{100, 200, 400, 800\}$.

(3) {w} and {11}.
(4) {10, 20, 30, 40, . . .} and {1, 2, 3, 4, . . .}.
(5) {0, 4, 8, 12, 16, . . .} and {x: x is a counting number}.

II. Determine which of the following sets can be placed in one-to-one correspondence with each other.

(1) $A = \{x, y, z\}$.
(2) $B = \{e, \#, \Sigma, \%)$.
(3) $C = \{1, 2, 3, 4, . . .\}$.
(4) $D = \{10, 20, 30, 40, . . .\}$.
(5) $E = \{1, 2, 3, 8\}$.
(6) $F = \{w, x, y, z\}$
(7) $G = \{1, 2, 4, 8\}$.
(8) $H = \{1, 2, 4, 8, . . .\}$.
(9) $I = \{2, 4, . . . , 20\}$.
(10) $J = \{1, 2, 3\}$.
(11) $K = \{x: x$ is a counting number and x is odd and x is less than 20$\}$.
(12) $L = \{x: x$ is a counting number and $x \neq 0\}$.

III. (1) State, without proof, which of the sets of Exercise II are infinite.
(2) State, without proof, which of the sets of Exercise II are finite.

IV. (1) Prove that the set {1, 2, 3, 4, . . .} is infinite. (*Hint.* Use Example 4 and Definition 5.)
(2) Prove that the set {1, 2} is finite. (*Hint.* Use Definition 6.)

V. Prove that {x: x is an even counting number} is infinite.

1.5 Universal Set, Complementation, and the Empty Set

In any discussion of sets we specify an all-inclusive set, called the *universal set* or *universe*, which contains all elements we wish to discuss. Frequently the universal set is understood from the context. However, if there is any danger of confusion, we should specify explicitly what the universal set is.

DEFINITION 7. The set U consisting of all elements under discussion is called the *universal set*, or *universe*.

The universal set U may change from one discussion to another. For example, in one discussion the universal set may be the set of counting numbers, whereas in another discussion the universal set may be the set of fractions. In fact, in some discussions the universal set may be the set of all human beings. In the study of first grade arithmetic, what is a universal set? In any discussion of a set A, it is understood that $A \subset U$. In cases of doubt, the universal set should be specified.

DEFINITION 8.   The *complement* of a set A (written $\tilde{A}$) is the set of all elements of U which do not belong to A.

We see from Definition 8 that $\tilde{A} = \{x: x \in U \text{ and } x \notin A\}$. An alternate notation for $\tilde{A}$ is $U \smallsetminus A$; that is, $U \smallsetminus A = \tilde{A}$.

Example 1.   If $U = \{0, 1, 2, 3, \ldots, 10\}$ and $A = \{1, 3, 5, 7, 9\}$, then $\tilde{A} = \{0, 2, 4, 6, 8, 10\}$.

Example 2.   If $U = \{0, 1, 2, 3, \ldots\}$ and $A = \{1, 3, 5, 7, 9, \ldots\}$, then $\tilde{A} = \{0, 2, 4, 6, \ldots\}$.

Example 3.   If $U = \{0, 1, 2, 3, \ldots\}$ and $A = \{1, 3, 5, 7, 9\}$, then $\tilde{A} = \{0, 2, 4, 6, 8, 10, 11, 12, 13, \ldots\}$.

Example 4.   If $U = \{x: x \text{ is a student enrolled in this school}\}$ and $A = \{x: x \text{ is a male student enrolled in this school}\}$, then $\tilde{A} = \{x: x \text{ is a female student enrolled in this school}\}$.

Since the universal set U is a subset of itself, Definition 8 tells us that $\tilde{U}$ is the set of all elements of U which do not belong to U. As U contains all of the elements under discussion, $\tilde{U}$ contains no elements. If we wish to consider $\tilde{U}$ to be a set, then we must introduce a new concept.

DEFINITION 9.   The *empty* set, or *null* set, is the set which contains no elements.

In this text the empty set will be denoted by the symbol $\varnothing$, or the empty braces, $\{\ \}$. From the definition of subset, it can be proved that the empty set is a subset of every set and, in particular, of the universal set. As we shall see in the next section, the concept of the empty set is a useful and convenient one.

From the above discussion, it follows that $\tilde{U} = \varnothing$ and $\tilde{\varnothing} = U$.

Exercise 1.5

I. Let $A = \{1, 2, 3, 4\}$. Tell whether each of the following is an element of A or a subset of A.

(1) $\{2, 3\}$ (3) 4

(2) $\{4\}$ (4) $\{1\}$

(5) 1
(6) {1, 2, 3, 4}
(7) {3}
(8) { }
(9) ∅
(10) {2}

(11) {3, 4}
(12) 3
(13) {2, 4}
(14) 2
(15) {2, 3, 4}
(16) {1, 2, 3}

II. The players of the New York Yankee baseball team constitute a set *Y*. Name three sets which contain *Y* as a subset and which may be considered universal sets.

III. Let $U = \{0, 2, 4, 6, 8, 10\}$. State the complement of each of the following sets.

(1) {0, 4, 8}
(2) {0, 6, 10}
(3) {2, 10}
(4) {2}
(5) {0}

(6) {4, 8}
(7) {0, 2, 4, 6, 8, 10}
(8) {0, 2, 8, 10}
(9) {0, 4, 6, 8, 10}
(10) { }

IV. Let $U = \{0, 1, 2, 3, \ldots\}$. State the complement of each of the following sets.

(1) {0, 2, 4, . . .}
(2) {1, 3, 5, . . .}
(3) {0, 1, 2, 3, . . .}

(4) {100, 101, 102, . . .}
(5) {*x*:*x* is even}
(6) {*x*:*x* is odd}

V. Given $U = \{x: x \text{ is a human being}\}$, state the complement of each of the following sets:

(1) $A = \{x: x \text{ is a female}\}$.
(2) $B = \{x: x \text{ is a human being and } x\text{'s age is less than or equal to 5}\}$.
(3) *C* is the set of all married persons.
(4) *D* is the set of all single persons.
(5) *E* is the set of all male human beings.

1.6 Union and Intersection

In this section we define *union* and *intersection*. To define *union*, we must agree on the meaning of the word *or*. In mathematics the word *or* means *and/or* used in legal documents. For example, the sentence, "Beverly will buy a movie projector *or* Beverly will buy a movie camera," is true if Beverly buys *either* a movie projector *or* a movie camera or if she buys *both*.

DEFINITION 10. The *union* of the two sets *A* and *B* (denoted by $A \cup B$) is the set consisting of all elements which belong to *A* or to *B*. That is,

$A \cup B = \{x: x \in A \text{ or } x \in B\}$.

Thus $A \cup B$ is the set consisting of all elements which belong to A or to B or to *both A and B*. The symbol $\cup$, sometimes called *cup*, is used to indicate the union of two sets, and $A \cup B$ is read *A union B*.

Example 1. If $A = \{0, 1, 2, 3, 4\}$ and $B = \{2, 4, 6, 8\}$, then $A \cup B = \{0, 1, 2, 3, 4, 6, 8\}$. (*Note.* We do *not* write $A \cup B = \{0, 1, 2, 3, 4, 2, 4, 6, 8\}$.)

Example 2. If $A = \{0, 1\}$ and $B = \{0, 1, 2\}$, then $A \cup B = \{0, 1, 2\}$. (*Note.* In this case, $A \subset B$, and hence $A \cup B = B$.)

Example 3. If $A = \{2, 4, 6, 8\}$ and $B = \{3, 5, 7\}$, then $A \cup B = \{2, 3, 4, 5, 6, 7, 8\}$.

Example 4. If $A = \{\text{Tony, Jackie, Lorraine}\}$, $B = \{\text{Barbara, Sadie, Ed, Jackie, Lloyd}\}$, then $A \cup B = \{\text{Tony, Jackie, Lorraine, Barbara, Sadie, Ed, Lloyd}\}$.

DEFINITION 11. The *intersection* of the two sets A and B (denoted by $A \cap B$) is the set of all elements which belong to both A and B.

That is, $A \cap B = \{x: x \in A \text{ and } x \in B\}$.

The symbol $\cap$, sometimes called *cap*, is used to indicate the intersection of two sets, and $A \cap B$ is read *A intersection B*.

Example 5. If $A = \{0, 1, 2, 3, 4\}$ and $B = \{2, 4, 6, 8\}$, then $A \cap B = \{2, 4\}$.

Example 6. If $A = \{0, 1\}$ and $B = \{0, 1, 2\}$, then $A \cap B = \{0, 1\}$. Note that in this case $A \subset B$ and hence $A \cap B = A$.

Example 7. If $A = \{2, 4, 6, 8\}$ and $B = \{3, 5, 7\}$, then $A \cap B = \{ \} = \emptyset$.

Example 8. If A is any set and $B = \emptyset$, then $A \cap B = A \cap \emptyset = \emptyset$.

Example 9. If $A = \{\text{Angie, Ann, Alice, Anita}\}$ and $B = \{\text{Bizer, Bea, Butch}\}$, then $A \cap B = \emptyset$.

Examples 7 and 9 provide further illustrations of the necessity and usefulness of the concept of the empty set. In order that the intersection of any two sets always be a set, as required by Definition 11, it is necessary to have the concept of the empty set.

DEFINITION 12. Two sets A and B are said to be *disjoint* (from each other) if and only if $A \cap B = \varnothing$.

Thus A and B in Example 7 and A and B in Example 9 are disjoint sets. Since $A \cap \varnothing = \varnothing$, for any set A, we see that every set is disjoint from the null set.

As each of the operators $\cup$ and $\cap$ operates on *two* sets to form a third set, the operators $\cup$ and $\cap$ are called *binary* operators.

Exercise 1.6

I. Compute $A \cup B$ in each of the following.

(1) $A = \{2, 4, 6, 8\}$, $B = \{2, 9\}$.
(2) $A = \{2, 4, 6, 8\}$, $B = \{2, 8\}$.
(3) $A = \{1, 3, 5\}$, $B = \{0, 2, 4\}$.
(4) $A = \{1, 3, 5, \ldots\}$, $B = \{0, 2, 4, \ldots\}$.
(5) $A = \{0, 1, 2, \ldots\}$, $B = \{1, 3, 5, \ldots\}$.
(6) $A = \{0\}$, $B = \{0, 1, 2, 3, \ldots\}$.
(7) $A = \{\ \}$, $B = \{0, 1, 2, 3, \ldots\}$.
(8) $A = \{0\}$, $B = \{1, 2, 3, \ldots\}$.
(9) $A = \{$Jessie, May, Bea$\}$, $B = \{$Janice, Craig, Lisa, Inez$\}$.
(10) $A = \{$Doris, Fannie, Bea, Jo$\}$, $B = \{$Bea, Hazel, Erenze, Elvina, Louise, Toby$\}$.

II. Compute $A \cap B$ in each part of Exercise I.

III. Compute $A \cup B$ and $A \cap B$ in each of the following.

(1) $A = \{0, 1\}$, $B = \{0, 1, 2\}$.
(2) $A = \{1, 2, 3\}$, $B = \{3, 4, 5\}$.
(3) $A = \{1, 2, 3\}$, $B = \{4, 5, 6\}$.
(4) $A = \{0, 1\}$, $B = \{0\}$.
(5) $A = \{1, 3, 5, \ldots\}$, $B = \{2, 4, 6, \ldots\}$.
(6) $A = \varnothing$, $B = \{1, 2, 3, 4, 5\}$.
(7) $A = \{\ \}$, $B = \{1, 2, 3, 4, 5\}$.
(8) $A = \{x: x$ is a counting number greater than 100$\}$,
    $B = \{x: x$ is a counting number less than or equal to 100$\}$.
(9) $A = \{x: x$ is a counting number greater than or equal to 100$\}$,
    $B = \{x: x$ is a counting number less than or equal to 100$\}$.
(10) $A = \{x: x$ is a counting number greater than 100$\}$,
    $B = \{x: x$ is a counting number less than 100$\}$.

(11) $A = \{x: x$ is a counting number greater than or equal to 100$\}$,
   $B = \{x: x$ is a counting number less than 100$\}$.

(12) A is the set of single persons, B is the set of married persons.

IV. What is the relationship of $A \cup B$ to $B \cup A$?

V. What is the relationship of $A \cap B$ to $B \cap A$?

VI. What is the relationship of $A \cap B$ to $A \cup B$?

1.7 Venn Diagrams

In the eighteenth century the Swiss mathematician Euler introduced the technique of the use of circles to indicate sets and relationships among sets. In the nineteenth century the British logician Venn refined and extended this idea to include other geometric figures. For this reason, these diagrams or figures are called Euler diagrams or Venn diagrams. In this text, we refer to them as *Venn diagrams*.

The elements of a set may be considered as points interior to a circle, square, rectangle, or other closed plane figure. To indicate that $A \subset B$, we may draw a circle interior to another circle or to a square or rectangle as indicated in Figure 1.1

FIGURE 1.1

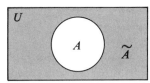

FIGURE 1.2

In Figure 1.1, you will notice that every point in the set A is also in the set B. As in Figure 1.1, throughout this text a rectangle will be used to indicate the universal set U. All sets in any discussion will be considered subsets of the universal set. You may wonder why we display the universal set. You will recall that the complement of a set B is defined if and only if the universal set is specified. The portrayal of the universal set makes it possible for us to indicate the complement of any set.

In Figure 1.2, the complement of A is indicated by the shaded region $\tilde{A}$. In Figure 1.1, what is the complement of B?

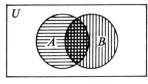

FIGURE 1.3

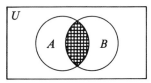

FIGURE 1.4

The shaded part of Figure 1.3 illustrates $A \cup B$. The shaded part of Figure 1.4 illustrates $A \cap B$. Note that the sets A and B illustrated in Figures 1.3 and 1.4 are not disjoint. The shaded parts of Figures 1.5 and 1.6 illustrate $A \cup B$ and $A \cap B$, respectively, when A and B are disjoint. The fact that $A \cap B = \emptyset$ is indicated in Figure 1.6 by the absence of shading.

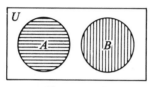

FIGURE 1.5

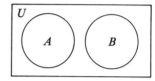

FIGURE 1.6

The shaded parts of Figures 1.7 and 1.8 illustrate $A \cup B$ and $A \cap B$ when $A \subset B$ and $A \neq B$. Note that $A \cup B = B$ and $A \cap B = A$.

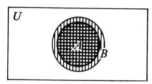

FIGURE 1.7

FIGURE 1.8

The following example illustrates an application of Venn diagrams.

Example. Let U = the set of all high school teachers, A = the set of all high school mathematics teachers, and B = the set of all high school coaches.

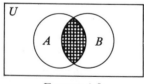

FIGURE 1.9

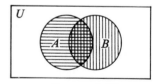

FIGURE 1.10

The shaded part of Figure 1.9 represents $A \cap B$; namely, the set of all high school coaches who are also high school mathematics teachers. The shaded part of Figure 1.10 represents $A \cup B$; namely, the set of all high school teachers who are mathematics teachers or who are coaches (or both). The unshaded part of Figure 1.10 represents $\overline{A \cup B}$; namely, the set of all high school teachers who are neither mathematics teachers nor coaches.

Exercise 1.7

I. Let U = the set of all human beings. Use Venn diagrams to illustrate each of the following.

    (1) A = the set of all students, B = the set of all high school students.

    (2) A = the set of all high school teachers, B = the set of all teachers.

    (3) A = set of all students, B = set of all persons under 1 year old.

    (4) A = set of all teachers, B = set of all parents.

    (5) A = set of all males over 21 years of age, B = set of all females over 21 years of age, C = set of all persons over 10 years of age.

II. Shade the union of A and B in each part of Exercise I.

III. Shade the intersection of A and B in each part of Exercise I.

IV. (1) Shade the union of A and C in Exercise I(5).

    (2) Shade the union of B and C in Exercise I(5).

    (3) Shade the union of A , B , and C in Exercise I(5).

    (4) Shade the intersection of A and C in Exercise I(5).

    (5) Shade the intersection of B and C in Exercise I(5).

    (6) Shade the intersection of A , B , and C in Exercise I(5).

V. In Figures 1.11, 1.12, 1.13, and 1.14, U = the set of all students. A = the set of all students of mathematics, B = the set of all students of chemistry, and C = the set of all students of speech.

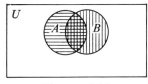

FIGURE 1.11

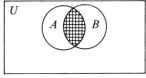

FIGURE 1.12

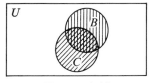

FIGURE 1.13

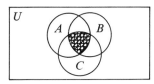

FIGURE 1.14

In terms of union, intersection, and complement (for example, $A \cup B$, $A \cap B$, or $\tilde{A}$), and in words, express what each of the following regions represents.

(1) The shaded region of Figure 1.11.
(2) The unshaded region of Figure 1.11.
(3) The shaded region of Figure 1.12.
(4) The unshaded region of Figure 1.12.
(5) The shaded region of Figure 1.13.
(6) The unshaded region of Figure 1.13.
(7) The shaded region of Figure 1.14.
(8) The unshaded region of Figure 1.14.

1.8 Algebra of Sets

So far we have concentrated our attention on unions and intersections of any *two* sets. In this section, we devote our attention to unions and intersections of more than two sets. Since $\cup$ and $\cap$ are binary operators and thus connect *two* sets only, we have to agree on the order in which the union or intersection of more than two sets is formed. For example, if $A = \{1, 2, 4\}$, $B = \{2, 3, 8\}$, and $C = \{1, 3, 8, 9\}$, then $A \cap B \cup C$ is ambiguous since it may be interpreted as $(A \cap B) \cup C$ or $A \cap (B \cup C)$. The following computations show that $(A \cap B) \cup C \neq A \cap (B \cup C)$.

$$
\begin{aligned}
(A \cap B) \cup C &= [\{1, 2, 4\} \cap \{2, 3, 8\}] \cup \{1, 3, 8, 9\} \\
&= \{2\} \cup \{1, 3, 8, 9\} \\
&= \{1, 2, 3, 8, 9\}. \\
A \cap (B \cup C) &= \{1, 2, 4\} \cap [\{2, 3, 8\} \cup \{1, 3, 8, 9\}] \\
&= \{1, 2, 4\} \cap \{1, 2, 3, 8, 9\} \\
&= \{1, 2\}.
\end{aligned}
$$

Hence $(A \cap B) \cup C \neq A \cap (B \cup C)$.

This example illustrates the necessity for punctuation. The parentheses are punctuation marks which indicate that the first operation ($\cup$ or $\cap$) to be performed is within the parentheses.

We learned from Definition 10 that the union of two sets A and B is itself a set, denoted by $A \cup B$. Thus the union of *two* sets is a *single* set. This property is called the *closure property for union*.

CLOSURE PROPERTY FOR UNION

If A and B are any sets, then $A \cup B$ is a unique set.

Recall that $A \cup B = \{x: (x \in A) \text{ or } (x \in B)\}$ and that $B \cup A = \{x: (x \in B) \text{ or } (x \in A)\}$. Since the sentence "$(x \in A)$ or $(x \in B)$"

is equivalent to "($x \in B$) or ($x \in A$)," it follows that $A \cup B = B \cup A$, for any sets A and B. This property is called the *commutative property for union*.

COMMUTATIVE PROPERTY FOR UNION

If A and B are any sets, then $A \cup B = B \cup A$.

For example, if $A = \{1, 5, 9, 13\}$ and $B = \{5, 13, 21\}$, then $A \cup B = \{1, 5, 9, 13, 21\}$ and $B \cup A = \{1, 5, 9, 13, 21\}$.

Next we consider $A \cup B \cup C$. We have already seen that, because $\cup$ is a binary operator, punctuation is necessary to indicate which operation is to be performed first. Thus we should compare $(A \cup B) \cup C$ and $A \cup (B \cup C)$. If $A = \{1, 3, 5, 7, 9\}$, $B = \{2, 5, 8, 11\}$, and $C = \{2, 4, 6, 8, 10\}$, then

$$(A \cup B) \cup C = \{1, 2, 3, 5, 7, 8, 9, 11\} \cup \{2, 4, 6, 8, 10\}$$
$$= \{1, 2, 3, 4, 5, 6, 7, 8, 9, 10, 11\},$$
and $\quad A \cup (B \cup C) = \{1, 3, 5, 7, 9\} \cup \{2, 4, 5, 6, 8, 10, 11\}$
$$= \{1, 2, 3, 4, 5, 6, 7, 8, 9, 10, 11\}.$$

In this example $(A \cup B) \cup C = A \cup (B \cup C)$. It is natural to wonder whether this relationship is true for *all* sets A, B, and C. This property, called the *associative property for union*, can be proved from the algebra of sentences studied in logic.

ASSOCIATIVE PROPERTY FOR UNION

If A, B, and C are any sets, then $(A \cup B) \cup C = A \cup (B \cup C)$.

Although it is frequently necessary to punctuate if we are to avoid ambiguity, the associative property makes it unnecessary to punctuate whenever the only operation is union. Thus, although $A \cap B \cup C$ is ambiguous, $A \cup B \cup C$ is *not* ambiguous. It may be proved from the associative property for union that $A_1 \cup A_2 \cup A_3 \cup \cdots \cup A_k$ is not ambiguous.

We have already seen that $A \cup \varnothing = A$ for any set A. For example, $\{1, 2, 3, 7, 11\} \cup \varnothing = \{1, 2, 3, 7, 11\}$. This property is called the *identity property for union*.

IDENTITY PROPERTY FOR UNION

If A is any set, then $A \cup \varnothing = A$.

It follows readily from the commutative property for union that $\varnothing \cup A = A$. The null set $\varnothing$ plays a role in the algebra of sets with respect to union similar to that of the number 0 in the algebra of numbers with respect to addition. In any algebra, the element with such a property with respect to a binary operation is called the *identity* element with respect to that binary operation. Thus 0 is the identity element with the respect to addition of numbers, and $\varnothing$ is the identity element with respect to union of sets.

Recall that $\tilde{A}$ is the complement of A; that is, $\tilde{A} = \{x: x \in U$ and $x \notin A\}$. Thus if $U = \{1, 2, 3, 4, 5, 6, 7\}$ and $A = \{1, 3, 5, 7\}$, then $\tilde{A} = \{2, 4, 6\}$. Moreover, you will notice that $A \cup \tilde{A} = U$. This property, which is an immediate consequence of Definition 8 and Defini-10, is called the *complement property for union*.

COMPLEMENT PROPERTY FOR UNION

If A is any set, then $A \cup \tilde{A} = U$.

This property is illustrated in Figure 1.15, in which $\tilde{A}$ is indicated by the shaded region.

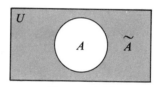

FIGURE 1.15

It follows readily from Definition 10 that $A \cup A = A$ for any set A. This property is called the *idempotent property for union*.

IDEMPOTENT PROPERTY FOR UNION

If A is any set, then $A \cup A = A$.

We state without proof the following properties for intersection.

CLOSURE PROPERTY FOR INTERSECTION

If A and B are any sets, then $A \cap B$ is a unique set.

COMMUTATIVE PROPERTY FOR INTERSECTION

If A and B are any sets, then $A \cap B = B \cap A$.

ASSOCIATIVE PROPERTY FOR INTERSECTION

If A, B, and C are any sets, then $(A \cap B) \cap C = A \cap (B \cap C)$.

IDENTITY PROPERTY FOR INTERSECTION

If A is any set, then $A \cap U = A$.

COMPLEMENT PROPERTY FOR INTERSECTION

If A is any set, then $A \cap \tilde{A} = \varnothing$.

IDEMPOTENT PROPERTY FOR INTERSECTION

If A is any set, then $A \cap A = A$.

Next we investigate $A \cap (B \cup C)$ and $(A \cap B) \cup (A \cap C)$. For example, if $A = \{1, 2, 4\}$, $B = \{2, 3, 8\}$, and $C = \{1, 3, 8, 9\}$, then

$$
\begin{aligned}
A \cap (B \cup C) &= \{1, 2, 4\} \cap [\{2, 3, 8\} \cup \{1, 3, 8, 9\}] \\
&= \{1, 2, 4\} \cap \{1, 2, 3, 8, 9\} \\
&= \{1, 2\}, \text{ and} \\
(A \cap B) \cup (A \cap C) &= [\{1, 2, 4\} \cap \{2, 3, 8\}] \cup [\{1, 2, 4\} \cap \{1, 3, 8, 9\}] \\
&= \{2\} \cup \{1\} \\
&= \{1, 2\}.
\end{aligned}
$$

Hence, in this example, $A \cap (B \cup C) = (A \cap B) \cup (A \cap C)$. This property, called the *distributive property for intersection over union*, can be proved for *any* sets A, B, and C.

THE DISTRIBUTIVE PROPERTY FOR INTERSECTION OVER UNION

If A, B, and C are any sets, then $A \cap (B \cup C) = (A \cap B) \cup (A \cap C)$.

This property is illustrated in the Venn diagram in Figure 1.16. The student should be cautioned, however, that there are many other possible arrangements of A, B, and C.

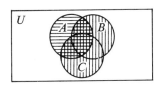

$$A \;\equiv$$
$$B \cup C \;|||||||$$
$$A \cap (B \cup C) \;\boxplus$$

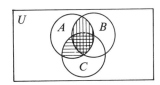

$$A \cap B \;|||||||$$
$$A \cap C \;\equiv$$
$$(A \cap B) \cup (A \cap C) \;(\textit{shaded region})$$

FIGURE 1.16

We now list some additional properties for union and intersection of sets and give examples and Venn diagrams.

THE DISTRIBUTIVE PROPERTY FOR UNION OVER INTERSECTION

If A, B, and C are any sets, then $A \cup (B \cap C) = (A \cup B) \cap (A \cup C)$.

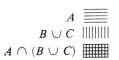

For example, if $A = \{1, 2, 4\}$, $B = \{2, 3, 8\}$, and $C = \{1, 3, 8, 9\}$, then

$$A \cup (B \cap C) = \{1, 2, 4\} \cup [\{2, 3, 8\} \cap \{1, 3, 8, 9\}]$$
$$= \{1, 2, 4\} \cup \{3, 8\}$$
$$= \{1, 2, 3, 4, 8\}, \text{ and}$$
$$(A \cup B) \cap (A \cup C) = [\{1, 2, 4\} \cup \{2, 3, 8\}] \cap [\{1, 2, 4\} \cup \{1, 3, 8, 9\}]$$
$$= \{1, 2, 3, 4, 8\} \cap \{1, 2, 3, 4, 8, 9\}$$
$$= \{1, 2, 3, 4, 8\}.$$

This property is illustrated in the Venn diagram in Figure 1.17. As previously stated, the student is cautioned that there are many other possible arrangements of *A*, *B*, and *C*.

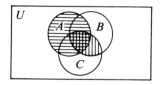

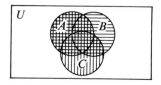

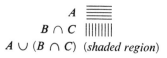

$$A \cup (B \cap C) \text{ (shaded region)}$$

FIGURE 1.17

THE DEMORGAN PROPERTY FOR UNION

If *A* and *B* are any sets, then $\widetilde{A \cup B} = \tilde{A} \cap \tilde{B}$.

For example, if $U = \{1, 2, 3, 4, 5, 6, 7, 8, 9, 10\}$,
$A = \{1, 5, 9, 10\}$,   and $B = \{1, 8, 9\}$,

then $A \cup B = \{1, 5, 8, 9, 10\}$

and hence $\widetilde{A \cup B} = \{2, 3, 4, 6, 7\}$.

Moreover, $\tilde{A} = \{2, 3, 4, 6, 7, 8\}$

and $\tilde{B} = \{2, 3, 4, 5, 6, 7, 10\}$

and hence $\tilde{A} \cap \tilde{B} = \{2, 3, 4, 6, 7\}$.

Hence, in this example, $\widetilde{A \cup B} = \tilde{A} \cap \tilde{B}$. This property can be proved for *any* sets *A* and *B*.

The DeMorgan property for union is illustrated in the Venn diagram in Figure 1.18.

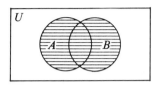
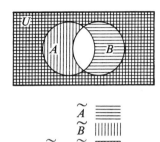

$A \cup B$ ▦
$\widetilde{A \cup B}$ *(unshaded region)*

$\tilde{A}$ ▦
$\tilde{B}$ ‖‖‖‖
$\tilde{A} \cap \tilde{B}$ ▦

FIGURE 1.18

THE DEMORGAN PROPERTY FOR INTERSECTION

If A and B are any sets, then $\widetilde{A \cap B} = \tilde{A} \cup \tilde{B}$.

For example, if $U = \{1, 2, 3, 4, 5, 6, 7, 8, 9, 10\}$,
                     $A = \{1, 5, 9, 10\}$,   and $B = \{1, 8, 9\}$,

then $A \cap B = \{1, 9\}$

and hence $\widetilde{A \cap B} = \{2, 3, 4, 5, 6, 7, 8, 10\}$.

Moreover, $\tilde{A} = \{2, 3, 4, 6, 7, 8\}$

and $\tilde{B} = \{2, 3, 4, 5, 6, 7, 10\}$

and hence $\tilde{A} \cup \tilde{B} = \{2, 3, 4, 5, 6, 7, 8, 10\}$.

Hence, in this example, $\widetilde{A \cap B} = \tilde{A} \cup \tilde{B}$. The DeMorgan property for intersection is illustrated in the Venn diagram in Figure 1.19.

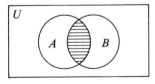
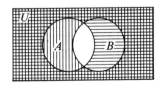

$A \cap B$ ▦
$\widetilde{A \cap B}$ *(unshaded region)*

$\tilde{A}$ ▦
$\tilde{B}$ ‖‖‖‖
$\tilde{A} \cup \tilde{B}$ *(shaded region)*

FIGURE 1.19

The *double complement property* follows readily from the definition of complement.

THE DOUBLE COMPLEMENT PROPERTY

If A is any set, then $\tilde{\tilde{A}} = A$.

The foregoing properties constitute the basic properties for the algebra of sets. Any other algebraic properties for sets can be derived from these basic properties.

Exercise 1.8

I. If $U = \{0, 1, 2, 3, 4, 5, 6, 7, 8, 9\}$, $A = \{0, 2, 4, 6\}$, $B = \{1, 4, 6, 8\}$, $C = \{1, 3, 5, 9\}$, and $D = \varnothing$, compute each of the following.

(1) $A \cup B$	(19) $U \cap D$
(2) $B \cup C$	(20) $A \cup D$
(3) $A \cap B$	(21) $A \cup \tilde{B}$
(4) $B \cap C$	(22) $A \cap \tilde{B}$
(5) $C \cap B$	(23) $\tilde{A} \cup \tilde{B}$
(6) $(B \cup A) \cup C$	(24) $\overline{A \cap B}$
(7) $(U \cap A) \cup B$	(25) $\tilde{D}$
(8) $U \cap (A \cup B)$	(26) $\tilde{U}$
(9) $C \cap (A \cup B)$	(27) $\tilde{U} \cap D$
(10) $(C \cap A) \cup B$	(28) $\tilde{U} \cup D$
(11) $(C \cup B) \cap (A \cup B)$	(29) $A \cup B \cup C$
(12) $(C \cap A) \cup (C \cap B)$	(30) $A \cup \overline{B \cup C}$
(13) $A \cap (B \cup C)$	(31) $(A \cup B) \cup \tilde{C}$
(14) $(A \cap B) \cup C$	(32) $A \cup (B \cup \tilde{C})$
(15) $(A \cup B) \cup C$	(33) $\overline{A \cap B \cap C}$
(16) $A \cup (B \cup C)$	(34) $A \cap B \cap C$
(17) $D \cap A$	(35) $(A \cap B) \cap \tilde{C}$
(18) $D \cap B$	(36) $A \cap (B \cap \tilde{C})$

II. (1) List the twelve possible ways in which the union of three sets A, B, and C can be formed.

(2) Are the resulting twelve sets equal? Why?

III. (1) Illustrate the distributive property $A \cap (B \cup C) = (A \cap B) \cup (A \cap C)$ by Venn diagrams. Use *two* arrangements, each different from the arrangement in Figure 1.16.

(2) Illustrate the distributive property $A \cup (B \cap C) = (A \cup B) \cap (A \cup C)$ by Venn diagrams. Use *two* arrangements, each different from the arrangement in Figure 1.17.

IV. Use the distributive properties and the commutative properties as stated in this section to prove each of the following properties.

(1) $(A \cup B) \cap C = (A \cap C) \cup (B \cap C)$.

(2) $(A \cap B) \cup C = (A \cup C) \cap (B \cup C)$.

(*Note*. These are alternate forms of the distributive properties.)

V. Let $U = C_0 = \{x : x$ is a counting number$\}$, $A = \{x : x$ is less than 100$\}$, $B = \{x : x$ is even$\}$, $C = \{x : x$ is odd$\}$, and $D = \{0, 3, 6, 9, \ldots\}$. Compute each of the following.

(1) $B \cap D$

(2) $C \cap D$

(3) $B \cap C$

(4) $B \cap A$

(5) $A \cap B$

(6) $A \cup C$

(7) $\tilde{C}$

(8) $\tilde{C} \cap A$

(9) $\tilde{B}$

(10) $A \cap (B \cup C)$

(11) $(B \cup C) \cap D$

(12) $(A \cup D) \cap C$

(13) $\overline{(A \cap C)} \cup (D \cap C)$

(14) $\overline{A \cup B}$

(15) $\tilde{A} \cap \tilde{B}$

(16) $A \cap \overline{(B \cup C)}$

(17) $A \cap (B \cup \tilde{C})$

(18) $\overline{A \cap (B \cup C)}$

(19) $(A \cap B) \cup \tilde{C}$

(20) $\overline{(A \cap B) \cup C}$

VI. Complete each of the following so that a true sentence results for all sets A, B, and C.

(1) $A \cup (B \cup C) = (A \cup B) \cup \underline{\qquad}$.

(2) $A \cup (B \cup C) = A \cup (C \cup \underline{\qquad})$.

(3) $A \cup (B \cap C) = (A \cup B) \cap (\underline{\qquad} \cup C)$.

(4) $B \cap (C \cup A) = (\underline{\qquad} \cap C) \cup (B \cap A)$.

(5) $C \cap (A \cup B) = (\underline{\qquad} \cap A) \cup (\underline{\qquad} \cap B)$.

(6) $A \cup (C \cap B) = (A \cup \underline{\qquad}) \cap (\underline{\qquad} \cup C)$.

(7) $(A \cap B) \cup C = (A \cup \underline{\qquad}) \cap (\underline{\qquad} \cup C)$.

(8) $(B \cup A) \cap C = (\underline{\qquad} \cap C) \cup (A \cap \underline{\qquad})$.

(9) $(A \cup B) \cap (A \cup C) = A \cup (\underline{\qquad} \cap C)$.

(10) $(A \cap C) \cup (A \cap B) = A \cap (\underline{\qquad} \cup B)$.

(11) $(A \cup C) \cup B = B \cup (A \cup \underline{\qquad})$.

(12) $\overline{(B \cap A)} \cap C = (A \cap \underline{\qquad}) \cap C$.

(13) $\overline{A \cup B \cup C} = (\tilde{A} \cap \tilde{B}) \cup \underline{\qquad}$.

(14) $A \cup \overline{(B \cup C)} = \underline{\qquad} \cup (\tilde{B} \cap \tilde{C})$.

(15) $A \cap \overline{(B \cup C)} = A \cap \tilde{B} \cap \underline{\qquad}$.

(16) $\overline{(B \cup C)} \cap A = \underline{\qquad} \cap \tilde{C} \cap A$.

(17) $\overline{A \cup B} \cap \tilde{C} = (\tilde{A} \cap \underline{\qquad}) \cap \tilde{C}$.

(18) $\tilde{A} \cup \overline{(B \cap C)} = (\tilde{A} \cup \underline{\qquad}) \cup \tilde{C}$.

(19) $\overline{A \cap (B \cup C)} = \tilde{A} \cup \tilde{B} \cup \underline{\qquad}$.

(20) $\overline{C \cup (B \cap A)} = \underline{\qquad} \cap \overline{B \cap A}$.

VII. State the name of the property which guarantees that each of the following sentences is true for all sets A, B, *and* C.

(1) $(A \cup B) \cup C = A \cup (B \cup C)$.

(2) $A \cup (C \cup B) = (A \cup C) \cup B$.

(3) $A \cup (B \cup C) = A \cup (C \cup B)$.

(4) $A \cup (B \cup C) = (B \cup C) \cup A$.

(5) $A \cap (B \cup C) = (A \cap B) \cup (A \cap C)$.

(6) $A \cup (B \cap C) = (A \cup B) \cap (A \cup C)$.

(7) $A \cup (B \cap C) = (C \cap B) \cup A$.

(8) $A \cap (B \cup C) = (C \cup B) \cap A$.

(9) $A \cup \widetilde{B \cap C} = A \cup (\tilde{B} \cup \tilde{C})$.

(10) $\widetilde{A \cup B} \cap C = (\tilde{A} \cap \tilde{B}) \cap C$.

VIII. State the truth value of each of the following sentences. The universal quantifier is understood; that is, the phrase "for all sets A, B, and C" is understood to be a part of each sentence.

(1) $(A \cap B) \cup C = A \cap (B \cup C)$.

(2) $A \cup (B \cap C) = (A \cup B) \cap C$.

(3) $A \cup (B \cap C) = (B \cap C) \cup A$.

(4) $B \cap (A \cup C) = (A \cup C) \cap B$.

(5) $B \cap (A \cup C) = (C \cup A) \cap B$.

(6) $A \cup (B \cap C) = (C \cap B) \cup A$.

(7) $\widetilde{A \cup B \cup C} = (\tilde{A} \cup \tilde{B}) \cup C$.

(8) $A \cap (B \cap C) = A \cap (\tilde{B} \cap \tilde{C})$.

(9) $\widetilde{A \cup B \cup C} = \tilde{A} \cap \tilde{B} \cap \tilde{C}$.

(10) $\widetilde{A \cap B \cap C} = \tilde{A} \cup \tilde{B} \cup \tilde{C}$.

1.9   Cartesian Product

We have already studied the binary operators $\cup$ and $\cap$ between any two sets A and B. You will recall that $A \cup B = \{x: x \in A \text{ or } x \in B\}$ and $A \cap B = \{x: x \in A \text{ and } x \in B\}$. Now we shall study another binary operator between two sets A and B. The set $A \times B$ (read *A cross B*) is called the *Cartesian product of A and B*.

DEFINITION 13.   The *Cartesian product* of two sets A and B (written $A \times B$) is the set of all pairs (a, b) such that $a \in A$ and $b \in B$.

In set notation $A \times B = \{(a, b) : a \in A \text{ and } b \in B\}$. *Equality* of pairs is identity; that is, $(a, b) = (c, d)$ if and only if $a = c$ and $b = d$. The elements (a, b) of $A \times B$ are called *ordered pairs*. The reason for the word *ordered* is that, in general, $(a, b) \neq (b, a)$; that is, the *order* in which the elements a and b are written is important. For example, if $A = \{1, 2\}$ and $B = \{0, 2, 4\}$, then $A \times B = \{(1, 0),$ $(1, 2),\ (1, 4),\ (2, 0),\ (2, 2),\ (2, 4)\}$ and $B \times A = \{(0, 1),\ (0, 2),$ $(2, 1),\ (2, 2),\ (4, 1),\ (4, 2)\}$. Thus $A \times B \neq B \times A$; that is, the operation is *not* commutative. The fact that this operation is *not* commutative should not surprise you. In mathematics and nature there are many noncommutative operations. For example, the operations of subtraction and division are noncommutative; that is, in general, $a - b \neq b - a$ and $a \div b \neq b \div a$. Henceforth, when we speak of the Cartesian product of A and B, without further qualification, we shall mean $A \times B$.

It is important to emphasize the distinction between the set $A \cap B$ and the set $A \times B$. Although the elements of $A \cap B$ are elements of A and also of B, the elements of $A \times B$ are *not* elements of A and are *not* elements of B. On the contrary, the elements of $A \times B$ are *ordered pairs* of elements—the first member of the pair being an element of A, and the second member of the pair being an element of B.

The concept of Cartesian product is extremely important in mathematics and applications. It is especially important in each of the following:

1. Developing the properties of the counting numbers with respect to multiplication,
2. Developing the properties of functions and their graphs,
3. Expressing the sample space of an experiment such as the roll of a pair of dice.

Example 1.

$$A = \{1, 3\} \text{ and } B = \{x, y\}.$$
$$A \times B = \{(1, x),\ (1, y),\ (3, x),\ (3, y)\}.$$
$$B \times A = \{(x, 1),\ (x, 3),\ (y, 1),\ (y, 3)\}.$$
$$A \cap B = \varnothing.$$
$$B \cap A = \varnothing.$$

Example 2.

$$A = \{1, 2, 4, 8\} \qquad \text{and} \qquad B = \{8, 9\}.$$
$$A \times B = \{(1, 8),\ (1, 9),\ (2, 8),\ (2, 9),\ (4, 8),\ (4, 9),$$
$$(8, 8),\ (8, 9)\}.$$
$$B \times A = \{(8, 1),\ (8, 2),\ (8, 4),\ (8, 8),\ (9, 1),\ (9, 2),$$
$$(9, 4),\ (9, 8)\}.$$
$$A \cap B = \{8\}.$$
$$B \cap A = \{8\}.$$

Example 3.

$$C_0 = \{0, 1, 2, 3, 4, \ldots\} \quad \text{and} \quad B = \{0, 1, 2, 3, 4\}.$$
$$C_0 \times B = \{(0, 0), \ (0, 1), \ (0, 2), \ (0, 3), \ (0, 4)$$
$$(1, 0), \ (1, 1), \ (1, 2), \ (1, 3), \ (1, 4)$$
$$\cdots$$
$$(k, 0), \ (k, 1), \ (k, 2), \ (k, 3), \ (k, 4),$$
$$\cdots \quad \}.$$
$$C_0 \cap B = \{0, 1, 2, 3, 4\} = B, \quad \text{and} \quad B \cap C_0 = B.$$

Example 4.

$$C_0 = \{0, 1, 2, 3, 4, \ldots\}$$
$$C_0 \times C_0 = \{(0, 0), \ (0, 1), \ (0, 2), \ (0, 3), \ (0, 4), \ldots$$
$$(1, 0), \ (1, 1), \ (1, 2), \ (1, 3), \ (1, 4), \ldots$$
$$\cdots$$
$$(k, 0), \ (k, 1), \ (k, 2), \ (k, 3), \ (k, 4), \ldots$$
$$\cdots \quad \}.$$

In Examples 3 and 4 it is not possible to list all elements of the Cartesian products. However, we have listed enough elements of $C_0 \times B$ so that the patterns are established. As before, the three dots indicate the omission of elements from the listing. One can *visualize* the forms of $C_0 \times B$ and $C_0 \times C_0$ even though he cannot actually *list* all of the elements.

We have already seen that the null set has special properties which make it particularly useful and interesting in the study of mathematics. In particular, $A \cup \varnothing = A$. This is analogous to $a + 0 = a$ in arithmetic. To complete the analogy, we shall conclude this section with a discussion of the Cartesian product of two sets, one of which is the null set. For example, if $A = \{2, 4, 6, 8\}$, then $A \times \varnothing = \varnothing$. By definition of $A \times B$, the second member b of the ordered pair (a, b) is an element of B. Since $B = \varnothing$, there are no elements b of B. Thus there is *no* second member b in B to pair with a in A to form an ordered pair (a, b); that is, there is *no* ordered pair (a, b) of $A \times B$. Hence $A \times B = \varnothing$. It is easy to see that $A \times \varnothing = \varnothing$ for *any* set A. In fact $A \times B = \varnothing$ if and only if $A = \varnothing$ or $B = \varnothing$. Now the analogy is complete: in arithmetic $a \times 0 = 0$ for any number a; in set theory $A \times \varnothing = \varnothing$ for any set A.

Exercise 1.9

I. Compute $A \times B$ for each of the following pairs of sets.

(1) $A = \{2\}$, $B = \{0\}$
(2) $A = \{2\}$, $B = \{ \ \}$

(3) $A = \{2\}$, $B = \{1, 2\}$
(4) $A = \varnothing$, $B = \{1, 3\}$
(5) $A = \{0, 1\}$, $B = \{1, 2, 3\}$
(6) $A = \{0, 1, 2, 3\}$, $B = \{1, 2, 3\}$
(7) $A = \{0\}$, $B = \{0, 1, 2, 3\}$
(8) $A = \{0\}$, $B = \{0, 1, 2, 3, \ldots\}$
(9) $A = \{10, 11, 12\}$, $B = \{1, 2, 3, 4, \ldots\}$
(10) $A = \{1, 2, 3, \ldots\}$, $B = C_0$

II. Compute $B \times A$ for each pair of sets in Exercise I.

III. (1) Give an example in which $(a, b) = (b, a)$.
(2) Under what condition is $(a, b) = (b, a)$?

IV. (1) Give an example in which $A \times B = B \times A$.
(2) Under what condition is $A \times B = B \times A$?

V. The Cartesian product $A \times B$ is given in each of the following. Compute A and B.

(1) $\{(1, 1),\ (1, 2),\ (1, 3),\ (5, 1),\ (5, 2),\ (5, 3)\}$
(2) $\{(1, 1),\ (1, 5),\ (2, 1),\ (2, 5),\ (3, 1),\ (3, 5)\}$
(3) $\{(0, 0),\ (0, 1),\ (0, 2)\}$

VI. (1) Count the elements in each finite set $A \times B$ in Exercise I.
(2) If A contains m elements and B contains k elements, intuitively, how many elements does $A \times B$ contain?

1.10 Equivalence Relation

Basic to the study of mathematics is the concept of *equivalence relation*. While Euclid used the equivalence relation in the writing of his *Elements of Geometry* and the student of geometry uses it today, the use is frequently tacit rather than explicit. Even the student of algebra frequently uses this concept without realizing it. For example, when we say, "if $a = b$, then $b = a$," we are using one of the properties of an equivalence relation.

The word *relation* has many common uses. We usually speak of the relation between objects or persons. One cubic foot of mercury weighs more than one cubic foot of lead. This is a relation between the densities of mercury and lead. Two persons may be related by blood; for example, one is the father of the other. Or they may be related by domicile; for example, each is the neighbor of the other. In mathematics the word *relation* has special significance.

Recall that $A = B$ if and only if $A \subset B$ and $B \subset A$. We note that $A = B$ expresses a relation between the set A and the set B. Similarly

$A \subset B$ expresses a relation between A and B. Consider the relation *is equal to*. First, notice that any set A is equal to itself; that is, $A = A$. Second, if $A = B$, then "A" and "B" are different names for the same set; that is, if $A = B$, then $B = A$. Third, if $A = B$ and $B = C$, then "A," "B," and "C" are different names for the same set; that is, if $A = B$ and $B = C$, then $A = C$. Because of the elegance and utility of this type of relation in mathematics, we give it the special name *equivalence relation*. The symbol R will be used to indicate a relation; that is, a R b means *a is related to b*. In this text we do not define the word *relation*. The examples will give you an intuitive idea of its meaning. In Definition 14 we define *equivalence relation* in terms of the undefined term *relation*.

DEFINITION 14. A relation R on a set S is an *equivalence relation* if and only if the following three properties are satisfied:
(a) *Reflexive Property* (if $a \in S$, then a R a);
(b) *Symmetric Property* (if $a, b \in S$ and a R b, then b R a);
(c) *Transitive Property* (if $a, b, c \in S$ and a R b and b R c, then a R c).

You should recall that a, b, and c need not be different elements. It is possible that any two are equal or all three are equal.

Example 1. Let S be a set of colored blocks. Let R be the relation *is of the same color as*. If a, b, and c are any blocks of the set, then

(a) a R a (any block a is of the same color as itself);
(b) if a R b, then b R a (if a is of the same color as b, then b is of the same color as a);
(c) if a R b and b R c, then a R c (if a is of the same color as b and b is of the same color as c, then a is of the same color as c).

Since the reflexive, symmetric, and transitive properties are satisfied, R is an equivalence relation.

Example 2. Let $U = \{0, 1, 2, 3, 4\}$. Let S be the collection of all subsets of U. Let the relation R be $\subset$.

(a) Since any set is a subset of itself, the reflexive property is obviously satisfied.
(b) If $A = \{1, 3\}$ and $B = \{1, 2, 3\}$, then $A \subset B$ but $B \not\subset A$. Hence the symmetric property is *not* satisfied.
(c) If $A \subset B$ and $B \subset C$, then $A \subset C$. Hence the transitive property is satisfied.

However, R is *not* an equivalence relation because only two of the three properties are satisfied.

Example 3. Let S be a collection of finite subsets of the counting numbers. Let R be the relation *contains the same number of elements as*. Then for any A, B, C in S:

(a) A contains the same number of elements as A;
(b) If A contains the same number of elements as B, then B contains the same number of elements as A;
(c) If A contains the same number of elements as B and B contains the same number of elements as C, then A contains the same number of elements as C.

Thus R is an equivalence relation; that is, the relation *contains the same number of elements as* is an equivalence relation.

Example 4. Let S be a collection of subsets of the counting numbers. Let R be the relation *is in one-to-one correspondence with*. Then for any subsets A, B, C of S:

(a) A R A (A is in one-to-one correspondence with A);
(b) If A R B, then B R A (if A is in one-to-one correspondence with B, then B is in one-to-one correspondence with A);
(c) If A R B and B R C, then A R C (if A is in one-to-one correspondence with B and B is in one-to-one correspondence with C, then A is in one-to-one correspondence with C).

Thus R is an equivalence relation; that is, the relation *is in one-to-one correspondence with* is an equivalence relation.

Example 5. Let S be a set of persons. Let R be the relation *is the mother of*. For any a in S, it is false that a is the mother of a. Since the reflexive property fails, R is *not* an equivalence relation. It is *not* necessary to check the symmetric and transitive properties.

Example 6. Let $S = \{1, 2, 3, 4, 5, 6, 7\}$, $A = \{1, 2, 3, 4\}$, $B = \{5, 6, 7\}$. For any $a, b \in S$, let a R b mean that *a and b are both in the same set A or both in B*. For example, 1 R 2 and 5 R 7, but 3 R̸ 7. Thus

(a) a R a (a is in the same subset as a);
(b) If a R b, then b R a (if a is in the same subset as b, then b is in the same subset as a);

(c) If a R b and b R c, then a R c (if a is in the same subset as b and b is in the same subset as c, then a is in the same subset as c).

Thus the relation R is an equivalence relation.
Note that the transitive property follows from the fact that $A \cap B = \varnothing$.

In the following example $A \cap B \neq \varnothing$, and the relation R is *not* an equivalence relation.

Example 7. Let $S = \{1, 2, 3, 4, 5, 6, 7\}$, $A = \{1, 2, 3, 4\}$, and $B = \{4, 5, 6, 7\}$. For any $a, b \in S$, let a R b mean that *a and b are both in the same set A or both in B*. For example, 1 R 2 and 5 R 7, but 3 Ɍ 7. Thus

(a) a R a (a is in the same subset as a);
(b) If a R b, then b R a (if a is in the same subset as b, then b is in the same subset as a);
(c) 3 R 4 because $3 \in A$ and $4 \in A$; 4 R 7 because $4 \in B$ and $7 \in B$. But 3 Ɍ 7 because $3 \in A$ and $7 \notin A$, and $7 \in B$ and $3 \notin B$.

Since the transitive property fails, we see that the relation R is *not* an equivalence relation. That is, it is *not* true that if a R b and b R c, then a R c.

The above discussion and examples illustrate that an equivalence relation on a set S separates the elements of S into mutually exclusive subsets; that is, into subsets such that $A = B$ or $A \cap B = \varnothing$ for all sets A and B. Thus in Example 1 the blocks in S are separated into mutually exclusive subsets such that all blocks of one color are in the same subset and no blocks of different colors are in the same subset. For a specified S the separation is shown in Figure 1.20.

$S = \{$ R^1 , B^2 , G^3 , R^4 , G^5 , G^6 , R^7 , B^8 , G^9 ,
G^{10} , R^{11} , B^{12} $\}$.
$A = \{$ R^1 , R^4 , R^7 , R^{11} $\}$,
$B = \{$ B^2 , B^8 , B^{12} $\}$,
$C = \{$ G^3 , G^5 , G^6 , G^9 , G^{10} $\}$.
$S = A \cup B \cup C,\ A \cap B = \varnothing,\ B \cap C = \varnothing,\ A \cap C = \varnothing$.

FIGURE 1.20

Exercise 1.10

I. In each of the following, a set S and a relation R are specified. Determine whether each relation is an equivalence relation. If R is not an equivalence relation, tell which property of Definition 14 fails.

(1) Let $S = \{0, 1, 2, 3, \ldots, 999\}$. Let R be the relation *has the same number of digits as*. Thus 57 R 91 and 301 R 817 but 3 R̸ 16.

(2) Two numbers are said to have the *same parity* if and only if they are both even or both odd. Let $S = \{0, 1, 2, 3, \ldots\}$ and R be the relation *has the same parity as*.

(3) Let S be the set of persons and let R be the relation *is of the same weight as*.

(4) Let S be the set of persons and let R be the relation *weighs within two pounds of*.

(5) Let S be the set of persons and let R be the relation *was born in the same month as*.

(6) Let S be the set of persons and let R be the relation *is the brother of*.

(7) Let S be the set of persons and let R be the relation *has the same parents as*.

(8) Let $S = \{\frac{1}{2}, \frac{2}{3}, \frac{4}{5}, \frac{2}{4}, \frac{3}{6}, \frac{8}{10}\}$ and let R be the relation defined as follows: $\frac{a}{b}$ R $\frac{c}{d}$ if and only if $ad = bc$.

(9) Let $S = \{0, 1, 2, 3, \ldots, 100\}$ and let R be the relation *ends in the same digit as*. For example, 17 R 67 but 17 R̸ 63.

(10) Let $S = \{0, 1, 2, 3, 4, \ldots, 23\}$ and R be the relation *leaves the same remainder when divided by 5*. Thus 3 R 8 and 3 R 23 but 3 R̸ 9.

II. Separate the sets in Exercise I–(1), (2), (5), (8), (9), (10) into mutually exclusive subsets such that any two elements of one subset are related but no two elements of different subsets are related. (*Hint.* Read the discussion concerning Example 1 and exhibit the mutually exclusive subsets as in Figure 1.20.)

III. (1) Let S be a set of triangles and let R be the relation *is congruent to (has the same size and shape as)*. Prove that R is an equivalence relation.

(2) Let S be a set of triangles and let R be the relation *is similar to (has the same shape as)*. Prove that R is an equivalence relation.

(3) Let S be a set of arrows and let R be the relation *has the same length as*. Prove that R is an equivalence relation.

CHAPTER 2

The Field of Real Numbers (A Review)

2.1 The Real Number System

You are already familiar with the real numbers and most of their properties. The study of *algebra* entails the real number system; i.e., in order to study algebra one must be familiar with the real numbers and their properties. In this chapter we review those properties of the real numbers which are essential to a systematic study of algebra.

You will recall that the sum of any two real numbers a and b is the unique real number $a + b$; that is, the sum of any two real numbers is well-defined. Similarly, you know that the sum of three real numbers $a, b,$ and c does not depend on the grouping. That is, if $a, b,$ and c are any real numbers, then $(a + b) + c = a + (b + c)$. For example, $(29 + 97) + 3 = 29 + (97 + 3)$. The real number 0 (called the *additive identity*) is the only real number such that $a + 0 = a$ for *every* real number a. If a is any real number, then there exists a unique real number ^-a (called the *additive inverse* of a) such that $a + {}^-a = 0$. For example, $7 + {}^-7 = 0$, $^-5 + {}^-(^-5) = 0$, and $\sqrt{2} + {}^-\sqrt{2} = 0$. Moreover, if a and b are any real numbers, then $a + b = b + a$. For example, $2.13 + 7.87 = 7.87 + 2.13$, and $2 + x = x + 2$ for every real number x.

These properties have familiar names.

CLOSURE PROPERTY FOR ADDITION

If a and b are any real numbers, then $a + b$ is a unique real number.

ASSOCIATIVE PROPERTY FOR ADDITION

If a, b, and c are any real numbers, then

$$(a + b) + c = a + (b + c).$$

IDENTITY PROPERTY FOR ADDITION

There exists a unique real number 0 (called the *additive identity*) such that $a + 0 = a$ for every real number a.

INVERSE PROPERTY FOR ADDITION

If a is any real number, then there exists a unique real number ^-a (called the *additive inverse of a* or *the negative of a*) such that $a + {^-a} = 0$.

COMMUTATIVE PROPERTY FOR ADDITION

If a and b are any real numbers, then $a + b = b + a$.

In a similar manner we can state analogous properties for multiplication.

CLOSURE PROPERTY FOR MULTIPLICATION

If a and b are any real numbers, then $a \times b$ is a unique real number.

ASSOCIATIVE PROPERTY FOR MULTIPLICATION

If a, b, and c are any real numbers, then $(a \times b) \times c = a \times (b \times c)$.

IDENTITY PROPERTY FOR MULTIPLICATION

There exists a unique real number 1 (called the *multiplicative identity*) such that $a \times 1 = a$ for every real number a.

INVERSE PROPERTY FOR MULTIPLICATION

If a is any nonzero real number, then there exists a unique real number $\frac{1}{a}$ (called the *multiplicative inverse of a* or *the reciprocal of a*) such that $a \times \frac{1}{a} = 1$.

COMMUTATIVE PROPERTY FOR MULTIPLICATION

If a and b are any real numbers, then $a \times b = b \times a$.

To illustrate the inverse property for multiplication we note that $5 \times \frac{1}{5} = 1$, $\sqrt{2} \times \frac{1}{\sqrt{2}} = 1$, $\frac{2}{7} \times \frac{1}{2/7} = 1$, and $\frac{\pi}{\sqrt{2}} \times \frac{1}{\frac{\pi}{\sqrt{2}}} = 1$. However, as there is no real number r such that $0 \times r = 1$, we see that 0 has no multiplicative inverse. Hence it is necessary to include the word *nonzero* in the inverse property for multiplication. Observe that the identity property for addition does not have this restriction.

The following property, called the *distributive property*, is another important property of the real numbers.

DISTRIBUTIVE PROPERTY

If a, b, and c are any real numbers, then

$$a \times (b + c) = a \times b + a \times c.$$

Recall that, by convention, multiplication takes precedence over addition, unless punctuation indicates otherwise. Thus in $a \times (b + c)$ the punctuation indicates that the *sum* $b + c$ is to be computed before the *product* $a \times (b + c)$. However, in $a \times b + a \times c$, convention indicates that the two products $a \times b$ and $a \times c$ are *first* computed and *then* the sum of these is computed. As examples of the distributive property, we observe that $2 \times (3 + 7) = 2 \times 3 + 2 \times 7$, $\sqrt{2} \times (a + 8) = \sqrt{2} \times a + \sqrt{2} \times 8$, and $8 \times (10 + 5) = 8 \times 10 + 8 \times 5$. Because of the commutative property, we may write $(10 + 5) \times 8 = 8 \times (10 + 5) = 8 \times 10 + 8 \times 5 = 10 \times 8 + 5 \times 8$. In general, $(b + c) \times a = b \times a + c \times a$ for any real numbers a, b, and c. Thus the right-hand distributive property follows readily from the (left-hand) distributive property.

The real number system is an example of an abstract system known as a *field*. As you will recall from your previous study, a *system* consists of a nonempty set of elements and one or more binary operators between elements of the set. In the following definition, precise meaning is given to the term *field*.

DEFINITION 1.   A mathematical system $(F, +, \times)$ consisting of a non-null set F and two binary operators $+$ and $\times$ is said to be a *field* if and only if the system possesses the properties $F1$ through $F11$.

$F1$.   If a and b are any elements of F, then $a + b$ is a unique element of F (*closure property for addition*).

$F2$.   If a, b, and c are any elements of F, then
$(a + b) + c = a + (b + c)$ (*associative property for addition*).

$F3$.   There exists a unique element 0 of F such that $a + 0 = a$ for any element of F (*identity property for addition*).

$F4$.   If a is any element of F, then there exists a unique element ^-a of F such that $a + {}^-a = 0$ (*inverse property for addition*).

$F5$.   If a and b are any elements of F, then $a + b = b + a$ (*commutative property for addition*).

*F*6.   If a and b are any elements of F, then $a \times b$ is a unique element of F (*closure property for multiplication*).

*F*7.   If a, b, and c are any elements of F, then $(a \times b) \times c = a \times (b \times c)$ (*associative property for multiplication*).

*F*8.   There exists a unique element 1 of F such that $a \times 1 = a$ for any element of F (*identity property for multiplication*).

*F*9.   If a is any nonzero element of F, then there exists a unique element $\frac{1}{a}$ of F such that $a \times \frac{1}{a} = 1$ (*inverse property for multiplication*).

*F*10. If a and b are any elements of F, then $a \times b = b \times a$ (*commutative property for multiplication*).

*F*11. If a, b, and c are any elements of F, then $a \times (b + c) = a \times b + a \times c$ (*distributive property*).

Throughout this text we employ the notation R to symbolize the *set* of real numbers. Thus the *real number system* $(R, +, \times)$ is a field. Frequently we indicate the product of a and b by $a \cdot b$, or ab, or $(a)(b)$, or $a(b)$, or $(a)b$. Thus $a \cdot b = ab = (a)(b) = a(b) = (a)b = a \times b$.

Two important aspects of mathematics (*generalization* and *abstraction*) will become more evident as we study the field properties and other properties which follow from the field properties.

Let I denote the set of *integers*; that is, $I = \{\ldots, {}^-3, {}^-2, {}^-1, 0, 1, 2, 3, \ldots\}$. Then $I \subset R$. Is $(I, +, \times)$ a field? It is easy to prove that $(I, +, \times)$ possesses all of the field properties except the inverse property for multiplication. The only elements of I which have multiplicative inverses in I are ${}^-1$ and 1. Hence $(I, +, \times)$ is not a field. Although I is a *subset* of R, $(I, +, \times)$ is not a *subfield* of $(R, +, \times)$.

Recall that the set of *rational numbers* is a proper subset of the set of real numbers. Denoting the set of rational numbers by R_a, we may write $R_a \subset R$. It is interesting to study the rational number system $(R_a, +, \times)$ and, in particular, to determine whether $(R_a, +, \times)$ is a field. Recall that a *rational number* is a real number which can be expressed in the form $\frac{a}{b}$, in which a is an integer and b is a nonzero integer, and equality defined such that $\frac{a}{b} = \frac{c}{d}$ if and only if $ad = bc$. For example, the rational number $\frac{5}{7}$ is the same rational number as the rational number $\frac{15}{21}$ because $5 \times 21 = 7 \times 15$. That is, $\frac{5}{7} = \frac{15}{21}$ because $5 \times 21 = 7 \times 15$. Similarly, $\frac{4}{-6} = \frac{-2}{3}$.

Since the sum of two rational numbers $\frac{a}{b}$ and $\frac{c}{d}$ is the unique rational number $\frac{(ad + bc)}{bd}$, we see that $(R_a, +, \times)$ has the closure property for addition; that is, if $\frac{a}{b}$ and $\frac{c}{d}$ are any rational numbers, then $\frac{a}{b} + \frac{c}{d} = \frac{(ad + bc)}{bd}$, and the sum is well-defined. For example, $\frac{2}{9} + \frac{3}{4} = \frac{(2 \times 4 + 9 \times 3)}{9 \times 4}$

$= \frac{(8 + 27)}{36} = \frac{35}{36}$, a rational number. It is easy to prove that $\left(\frac{a}{b} + \frac{c}{d}\right) + \frac{e}{f} = \frac{a}{b} + \left(\frac{c}{d} + \frac{e}{f}\right)$ for any rational numbers $\frac{a}{b}, \frac{c}{d}$, and $\frac{e}{f}$. The unique additive identity is the rational number 0, which can be expressed as $\frac{0}{1}, \frac{0}{2}, \frac{0}{3}, \cdots$. Thus $\frac{a}{b} + 0 = \frac{a}{b}$ and $0 + \frac{a}{b} = \frac{a}{b}$. The unique additive inverse of the rational number $\frac{a}{b}$ is the rational number $\frac{-a}{b}$; that is, if $\frac{a}{b}$ is any rational number, then there exists a rational number $\frac{-a}{b}$ such that $\frac{a}{b} + \frac{-a}{b} = 0$ and $\frac{-a}{b} + \frac{a}{b} = 0$. Hence $-\left(\frac{a}{b}\right) = \frac{-a}{b}$. The commutative property for addition follows readily from the definition of $\frac{a}{b} + \frac{c}{d}$. Thus if $\frac{a}{b}$ and $\frac{c}{d}$ are any rational numbers, then $\frac{a}{b} + \frac{c}{d} = \frac{c}{d} + \frac{a}{b}$.

Since the product $\frac{a}{b} \cdot \frac{c}{d}$ (that is, $\frac{a}{b} \times \frac{c}{d}$) of the rational numbers $\frac{a}{b}$ and $\frac{c}{d}$ is the unique rational number $\frac{(a \times c)}{(b \times d)}$, we see that $(R_a, +, \times)$ possesses the closure property for multiplication. The associative property follows readily from the definition of $\frac{a}{b} \times \frac{c}{d}$. The unique multiplicative identity is the rational number $\frac{1}{1}$ or simply 1. Thus, if $\frac{a}{b}$ is any rational number, then $\frac{a}{b} \times 1 = \frac{a}{b}$ and $1 \times \frac{a}{b} = \frac{a}{b}$ and, moreover, 1 is the only rational number with this property. If $\frac{a}{b} \neq 0$ (i.e., if $a \neq 0$), then the unique rational number $\frac{b}{a}$ exists such that $\frac{a}{b} \times \frac{b}{a} = 1$ and $\frac{b}{a} \times \frac{a}{b} = 1$. Thus $\frac{b}{a}$ is the unique multiplicative inverse of the nonzero rational number $\frac{a}{b}$; that is, $\frac{1}{a/b} = \frac{b}{a}$. If $\frac{a}{b}$ and $\frac{c}{d}$ are any rational numbers, then $\frac{a}{b} \times \frac{c}{d} = \frac{c}{d} \times \frac{a}{b}$; that is, $(R_a, +, \times)$ possesses the commutative property for multiplication. The distributive property is readily proved. Hence if $\frac{a}{b}, \frac{c}{d}$, and $\frac{e}{f}$ are any rational numbers, then $\frac{a}{b} \times \left(\frac{c}{d} + \frac{e}{f}\right) = \frac{a}{b} \times \frac{c}{d} + \frac{a}{b} \times \frac{e}{f}$.

Although the integer system $(I, +, \times)$ is *not* a field, we see that the rational number system $(R_a, +, \times)$ is a field.

Observe that the set $\{0, 1, 2, 3, \ldots\}$ of *counting numbers* is a subset of $\{\ldots, -3, -2, -1, 0, 1, 2, 3, \ldots\}$. Letting $C_0 = \{0, 1, 2, 3, \ldots\}$, we see that $C_0 \subset I$. Recall that $(I, +, \times)$ is not a field. Is $(C_0, +, \times)$ a field? That is, does $(C_0, +, \times)$ possess all field properties? Since 0 is the only element of C_0 which has an additive inverse and 1 is the only element of C_0 which has a multiplicative inverse, we see that $(C_0, +, \times)$ does not possess either inverse property. Thus although $(R, +, \times)$ and $(R_a, +, \times)$ are fields, we see that $(I, +, \times)$ and $(C_0, +, \times)$ are *not* fields.

Exercise 2.1

I. (1) Prove that $(C_0, +, \times)$ possesses all field properties except $F4$ and $F9$.

    (2) Prove that $(I, +, \times)$ possesses all field properties except $F9$.

(3) Prove that $(R_a, +, \times)$ possesses all field properties. [You may assume the properties in (1) and (2).]

(4) Let $I^+ = \{1, 2, 3, \ldots\}$ (the set of *positive integers*). Which field properties does $(I^+, +, \times)$ possess?

(5) Let $I^- = \{^-1, ^-2, ^-3, \ldots\}$ (the set of *negative integers*). Which field properties does $(I^-, +, \times)$ possess?

(6) Let $A = \{0, 1, 2\}$. Which field properties does $(A, +, \times)$ possess?

(7) Let $B = \{1\}$. Which field properties does $(B, +, \times)$ possess?

(8) Let $C = \{0\}$. Which field properties does $(C, +, \times)$ possess?

II. Let $S = \{a + b\sqrt{2} : a \in R_a \text{ and } b \in R_a\}$. Which field properties does $(S, +, \times)$ possess?

2.2 The Need for Real Numbers

In Section 2.1 we learned that the real number system, $(R, +, \times)$, is a field and the rational number system, $(R_a, +, \times)$, is a field. However, the system of integers, $(I, +, \times)$, and the counting number system, $(C_0, +, \times)$, are not fields. In Exercise I (4) of Section 2.1, we learned that the system of positive integers, $(I^+, +, \times)$, is not a field.

Historically, the first numbers invented were the positive integers. Recall that the set of positive integers is the set consisting of the numbers $1, 2, 3, 4, 5, \ldots$ That is, $I^+ = \{1, 2, 3, 4, 5, \ldots\}$. We use the positive integers when we count the elements in any finite nonempty set. In fact, the reason that the first numbers invented were the positive integers is that primitive man's principal use of arithmetic consisted of counting.

As man progressed, his daily needs required him to solve certain equations. For example, to solve the equation $x + 2 = 5$, the set of positive integers suffice. The solution is 3. However, if we wish to solve the equation $x + 5 = 5$, we discover that there is no solution in the set of positive integers. For this reason we extend the set of positive integers to *the set of counting numbers, C_0, which contains 0 as an element*. The equation $x + 5 = 5$ has a solution in C_0.

However, if we wish to solve the equation $x + 7 = 5$, we discover that there is no solution in the set of counting numbers. Similarly, if we wish to solve the equation $x + a = 0$, for any positive integer a, we discover that there is no solution in C_0. Hence we extend C_0 to *the set of integers, I*, which contains the negative integers, $^-1, ^-2, ^-3, \ldots$. The equation $x + a = 0$ has a solution in I.

Similarly, if we try to solve the equation $5x + ^-2 = 0$, we discover that there is no solution in the set of integers. Similarly, there is no solution of the equation $bx + a = 0$, for all nonzero integers b and all integers a, in I, unless b divides a. Consequently we extend the set of integers to *the set of rational numbers, R_a,* which contains the set of fractions as a proper subset. The equation $bx + a = 0$ has a solution in R_a.

If we try to solve the equation $x^2 = 2$, we discover that there is no solution in the set of rational numbers. Similarly, there is no solution of the equation $9x^2 = 2$ in the set of rational numbers. In general, if either a or b is not the square of an integer, there is no solution of the equation $bx^2 = a$ in the set of rational numbers. Consequently we extend the set of rational numbers to *the set of real numbers, R,* which contains the set of irrational numbers as a proper subset. If a and b are any positive integers, the equation $bx^2 = a$ has a solution (in fact, two solutions) in R.

The relationship of the set of real numbers to the above mentioned subsets is illustrated in Figure 2.1.

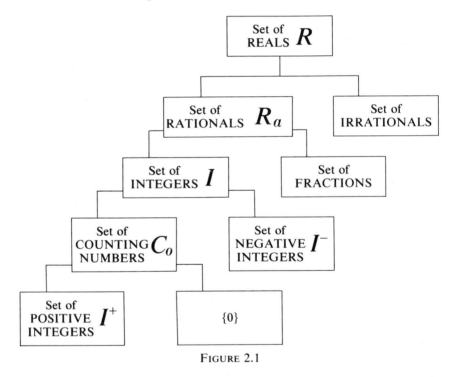

FIGURE 2.1

Exercise 2.2

I. Decide whether each of the following open sentences can be converted to a true sentence by replacement of the variable by a positive integer. That is, decide whether each of the following equations has a solution in I^+. If it does, solve the equation.

(1) $x + 2 = 7$ (11) $5x = 7$
(2) $3x + 5 = 17$ (12) $7x = 5$
(3) $3x + 2 = 2 + 2x$ (13) $5x^2 = 45$
(4) $2x + 3 = 3$ (14) $9x^2 = 36$
(5) $4x + 11 = 7$ (15) $9x^2 = 5$
(6) $5x + 1 = 6$ (16) $5x^2 = 9$
(7) $x^2 + 2 = 6$ (17) $x^2 + 4 = 7$
(8) $3x + 4 = 5$ (18) $4x^2 = 5$
(9) $3x + 5 = 4$ (19) $x^2 + 7 = 6$
(10) $x^2 + 5 = 9$ (20) $x^2 + 9 = 5$

II. Decide whether each of the equations in Exercise I has a solution in C_0. If it does, solve the equation.

III. Decide whether each of the equations in Exercise I has a solution in I. If it does, solve the equation.

IV. Decide whether each of the equations in Exercise I has a solution in R_a. If it does, solve it.

V. Decide whether each of the equations in Exercise I has a solution in R. If it does, solve it.

2.3   Consequences of the Field Properties

We have learned that the real number system $(R, +, \times)$ is a field and that the rational number system $(R_a, +, \times)$ is a field also. However, neither $(C_0, +, \times)$ nor $(I, +, \times)$ is a field. In this section we consider some properties of $(R, +, \times)$ which are consequences of the field properties. These properties, which are of frequent use in algebra, are, therefore, properties of *every* field — not merely of the real number field. Hence any deductions made from the field properties are valid in *any* field.

One important property is the *cancellation property for addition*.

CANCELLATION PROPERTY FOR ADDITION

If a, b, and c are any elements of a field such that $a + c = b + c$, then $a = b$.

For example, if $a + 2 = \sqrt{3} + 2$, then $a = \sqrt{3}$; and if $x + y = 3 + y$, then $x = 3$.

To prove the cancellation property for addition, we employ the closure, associative, inverse, and identity properties for addition as follows:

$$a + c = b + c$$
$$(a + c) + {}^-c = (b + c) + {}^-c$$
$$a + (c + {}^-c) = b + (c + {}^-c)$$
$$a + 0 = b + 0$$
$$a = b. \diamondsuit$$

In a similar manner we state and prove the *cancellation property for multiplication*.

CANCELLATION PROPERTY FOR MULTIPLICATION

If a, b, and c are any elements of a field such that $ac = bc$ and $c \neq 0$, then $a = b$.

For example, if $a\pi = 3\pi$, then $a = 3$; and if $xy = \frac{2}{3}y$ and $y \neq 0$, then $x = \frac{2}{3}$.

The proof depends on the closure, associative, inverse, and identity properties for multiplication as follows:

$$ac = bc \qquad (c \neq 0)$$
$$(ac) \times \left(\tfrac{1}{c}\right) = (bc) \times \left(\tfrac{1}{c}\right)$$
$$a \times \left(c \times \tfrac{1}{c}\right) = b \times \left(c \times \tfrac{1}{c}\right)$$
$$a \times 1 = b \times 1$$
$$a = b. \diamondsuit$$

A useful alternative statement of the cancellation property for multiplication is the *multiplication property of zero*. In a field, these two apparently different properties are equivalent. The multiplication property of zero is used extensively in algebra, particularly in the solution of quadratic equations.

MULTIPLICATION PROPERTY OF ZERO

If a and b are any elements of a field, then $ab = 0$ if and only if $a = 0$ or $b = 0$.

For example, if $3x = 0$, then $x = 0$; if $3(x + 1) = 0$, then $x + 1 = 0$ and thus $x = {}^-1$; and if $(x + {}^-1)(x + 1) = 0$, then $x = 1$ or $x = {}^-1$.

The multiplication property of zero is really a statement of *two* facts: (1) if $a = 0$ or $b = 0$, then $ab = 0$; (2) if $ab = 0$, then $a = 0$ or $b = 0$. The proof of the multiplication property of zero depends on the identity property for addition, the distributive property, the cancellation property for addition, and the cancellation property for multiplication as follows:

Now $a + 0 = a$.

$a(a + 0) = a \times a$.

$a \times a + a \times 0 = a \times a$.

But $a \times a + 0 = a \times a$.

Hence $a \times a + a \times 0 = a \times a + 0$.

Thus, $a \times 0 = 0$ (by the cancellation property for addition).

Hence, if $b = 0$, then $ab = 0$.

Conversely, let $ab = 0$ and $a \neq 0$.

Now $a \times 0 = 0$.

Hence $ab = a \times 0$ and $a \neq 0$.

Thus $b = 0$ (by the cancellation property for multiplication)

Hence if $ab = 0$, then $a = 0$ or $b = 0$. $\diamond$

The *double negative* property is a useful rule of algebra. According to this property, the additive inverse of the additive inverse of the real number a is a itself. For example, $^-(^-7) = 7$ and $^-(^-\sqrt{2}) = \sqrt{2}$.

DOUBLE NEGATIVE PROPERTY

If a is any element of a field, then $^-(^-a) = a$.

Since the main part of this text is concerned with the real number system, the usual terminology of real numbers is used in the names of the properties. For example, the Double Negative Property derives its name from the fact that the negative of the negative of any real number a is a itself. However, the reader is warned that the property, as stated, is valid in *any* field and that the symbol "^-a" represents *the additive inverse of* a, and not necessarily the negative of the real number a. In fact, the word *negative*, as pertains to real numbers, is meaningless in some fields. In Chapter 7 the reader will learn that there are fields which do not possess the familiar order properties of the field of real numbers and hence that we cannot define *positive* numbers and *negative* numbers, in the usual manner, unless we postulate an order relation in the field.

Similarly, the symbol "0" represents the *additive identity* (not necessarily the real number *zero*), the symbol "1" represents the *multiplicative identity* (not necessarily the real number *one*), and the symbol "$\frac{1}{a}$" represents the multiplicative inverse of the element a, provided $a \neq 0$. The qualifying adjective *nonzero* in $F9$ is used to indicate that every element of F *except* 0 (the additive identity) has a unique multiplicative inverse.

The *sign property for addition* is a useful property in algebra. In particular, it enables us to express the additive inverse (or negative) of a sum of two real numbers as the sum of the additive inverses of the two real numbers.

SIGN PROPERTY FOR ADDITION

If a and b are any elements of a field, then $^-(a + b) = {}^-a + {}^-b$. For example, $^-(x + 3) = {}^-x + {}^-3$ and $^-(x + {}^-3) = {}^-x + {}^-({}^-3) = {}^-x + 3$. Similarly, $^-({}^-x + y + {}^-5) = {}^-[({}^-x + y) + {}^-5] = {}^-({}^-x + y) + {}^-({}^-5) = (x + {}^-y) + 5 = x + ({}^-y + 5)$.

The proof of the sign property for addition depends on the inverse, commutative, associative, identity, and cancellation properties for addition as follows:

Now $^-(a + b) + (a + b) = 0$.
Moreover, $({}^-a + {}^-b) + (a + b) = ({}^-a + a) + ({}^-b + b)$
$$= 0 + 0$$
$$= 0.$$
Thus $^-(a + b) + (a + b) = ({}^-a + {}^-b) + (a + b)$
Hence $^-(a + b) = {}^-a + {}^-b.\diamondsuit$

The sign property for addition can be generalized to the sum of any number of elements in any field. The generalized sign property may be stated as follows: If $a_1, a_2, \ldots, a_k$ *are any elements of F, then* $^-(a_1 + a_2 + \cdots + a_k) = {}^-a_1 + {}^-a_2 + \cdots + {}^-a_k$.

A useful rule of algebra is that *the product of a positive number and a negative number is a negative number.* Another useful rule is that *the product of two negative numbers is a positive number.* Both of these rules are special cases of the *sign property for multiplication.* The reader should recall the comments after the double negative property.

SIGN PROPERTY FOR MULTIPLICATION

If a and b are any elements of a field, then

(a) $^-a \times b = {}^-(a \times b)$;
(b) $a \times {}^-b = {}^-(a \times b)$;
(c) $^-a \times b = a \times {}^-b$;
(d) $^-a \times {}^-b = a \times b$.

For example, $^-2 \times 3 = {}^-(2 \times 3) = {}^-6$; $2 \times {}^-3 = {}^-(2 \times 3) = {}^-6$; $^-2 \times 3 = 2 \times {}^-3$; and $^-2 \times {}^-3 = 2 \times 3 = 6$.

The proof of the sign property for multiplication depends on the distributive property, the additive inverse property, the multiplication property of zero, and the cancellation property as follows:

(a) Now $^-a(b) + a(b) = ({}^-a + a)b$
$$= (0)b$$
$$= 0.$$

Moreover, $^-(ab) + ab = 0$.
Hence $^-a(b) + a(b) = {}^-(ab) + ab$.
Thus $^-a(b) = {}^-(ab)$. $\diamondsuit$

(b) Now $a(^-b) + a(b) = a(^-b + b)$
$$= a(0)$$
$$= 0.$$
Moreover, $^-(ab) + ab = 0$.
Hence $a(^-b) + ab = {}^-(ab) + ab$.
Thus $a(^-b) = {}^-(ab)$. $\diamondsuit$

(c) Since $^-a(b) = {}^-(ab)$ and $a(^-b) = {}^-(ab)$, it follows that
$^-a(b) = a(^-b)$. $\diamondsuit$

(d) Now $(^-a)(^-b) + (^-a)(b) = {}^-a(^-b + b)$
$$= {}^-a(0)$$
$$= 0.$$
Moreover, $ab + (^-a)(b) = ab + {}^-(ab)$
$$= 0.$$
Hence $(^-a)(^-b) + (^-a)(b) = ab + (^-a)(b)$.
Thus $(^-a)(^-b) = ab$. $\diamondsuit$

Observe the dominant role the distributive property plays in the proof of the fact that $^-a \times {}^-b = a \times b$.

By property $F3$, the real number 0 has the property that $a + 0 = a$ for every real number a. Is 0 the only real number with this property? In other words, is there another real number z such that $a + z = a$ for some real number a? To prove that there is no real number z (other than 0) such that $a + z = a$, we assume that there is and prove that $z = 0$, as follows:

Assume $a + z = a$.
But $a + 0 = a$.
Hence $a + z = a + 0$.
Thus $z = 0$.
Hence, for every real number a, $a + z = a$ if and only if $z = 0$.
Thus *the additive identity is unique.* $\diamondsuit$

In a similar manner, we prove that the multiplicative identity 1 is unique, as follows:

Assume that there exists a real number u such that $a \times u = a$
for some real number $a \neq 0$.
But $a \times 1 = a$ for every real number $a \neq 0$.
Hence $a \times u = a \times 1$.
But $a \neq 0$.
Hence $u = 1$.
That is, *the multiplicative identity is unique.* $\diamondsuit$

The two proofs above make it unnecessary for us to use the word *unique* in F3 and F8. Even if we omitted the word, the uniqueness would follow.

Because of F4, *the inverse property for addition,* we can define *subtraction* of any two elements of a field as follows:

DEFINITION 2.   The *difference*, $a - b$, in the subtraction of the element b from the element a in any field F is that element c of F such that $a = b + c$. That is, $a - b = c$ if and only if $a = b + c$.

The following examples illustrate Definition 2.

Example 1. $8 - 5 = 3$ because $5 + 3 = 8$.

Example 2. $8 - {}^-5 = 13$ because
$$\begin{aligned}
{}^-5 + 13 &= {}^-5 + (5 + 8)\\
&= ({}^-5 + 5) + 8\\
&= 0 + 8\\
&= 8.
\end{aligned}$$

Example 3. $5 - {}^-8 = 13$ because
$$\begin{aligned}
{}^-8 + 13 &= {}^-8 + (8 + 5)\\
&= ({}^-8 + 8) + 5\\
&= 0 + 5\\
&= 5.
\end{aligned}$$

Example 4. ${}^-5 - {}^-8 = 3$ because
$$\begin{aligned}
{}^-8 + 3 &= {}^-(5 + 3) + 3\\
&= ({}^-5 + {}^-3) + 3\\
&= {}^-5 + ({}^-3 + 3)\\
&= {}^-5 + 0\\
&= {}^-5.
\end{aligned}$$

Example 5. ${}^-8 - {}^-5 = {}^-3$ because
$$\begin{aligned}
{}^-5 + {}^-3 &= {}^-(5 + 3)\\
&= {}^-8.
\end{aligned}$$

The following important properties can be proved from Definition 2:

1. $a - b = a + {}^-b$, and
2. $a - {}^-b = a + b$,

for all real numbers a and b.

Because of F9, *the inverse property for multiplication,* we can define *division* of any element of F by and nonzero element of F as follows.

DEFINITION 3.   The *quotient*, $a \div b$, in the division of the element a by the nonzero element b in any field F is that element c of F such that $a = b \times c$. That is, $a \div b = c$ if and only if $a = b \times c$.

The quotient $a \div b$ is frequently indicated by $\frac{a}{b}$ or a/b. For example, $2 \div 3 = \frac{2}{3} = 2/3$, and $\pi \div \sqrt{2} = \frac{\pi}{\sqrt{2}} = \pi/\sqrt{2}$. The above examples from the field of real numbers emphasize that a may be any element of the field, and b may be any element except 0. Thus $\frac{a}{b}$ is not necessarily a rational number.

The following examples illustrate Definition 3.

Example 6. $^-15 \div 3 = {}^-5$ because $^-15 = 3 \times {}^-5$.

Example 7. $^-15 \div {}^-3 = 5$ because $^-15 = {}^-3 \times 5$.

Example 8. $15 \div {}^-3 = {}^-5$ because $15 = {}^-3 \times {}^-5$.

Example 9. $3 \div \frac{4}{5} = \frac{15}{4}$ because $\frac{4}{5} \times \frac{15}{4} = 3$.

Example 10. $\frac{2}{3} \div \frac{5}{7} = \frac{14}{15}$ because $\frac{5}{7} \times \frac{14}{15} = \frac{2}{3}$.

The following important properties can be proved from Definition 3:

1. $a \div b = a \times \frac{1}{b}$,
2. $^-a \div b = {}^-(a \div b) = {}^-\!\left(\frac{a}{b}\right)$,
3. $a \div {}^-b = {}^-(a \div b) = {}^-\!\left(\frac{a}{b}\right)$,
4. $^-a \div {}^-b = a \div b = \frac{a}{b}$, and
5. $\frac{a}{b} \div \frac{c}{d} = \frac{a}{b} \times \frac{d}{c} = \frac{ad}{bc}$,

for all real numbers a and all nonzero real numbers b, c, and d. The last property above is the familiar *invert and multiply rule*.

Exercise 2.3

I. Use the cancellation property for addition and the cancellation property for multiplication to compute that real number a which obeys each of the following conditions.

(1) $2a + 5 = 6 + 5$ (6) $2a = 5$
(2) $3a + 2 = 6 + 2$ (7) $6a - 3 = 4$
(3) $2a + 7 = 3 + 7$ (8) $6a - 4 = 3$
(4) $2a + 3 = 5 + 3$ (9) $\sqrt{2}a = 5\sqrt{2}$
(5) $2a = 7$ (10) $\pi a = 6\pi$

II. Apply the sign property for addition to each of the following.

(1) $^-(6 + \pi)$ (4) $^-(\pi + {}^-2)$

(2) $^-(\sqrt{2} + 7)$ (5) $^-(2 + {}^-\pi + \sqrt{2})$

(3) $^-(^-3 + \sqrt{2})$ (6) $^-(3 + {}^-\sqrt{2} + {}^-\pi)$

III. Employ the sign property for multiplication to compute each of the following.

(1) $^-2 \times 5$ (6) $^-(^-5 \times 3)$

(2) $3 \times {}^-4$ (7) $^-(8 \times {}^-4 \times 5)$

(3) $^-(3 \times 2)$ (8) $^-(8 \times 4 \times {}^-5)$

(4) $^-(5 \times 7)$ (9) $^-(^-2 \times {}^-3 \times {}^-4)$

(5) $^-(2 \times {}^-4)$ (10) $^-(^-3 \times {}^-5 \times {}^-2)$

IV. Employ the distributive property and the multiplication property of zero to prove that each of the following is 0.

(1) $6(5) + {}^-6(5)$ (5) $3\pi(4) + 3\pi(^-4)$

(2) $5(6) + 5(^-6)$ (6) $2\pi(^-5) + 2\pi(5)$

(3) $\sqrt{2}(^-3) + \sqrt{2}(3)$ (7) $\pi(^-4) + {}^-\pi(^-4)$

(4) $\sqrt{3}(^-2) + \sqrt{3}(2)$ (8) $\sqrt{2}(^-3) + {}^-\sqrt{2}(^-3)$

V. Employ Definition 2 and its consequences to compute each of the following differences.

(1) $5 - 3$ (11) $^-4 - 4$

(2) $3 - 5$ (12) $4 - 4$

(3) $0 - 2$ (13) $6.7 - 8.1$

(4) $0 - {}^-2$ (14) $6.7 - {}^-8.1$

(5) $8 - {}^-2$ (15) $^-6.7 - {}^-8.1$

(6) $^-2 - 8$ (16) $^-6.7 - 8.1$

(7) $^-2 - {}^-8$ (17) $3\pi - {}^-5\pi$

(8) $^-7 - 2$ (18) $2\sqrt{2}\pi - 5\sqrt{2}\pi$

(9) $^-4 - {}^-4$ (19) $^-2\sqrt{2}\pi - 5\sqrt{2}\pi$

(10) $4 - {}^-4$ (20) $^-2\sqrt{2}\pi - {}^-5\sqrt{2}\pi$

VI. Employ Definition 3 and its consequences to compute each of the following quotients.

(1) $39 \div {}^-3$ (7) $^-2 \div \frac{4}{5}$

(2) $^-39 \div 3$ (8) $\frac{^-4}{5} \div {}^-2$

(3) $^-39 \div {}^-3$ (9) $^-2 \div \frac{^-4}{5}$

(4) $^-39 \div 5$ (10) $\frac{^-2}{5} \div {}^-4$

(5) $^-39 \div {}^-5$ (11) $\frac{4}{5} \div \frac{7}{9}$

(6) $39 \div {}^-5$ (12) $\frac{7}{9} \div \frac{4}{5}$

(13) $\frac{5}{4} \div \frac{7}{9}$ (17) $\frac{-4}{5} \div \frac{5}{4}$

(14) $\frac{5}{4} \div \frac{9}{7}$ (18) $\frac{4}{5} \div \frac{-4}{5}$

(15) $\frac{4}{5} \div \frac{9}{7}$ (19) $\frac{-5}{4} \div \frac{5}{-4}$

(16) $\frac{7}{9} \div \frac{5}{4}$ (20) $\frac{4}{7} \div \frac{7}{4}$

VII. (1) Prove that the multiplication property of zero follows from the cancellation property for multiplication.

(2) Prove that the cancellation property for multiplication follows from the multiplication property of zero.

(3) Prove that $\frac{1}{1/a} = a$ for any nonzero real number a.

(4) Prove that the property $a - {}^-b = a + b$ follows from the property $a - b = a + {}^-b$ and the double negative property.

(5) Prove that $\frac{a}{a} = 1$ for every real number a except 0, and $\frac{a}{1} = a$ for every real number a.

2.4 Primes, Composites, Greatest Common Divisor, and Least Common Multiple

Later it will be necessary to simplify certain *algebraic* expressions and to combine certain rational expressions by means of the operations of addition, subtraction, multiplication, and division. Since these procedures are similar to those in combining *numerical* expressions, we present a brief review of the procedures involved in combining numerical expressions. The concepts and terminology introduced in the following definitions are essential in the development.

DEFINITION 4. (a) The integer b *divides* the integer a (written $b|a$) if and only if there exists an integer k such that $a = bk$.

(b) The integer b is a *divisor* (or *factor*) of the integer a if and only if b divides a.

(c) The integer a is a *multiple* of the integer b if and only if b is a *divisor* of a.

(d) The integer a *is divisible by* the integer b if and only if a is a multiple of b.

The following examples illustrate Definition 4.

Example 1. $5|15$ because $5 \times 3 = 15$. Thus 5 is a divisor of 15, 15 is a multiple of 5, and 15 is divisible by 5.

Example 2. $^-5|15$ because $^-5 \times {}^-3 = 15$. Thus $^-5$ is a divisor of 15, 15 is a multiple of $^-5$, and 15 is divisible by $^-5$.

Example 3. $^-5|^-15$ because $^-5 \times 3 = {}^-15$. Thus $^-5$ is a divisor of $^-15$, $^-15$ is a multiple of $^-5$, and $^-15$ is divisible by $^-5$.

Observe from Definition 4 that if $b|a$ and $b \neq 0$, then $\frac{a}{b}$ is a unique integer. If $b|a$ and $b = 0$, then $a = 0$ also, and $\frac{a}{b}$ is not defined. If $b = 0$ and $a \neq 0$, then $b \nmid a$, and $\frac{a}{b}$ is not defined. Thus, if $b|a$ and $b \neq 0$, the integer k of Definition 4 is unique. The following divisibility properties follow from Definition 4.

THEOREM 1. *(a) If $a|b$ and $a|c$, then $a|(b + c)$.*
(b) If $a|b$ and $b|c$, then $a|c$.

It follows immediately from Definition 4 that $^-1|a$, $1|a$, $a|a$, and $^-a|a$ for every integer a. Hence every integer, except 1 and $^-1$, has at least *four* divisors, two negative divisors and two positive divisors. Any positive integer which has *exactly* two positive divisors is given a special name.

DEFINITION 5. The positive integer p is called a *prime number* (or *prime*) if and only if p has exactly two positive divisors, 1 and p.

According to Definition 5, 1 is *not* a prime. Moreover, 4, 6, 8, 9, 10, and 15 are *not* primes. The first 10 primes are 2, 3, 5, 7, 11, 13, 17, 19, 23, and 29. Observe that some odd numbers are not primes and that the even number 2 is a prime. Any positive integer greater than 1 which is not prime is given a special name.

DEFINITION 6. The positive integer c is called a *composite number* (or simply a *composite*) if and only if $c \neq 1$ and c is not a prime.

The first 10 composites are 4, 6, 8, 9, 10, 12, 14, 15, 16, and 18.
It follows from Definitions 5 and 6 that 1 is neither prime nor composite. This choice is arbitrary. We *could* have defined the words *prime* and *composite* so that 1 would be a prime. However, in more advanced mathematics time is saved in statements and proofs of theorems if 1 is not considered a prime. If 1 were considered to be a prime, then many theorems would have to be stated with exceptions and special cases. The positive integer 1 is called a *unit*.
For centuries mathematicians have been fascinated by many interesting questions concerning primes. Although many of these questions have been answered, some of them remain unanswered even today. Many problems in number theory are easily stated but not easily solved. In fact, most problems are so easily stated that the average high school student can understand them. However, their solutions have evaded the most eminent mathematicians.

The concepts of *common divisor* and *greatest common divisor* are important.

DEFINITION 7.   The positive integer c is said to be a *common divisor* of the integers a and b if and only if $c|a$ and $c|b$.

For example, 5 is a common divisor of 20 and 30 because $5|20$ and $5|30$. Other common divisors of 20 and 30 are 1, 2, and 10. Definition 7 is easily extended to include a common divisor of more than two integers; *any common divisor is a divisor of each of the integers.* For example, 3 is a common divisor of 6, 12, and 15. The reader should notice that Definition 7 restricts consideration of .common divisors to positive divisors only.

Since 1 divides every positive integer, we see that 1 is a common divisor of any two positive integers a and b. That is, if a and b are any positive integers, then there exists a common divisor of a and b.

Now let us consider the set of all common divisors of a and b. Since any common divisor of a and b divides a, we see that the set of all common divisors of a and b is a subset of $\{1, 2, 3, \dots, a\}$. Thus the set of all common divisors of a and b is a finite set. Hence it contains a largest element. In Definition 8, we give a name to the largest element of the set of all common divisors of two positive integers.

DEFINITION 8.   The largest member of the set of all common divisors of the positive integers a and b is called the *greatest common divisor* (*gcd*) of a and b.

For example, the set of all common divisors of 210 and 20 is equal to $\{1, 2, 5, 10\}$. Thus the gcd of 210 and 20 is equal to 10. Notice that every element of $\{1, 2, 5, 10\}$ divides 10. This example and other similar ones lead us to suspect that the greatest common divisor of any two positive integers a and b is divisible by every common divisor of a and b. It may be proved as a theorem that the gcd of a and b is divisible by every common divisor of a and b.

By Definition 4, a is a multiple of b if and only if b is a divisor of a. Thus 35 is a multiple of 5 because 5 is a divisor of 35; that is, $35 = 5 \times 7$. We see also that $7|35$ and that 35 is a multiple of 7. Some multiples of 9 are 9, 18, 27, 36, 45, 54, 63, 72, and some multiples of 12 are 12, 24, 36, 48, 60, 72. From these two sets of multiples we see that 36 and 72 are multiples of 9 and of 12; that is, 36 is a common multiple of 9 and 12, and so is 72. The concepts of *common multiple* and *least common multiple* are important.

DEFINITION 9.   The positive integer c is said to be a *common multiple* of the positive integers a and b if and only if c is a multiple of a and c is a multiple of b.

For any pair of positive integers a and b, we know that a common multiple exists; namely, ab. In fact, for any positive integer k, kab is a common multiple of a and b. Thus, since 36 is a common multiple of 9 and 12, we see that 2×36, 3×36, 4×36, . . . are also common multiples of 9 and 12. The set $M = \{m_1, m_2, \ldots\}$ of all common multiples of a and b is a subset of C_0. By the *well-ordering property*,* there is a least element m of M. For example, the set $\{36, 72, 108, 144, \ldots\}$ of all common multiples of 9 and 12 contains the least element 36. For this reason we say that 36 is the least common multiple of 9 and 12.

DEFINITION 10.   The *least commom multiple (lcm)* of a and b is the least element, m, of the set of all common multiples of a and b.

The lcm of 9 and 12 is 36, and the lcm of 5 and 7 is 35.

Recall from Definition 4 that b is called a *factor* of a if and only if $a = bk$ for some integer k. By this same definition we see that k is also a factor of a. When an integer has been expressed as a product of factors, we say that it has been *factored*. Thus a has been factored into its factors b and k. In particular, 21 can be factored as 3×7 and 30 may be factored as 6×5. Since $6 = 2 \times 3$, we can factor 30 into a product of three factors; thus $30 = 2 \times 3 \times 5$. Notice that the three factors of 30 are primes. Thus 30 has been expressed as a product of prime factors. Similarly, when we write, "$21 = 3 \times 7$," we are expressing 21 as a product of *prime* factors.

DEFINITION 11.   (a) The integer a is said to be *factored* if and only if it is expressed as a product of factors.

(b) The integer a is said to be *factored into prime factors* if and only if it is expressed as a product of prime factors.

(c) A *prime factorization* of the integer a is any product of primes $p_1, p_2, \ldots, p_k$ such that $a = p_1 p_2 \ldots p_k$.

Thus $2 \times 3 \times 5$ is a prime factorization of 30. Other prime factorizations of 30 are $2 \times 5 \times 3$, $3 \times 5 \times 2$, $5 \times 2 \times 3$, and $5 \times 3 \times 2$. The only difference between any two of these prime factorizations of

---

* The *well-ordering property* will be discussed in Section 2.7.

30 is the order in which the prime factors occur. If we disregard the order, we see that there is *exactly one* prime factorization of 30.

Now we state an important theorem known as the *unique prime factorization theorem* (or *fundamental theorem of arithmetic*).

THEOREM 2. *(a) If a is any composite, then a can be expressed as a product of primes, $a = p_1p_2 \ldots p_k$.*

(b) Except for the order in which the primes occur, the prime factorization of a is unique.

We may employ the unique prime factorization theorem to compute the *gcd* and *lcm* of any two positive integers. For convenience, we make the following definitions: (1) $a^0 = 1$ for any nonzero integer a, and (2) $a^m = \underbrace{a \times a \times \ldots \times a}_{m \text{ factors}}$ for any integer a and any positive integer

m (m is called the *exponent*). Later in Section 2.5 we shall define a^0 for any nonzero real number a, and a^m for any real number a and any integer m and discuss the advantages of the notation.

Example 4. Compute the *lcm* of 12 and 9.
First we factor 12 and 9 as follows:

$12 = 2 \times 2 \times 3 = 2^2 \times 3,$
$9 = 3 \times 3 = 3^2.$

From these factorizations we see that any common multiple of 12 and 9 must contain the factor $2^2 \times 3$ *and* the factor 3^2. The smallest positive integer which contains *both* of these factors ($2^2 \times 3$ *and* 3^2) is $2^2 \times 3^2$. Hence the lcm of 12 and 9 is 36.

Example 5. Compute the *lcm* of 360 and 84.
First we exhibit the prime factorizations of 360 and 84 as follows:

$360 = 2^3 \times 3^2 \times 5^1,$
$84 = 2^2 \times 3^1 \times 7^1.$

Although we could compute the lcm as in Example 4, instead we compute the lcm of 360 and 84 in a way which enables us to develop a general systematic procedure for computing the lcm of any two numbers. From the factorization of 360 we see that the lcm must contain the factors 2, 3, and 5. From the factorization of 84 we see that the lcm must contain the factors 2, 3, and 7.

Hence the lcm must be of the form $2^j \times 3^k \times 5^l \times 7^m$, in which $j, k, l,$ and m are counting numbers. Since the lcm of 360 and 84 is the *smallest* positive integer which is a multiple of *both* 360 and 84, we determine *j, k, l,* and *m* from the fact that $2^j \times 3^k \times 5^l \times 7^m$ must be a multiple of 2^3 *and* 2^2, 3^2 *and* 3^1, 5^1 *and* 1, and 1 and 7^1. That is, the lcm must contain the factors 2^3, 3^2, 5^1, and 7^1 (the factors with the larger exponents).

Hence the lcm is

$$2^3 \times 3^2 \times 5^1 \times 7^1.$$

From the procedure in Example 5 we see that it is advantageous to express the factorization of each number by listing *all* prime factors of *both* numbers. For example,

$360 = 2^③ \times 3^② \times 5^① \times 7^0$, and
$84 = 2^2 \times 3^1 \times 5^0 \times 7^①$.

From these factorizations we can compute the lcm almost mechanically by choosing the *larger* of the two exponents of each prime factor of the two numbers. Thus the lcm of 360 and 84 is $2^3 \times 3^2 \times 5^1 \times 7^1$. The larger exponents are circled in the factorizations of 360 and 84.

Example 6.   Compute the *lcm* of 40320 and 2376.

$40320 = 2^7 \times 3^2 \times 5 \times 7 = 2^7 \times 3^2 \times 5^1 \times 7^1 \times 11^0$.
$2376 = 2^3 \times 3^3 \times 11 = \quad\; 2^3 \times 3^3 \times 5^0 \times 7^0 \times 11^1$.

Thus the lcm of 40320 and 2376 is $2^7 \times 3^3 \times 5 \times 7 \times 11$.

Example 7.   Compute the *lcm* of 105 and 22.

$105 = 3 \times 5 \times 7 = 2^0 \times 3^1 \times 5^1 \times 7^1 \times 11^0$.
$22 = 2 \times 11 = \quad\; 2^1 \times 3^0 \times 5^0 \times 7^0 \times 11^1$.

Thus the lcm of 105 and 22 is $2^1 \times 3^1 \times 5^1 \times 7^1 \times 11^1$.

The following theorem justifies the procedure for computing the *lcm* of any two positive integers *a* and *b*.

THEOREM 3.   *If a and b are any positive integers such that*

$a = p_1^{s_1} p_2^{s_2} \cdots p_k^{s_k},$
$b = p_1^{t_1} p_2^{t_2} \cdots p_k^{t_k},$

and the primes $p_1, p_2, \ldots, p_k$ *are all distinct, then the lcm of a and b is*

$$p_1^{w_1} p_2^{w_2} \cdots p_k^{w_k},$$

where w_1 *is the maximum of* s_1 *and* t_1, w_2 *is the maximum of* s_2 *and* t_2, *..., and* w_k *is the maximum of* s_k *and* t_k.

The reader should notice that some of the exponents may be 0.

To illustrate again the notation of Theorem 3, we reconsider Example 6. In Example 6, $a = 40320 = 2^7 \times 3^2 \times 5^1 \times 7^1 \times 11^0$, $p_1 = 2$, $s_1 = 7$, $p_2 = 3$, $s_2 = 2$, $p_3 = 5$, $s_3 = 1$, $p_4 = 7$, $s_4 = 1$, and $p_5 = 11$, $s_5 = 0$. Similarly, $b = 2376 = 2^3 \times 3^3 \times 5^0 \times 7^0 \times 11^1$, $t_1 = 3$, $t_2 = 3$, $t_3 = 0$, $t_4 = 0$, and $t_5 = 1$. Thus $w_1 = 7 =$ maximum of 7 and 3, $w_2 = 3$ = maximum of 2 and 3, $w_3 = 1 =$ maximum of 1 and 0, $w_4 = 1$ = maximum of 1 and 0, and $w_5 = 1 =$ maximum of 0 and 1. Consequently the lcm of 40,320 and 2376 is $2^7 \times 3^3 \times 5^1 \times 7^1 \times 11^1$.

Similarly, we may employ the unique prime factorization theorem to compute the gcd of any two positive integers. The following examples illustrate the method.

Example 8.   Compute the *gcd* of 12 and 9.

$12 = 2 \times 2 \times 3$
$9 = 3 \times 3$

Since the gcd of 12 and 9 divides 12, we see that the gcd must be a factor of 12.

Since the gcd of 12 and 9 divides 9, we see that the gcd of 12 and 9 must be a factor of 9.

Clearly, the largest positive integer which is a factor of both 12 and 9 is 3.

Hence, the gcd of 12 and 9 is 3.

Example 9.   Compute the *gcd* of 360 and 84.

$360 = 2^3 \times 3^2 \times 5 = 2^3 \times 3^2 \times 5^1 \times 7^0$.
$84 = 2^2 \times 3 \times 7 = 2^2 \times 3^1 \times 5^0 \times 7^1$.

Thus the gcd of 360 and 84 is $2^2 \times 3^1 \times 5^0 \times 7^0$, which is equal to 12.

Example 10.   Compute the *gcd* of 40320 and 2376.

$40320 = 2^7 \times 3^2 \times 5 \times 7 = 2^7 \times 3^2 \times 5^1 \times 7^1 \times 11^0$.
$2376 = 2^3 \times 3^3 \times 11 = 2^3 \times 3^3 \times 5^0 \times 7^0 \times 11^1$.

Thus the gcd of 40320 and 2376 is $2^3 \times 3^2 \times 5^0 \times 7^0 \times 11^0$, which is equal to 72.

Example 11.   Compute the *gcd* of 105 and 22.

$105 = 2^0 \times 3^1 \times 5^1 \times 7^1 \times 11^0$.
$22 = 2^1 \times 3^0 \times 5^0 \times 7^0 \times 11^1$.

Thus the gcd of 105 and 22 is $2^0 \times 3^0 \times 5^0 \times 7^0 \times 11^0$, which is equal to 1.

The following theorem justifies the procedure for computing the gcd of any two positive integers a and b.

THEOREM 4. *If a and b are any positive integers such that*

$$a = p_1^{s_1} p_2^{s_2} \cdots p_k^{s_k},$$
$$b = p_1^{t_1} p_2^{t_2} \cdots p_k^{t_k},$$

and the primes $p_1, p_2, \ldots, p_k$ are all distinct, then the gcd of a and b is

$$p_1^{v_1} p_2^{v_2} \cdots p_k^{v_k},$$

where v_1 is the minimum of s_1 and t_1, v_2 is the minimum of s_2 and $t_2, \ldots$, and v_k is the minimum of s_k and t_k.

The reader should notice that some of the exponents may be 0. In Example 10 above, $p_1 = 2$, $p_2 = 3$, $p_3 = 5$, $p_4 = 7$, $p_5 = 11$; $s_1 = 7$, $s_2 = 2$, $s_3 = 1$, $s_4 = 1$, $s_5 = 0$; $t_1 = 3$, $t_2 = 3$, $t_3 = 0$, $t_4 = 0$, $t_5 = 1$; $v_1 = 3$, $v_2 = 2$, $v_3 = 0$, $v_4 = 0$, $v_5 = 0$.

In computing the sum of two rational numbers, we usually express the rational numbers with a common denominator, the *lcm* of the denominators. The following examples illustrate the procedure employed.

Example 12. Compute $\frac{5}{9} + \frac{1}{12}$.

$$
\begin{aligned}
\frac{5}{9} + \frac{1}{12} &= \frac{5}{3^2} + \frac{1}{(2^2 \times 3)} \\
&= \frac{(5 \times 2^2)}{(3^2 \times 2^2)} + \frac{(1 \times 3)}{[(2^2 \times 3) \times 3]} \\
&= \frac{(5 \times 2^2)}{(3^2 \times 2^2)} + \frac{(1 \times 3)}{(2^2 \times 3^2)} \\
&= \frac{20}{(2^2 \times 3^2)} + \frac{3}{(2^2 \times 3^2)} \\
&= \frac{(20 + 3)}{(2^2 \times 3^2)} \\
&= \frac{23}{36}.
\end{aligned}
$$

The reason we chose the denominator $2^2 \times 3^2$ is that the least common multiple of 9 and 12 is $2^2 \times 3^2$.

Example 13. Compute $\frac{7}{12} + \frac{5}{144}$.

$$
\begin{aligned}
\frac{7}{12} + \frac{5}{144} &= \frac{(7 \times 12)}{(12 \times 12)} + \frac{5}{144}. \\
&= \frac{84}{144} + \frac{5}{144} \\
&= \frac{89}{144}.
\end{aligned}
$$

Example 14. Compute $\frac{1}{12} + \frac{1}{15}$.

$$
\begin{aligned}
\frac{1}{12} + \frac{1}{15} &= \frac{1}{(2^2 \times 3)} + \frac{1}{(3 \times 5)} \\
&= \frac{(1 \times 5)}{[(2^2 \times 3) \times 5]} + \frac{(2^2 \times 1)}{[2^2 \times (3 \times 5)]} \\
&= \frac{5}{(2^2 \times 3 \times 5)} + \frac{4}{(2^2 \times 3 \times 5)} \\
&= \frac{9}{(2^2 \times 3 \times 5)} \\
&= \frac{(3 \times 3)}{[(2^2 \times 5) \times 3]} \\
&= \frac{3}{(2^2 \times 5)} \\
&= \frac{3}{20}.
\end{aligned}
$$

The above examples illustrate that the procedure is to compute the least common multiple of the denominators, b and d, and then express the two rational numbers with the lcm of b and d as their common denominator.

DEFINITION 12. *The least common denominator* of two rational numbers $\frac{a}{b}$ and $\frac{c}{d}$ is the least common multiple of their denominators.

After we have added two rational numbers to obtain their sum, a rational number, we usually employ the gcd to reduce their sum to *lowest terms*. For example, we reduce $\frac{26}{39}$ to lowest terms by dividing 26 and 39 by their gcd. Hence $\frac{26}{39} = \frac{13 \times 2}{13 \times 3} = \frac{2}{3}$. The following theorem guarantees that every rational number has such a unique representation.

THEOREM 5. *Every rational number except 0 has a unique representation of the form $\frac{a}{b}$, in which a is an integer, b is a positive integer, and the gcd of a and b is 1.*

DEFINITION 13. A representation of a rational number is in *lowest terms* if and only if it is the unique representation of Theorem 5.

For example, $\frac{2}{3}$ is in lowest terms, $\frac{-4}{5}$ is in lowest terms, $\frac{26}{39}$ is *not* in lowest terms and $\frac{4}{-5}$ is *not* in lowest terms.

Exercise 2.4

I. (1) List all primes less than 100.
  (2) List all composites less than 100.
  (3) List all odd composites between 14 and 84.
  (4) List all even primes.

II. Compute the lcm of each of the following number pairs.

(1) 2 and 3   (6) 840 and 63
(2) 10 and 15   (7) 84 and 630
(3) 9 and 6   (8) 98 and 56
(4) 22 and 77   (9) 55 and 22
(5) 630 and 42   (10) 15 and 7

III. Compute the gcd of each pair of numbers in Exercise II.

IV. Compute the lcm and the gcd of each of the following number triplets.

(1) 12, 15, 33   (6) 24, 16, 9
(2) 12, 6, 18   (7) 4, 5, 9
(3) 12, 21, 77   (8) 6, 3, 9
(4) 50, 125, 8   (9) 100, 200, 250
(5) 77, 121, 49   (10) 10, 20, 25

V. Compute the gcd of each number triplet in Exercise IV.

VI. Express each of the following sums as a rational number in lowest terms.

(1) $\frac{1}{2} + \frac{1}{3}$ (6) $\frac{9}{840} + \frac{5}{63}$
(2) $\frac{1}{10} + \frac{1}{15}$ (7) $\frac{9}{84} + \frac{1}{630}$
(3) $\frac{5}{9} + \frac{5}{6}$ (8) $\frac{3}{98} + \frac{5}{56}$
(4) $\frac{9}{22} + \frac{8}{77}$ (9) $\frac{2}{55} + \frac{3}{22}$
(5) $\frac{1}{630} + \frac{9}{42}$ (10) $\frac{7}{15} + \frac{15}{7}$

VII. Express each of the following sums and differences as a rational number in lowest terms.

(1) $\frac{1}{12} + \frac{1}{15} + \frac{1}{33}$ (6) $\frac{7}{24} + \frac{5}{16} - \frac{4}{9}$
(2) $\frac{1}{12} + \frac{1}{6} + \frac{1}{18}$ (7) $\frac{3}{4} + \frac{4}{5} - \frac{5}{9}$
(3) $\frac{5}{12} + \frac{5}{21} - \frac{5}{77}$ (8) $\frac{5}{6} - \frac{2}{3} + \frac{4}{9}$
(4) $\frac{3}{50} - \frac{3}{125} + \frac{3}{8}$ (9) $\frac{3}{100} - \frac{3}{200} - \frac{7}{250}$
(5) $\frac{6}{77} - \frac{6}{121} + \frac{6}{49}$ (10) $\frac{3}{10} - \frac{7}{20} - \frac{1}{25}$

VIII. Prove

(1) If $a|b$ and $a|c$, then $a|(b + c)$.
(2) If $a|b$ and $a|c$, then $a|(b - c)$.
(3) If $a|b$ and $b|c$, then $a|c$.

2.5 Exponents, Radicals, and Decimals

The unique prime factorization theorem guarantees that any composite number can be expressed uniquely as a product of primes. For example, $360 = 2 \times 2 \times 2 \times 3 \times 3 \times 5 = 2^3 \times 3^2 \times 5$. When a number is expressed in the form a^m, that number is expressed in *exponential* form. In this example, 2^3 and 3^2 are the exponential forms of 8 and 9, respectively.

DEFINITION 14.   For any real number a and any positive integer m

(a) $a^m = \underbrace{a \times a \times \ldots \times a}_{m\text{-factors}}.$

(b) The real number a is called the *base*.

(c) The positive integer m is called the *exponent*.

(d) The real number a^m is said to be in *exponential form*.

Example 1. $\left(\frac{2}{3}\right)^4 = \left(\frac{2}{3}\right)\left(\frac{2}{3}\right)\left(\frac{2}{3}\right)\left(\frac{2}{3}\right) = \frac{(2)(2)(2)(2)}{(3)(3)(3)(3)} = \frac{2^4}{3^4}.$

Example 2. $(^-5)^4 = (^-5)(^-5)(^-5)(^-5) = 625 = 5^4.$

Example 3. $(^-5)^3 = (^-5)(^-5)(^-5) = ^-125 = ^-5^3.$

Example 4. $(2 \times 3)^4 = (2 \times 3)(2 \times 3)(2 \times 3)(2 \times 3)$
$= (2 \times 2 \times 2 \times 2)(3 \times 3 \times 3 \times 3) = 2^4 \times 3^4.$

Example 5. $\left(\frac{2}{5}\right)^3 \times \left(\frac{2}{5}\right)^4 = \left(\frac{2}{5}\right)\left(\frac{2}{5}\right)\left(\frac{2}{5}\right)\left[\left(\frac{2}{5}\right)\left(\frac{2}{5}\right)\left(\frac{2}{5}\right)\left(\frac{2}{5}\right)\right] = \left(\frac{2}{5}\right)^7.$

Example 6. $\left(\frac{4}{7}\right)^1\left(\frac{4}{7}\right)^5 = \left(\frac{4}{7}\right)\left[\left(\frac{4}{7}\right)\left(\frac{4}{7}\right)\left(\frac{4}{7}\right)\left(\frac{4}{7}\right)\left(\frac{4}{7}\right)\right] = \left(\frac{4}{7}\right)^6.$

Example 7. $\frac{5^6}{5^3} = \frac{5^3}{5^3} \times 5^3 = \left(\frac{5}{5}\right)^3 5^3 = 1^3 \times 5^3 = 1 \times 5^3 = 5^3.$

Example 8. $\frac{6^5}{6^3} = \frac{6^3}{6^3} \times 6^2 = 1(6)^2 = 6^2.$

Example 9. $\frac{4^3}{4^5} = \frac{4^3}{4^3 \times 4^2} = \frac{4^3}{4^3} \times \frac{1}{4^2} = 1 \times \frac{1}{4^2} = \frac{1}{4^2}.$

Example 10. $\frac{(10.1)^7}{(10.1)^8} = \frac{(10.1)^7}{(10.1)^7(10.1)^1} = \frac{(10.1)^7}{(10.1)^7} \times \frac{1}{(10.1)^1} = \frac{1}{(10.1)^1} = \frac{1}{10.1}.$

The above examples, which illustrate Definition 14, also motivate the following theorems.

THEOREM 6.   *If a is any real number and k and m are any positive integers, then $a^k \times a^m = a^{k+m}$.*

THEOREM 7.   *If a is any nonzero real number and k and m are any positive integers such that $k < m$, then $\frac{a^m}{a^k} = a^{m-k}$.*

THEOREM 8.   *If a is any nonzero real number and k and m are any positive integers such that* $m < k$, *then* $\dfrac{a^m}{a^k} = \dfrac{1}{a^{k-m}}$.

Theorems 6, 7, and 8 can be proved by means of the technique
employed in Examples 5, 7, and 9, respectively.

The following examples illustrate the above theorems.

Example 11. $(8.2)^5(8.2)^8 = (8.2)^{5+8} = (8.2)^{13}$.

Example 12. $\dfrac{(2.71)^{11}}{(2.71)^8} = (2.71)^{11-8} = (2.71)^3$.

Example 13. $\dfrac{(32.7)^6}{(32.7)^5} = (32.7)^{6-5} = (32.7)^1 = 32.7$.

Example 14. $\dfrac{(91)^4}{(91)^9} = \dfrac{1}{(91)^{9-4}} = \dfrac{1}{91^5}$.

Example 15. $\dfrac{a^5}{a^8} = \dfrac{1}{a^{8-5}} = \dfrac{1}{a^3}$, provided $a \neq 0$.

As we would like to combine Theorem 7 and Theorem 8 into one
theorem, regardless of whether $k < m$, $m < k$, or $m = k$, we make
the following definition.

DEFINITION 15.   For any real number $a \neq 0$ and any positive integer k,

$$\text{(a) } a^{-k} = \frac{1}{a^k},$$
$$\text{(b) } a^0 = 1.$$

According to Definition 10, $91^{-5} = \frac{1}{91^5}$ and $(91)^0 = 1$.

Theorem 6 can now be extended, and Theorems 7 and 8 may be
combined and extended as in the following theorems.

THEOREM 9.   *If a is any nonzero real number and k and m are any
integers, then* $a^k \times a^m = a^{k+m}$.

THEOREM 10.   *If a is any nonzero real number and k and m are any
integers, then* $\dfrac{a^m}{a^k} = a^{m-k}$.

You may prove the above theorems by considering the various cases.
The following examples illustrate the theorems.

Example 16. $5^2 \times 5^{-3} = 5^{2+\,-3} = 5^{-1} = \frac{1}{5^1} = \frac{1}{5}$.

Example 17. $(7.1)^{-6} \times (7.1)^6 = (7.1)^{-6+6} = (7.1)^0 = 1$.

Example 18. $\dfrac{(8.3)^2}{(8.3)^3} = (8.3)^{2-3} = (8.3)^{-1} = \frac{1}{(8.3)^1} = \frac{1}{(8.3)}$.

Example 19. $\dfrac{(11.7)^5}{(11.7)^{-3}} = (11.7)^{5-\,-3} = (11.7)^{5+3} = (11.7)^8$.

Example 20. $\dfrac{a^5}{a^6} = a^{5-6} = a^{-1} = \frac{1}{a}$,   provided $a \neq 0$.

The following theorems can be proved by use of a technique similar to that employed in Examples 4 and 1, respectively.

THEOREM 11.   *If a and b are any real numbers and k is any integer such that ab $\neq$ 0 or 0 < k, then $(ab)^k = a^k b^k$.*

THEOREM 12.   *If a is any real number, b is any nonzero real number, and k is any integer, then $(\frac{a}{b})^k = \frac{a^k}{b^k}$.*

The following examples suggest that $(a^k)^m = (a^m)^k = a^{km}$ for any nonzero real number a and any integers k and m.

Example 21. $(5^2)^3 = 5^2 \ 5^2 \ 5^2 = 5^{2+2+2} = 5^6$, and $(5^3)^2 = 5^3 \ 5^3 = 5^{3+3} = 5^6$.

Example 22. $(8^{-2})^3 = 8^{-2} \ 8^{-2} \ 8^{-2} = 8^{-2 + ^-2 + ^-2} = 8^{-6}$, and $(8^3)^{-2} = 1/(8^3)^2 = 1/(8^3 \ 8^3) = 1/8^{3+3} = 1/8^6 = 8^{-6}$.

The following theorem, which is stated without proof, asserts that the conjecture is correct.

THEOREM 13.   *If a is any nonzero real number and k and m are any integers, then $(a^k)^m = (a^m)^k = a^{km}$.*

The following definition of *square root* is based on exponents.

DEFINITION 16.   The real number a is said to be a *square root* of the real number b if and only if $a^2 = b$.

For example, 3 is a square root of 9 because $3^2 = 9$ and $^-3$ is a square root of 9 because $(^-3)^2 = 9$. It follows from the sign property for multiplication and the Dedekind property, which will be discussed in Section 2.7, that every positive real number has two squares roots, one negative and one positive. The positive square root of a positive real number is given a special name and notation.

DEFINITION 17.   The positive square root of the positive real number b is called *the principal square root of b* (briefly, *the square root of b*) and is denoted by $\sqrt{b}$.*

For example, $\sqrt{9} = 3$ (not $^-3$) and $\sqrt{16} = 4$. If $b = 0$, then there is only *one* square root of b; $\sqrt{b} = 0$ if and only if $b = 0$. If $b < 0$,

---

* The symbol "$\sqrt{\ }$" or in general "$\sqrt[k]{\ }$" is called a *radical*.

then there is no real number a such that $a^2 = b$; that is, $\sqrt{b}$ does not exist if $b < 0$. As the square root of 2 is *not* a rational number, the simplest exact expression for the square root of 2 is $\sqrt{2}$. Although $\sqrt{2}$ is not a rational number, it can be approximated by a rational number. The following examples further illustrate the above definitions and theorems.

Example 23. $(\sqrt{2})^3(\sqrt{5})^7/(\sqrt{2})^5(\sqrt{5})^3 = (\sqrt{2})^3/(\sqrt{2})^5 \times (\sqrt{5})^7/(\sqrt{5})^3$
$= (\sqrt{2})^{3-5} \times (\sqrt{5})^{7-3} = (\sqrt{2})^{-2} \times (\sqrt{5})^4 = (\sqrt{5})^4/(\sqrt{2})^2 = (\sqrt{5})^2(\sqrt{5})^2/(\sqrt{2})^2$
$= 5 \times 5/2 = 25/2.$

Example 24. $(1.6)^3 \ a^6 \ b^2/(1.6)^2 ab^5 = (1.6)^{3-2} \ a^{6-1} \ b^{2-5} = 1.6a^5b^{-3}$
$= 1.6a^5/b^3.$

Example 25. $(\sqrt{2})^5(-b)^9c^2/(\sqrt{2})^5(-b)^3c^5 = (\sqrt{2})^{5-5} \ (-b)^{9-3} \ c^{2-5}$
$= (\sqrt{2})^0(-b)^6(c)^{-3} = (\sqrt{2})^0(-b)^6/c^3 = 1 \times (-b)^6/c^3 = b^6/c^3,$ provided $bc \neq 0$.

Example 26.
$(a + b)^7(6 - c)^3/(a + b)^3(c - 6)^5$
$= \frac{(a+b)^7 \times {}^-(c-6)^3}{(a+b)^3 \times (c-6)^5}$
$= \frac{-1(a+b)^7(c-6)^3}{(a+b)^3(c-6)^5}$
$= \frac{-1(a+b)^4}{(c-6)^2}$
$= \frac{-(a+b)^4}{(c-6)^2},$ provided $(a + b)(c - 6) \neq 0$.

Example 27. $\frac{5a^2b^6}{a^3b^6} = 5a^{-1}b^0 = 5a^{-1} = 5(\frac{1}{a}) = \frac{5}{a},$ provided $ab \neq 0$.

Notice that $5a^{-1} = \frac{5}{a}$ and *not* $\frac{1}{5a}$.

The following theorem states that $\sqrt{2}$ is *not* a rational number.

THEOREM 14.   *There is no rational number whose square is equal to 2.*

Proof. Assume there exists a rational number $\frac{a}{b}$ such that $\left(\frac{a}{b}\right)^2 = 2$. Obviously, $a \neq 1$ and $b \neq 1$. Then $\left(\frac{a}{b}\right)\left(\frac{a}{b}\right) = 2$. Thus $aa = 2bb$.

By the unique prime factorization theorem, a and b may be factored uniquely into prime factors. Thus $a = p_1p_2 \ldots p_k$ and $b = q_1q_2 \ldots q_m$. Hence $(p_1p_2 \ldots p_k)(p_1p_2 \ldots p_k) = 2(q_1q_2 \ldots q_m)(q_1q_2 \ldots q_m)$.

The factor 2 occurs an even number of times in aa and an odd number of times in $2bb$. Thus the unique prime factorization of aa is different from the unique prime factorization of $2bb$. But $aa = 2bb$. This is a contradiction to the unique prime factorization theorem. Hence the assumption is false.

Thus there is no rational number $\frac{a}{b}$ such that $\left(\frac{a}{b}\right)^2 = 2$. ◇

A real number which is not a rational number is called an *irrational number*. The above theorem asserts the existence of irrational numbers. It is obvious that the set of real numbers is the union of the set of rational numbers and the set of irrational numbers, and these two sets are disjoint. Every terminating decimal represents a rational number. For example, $3.14 = \frac{314}{100} = \frac{107}{50}$, and $0.125 = \frac{125}{1000} = \frac{1}{8}$.

The following examples illustrate the fact that every repeating decimal represents a rational number.

Example 28. Let $a = 0.\overline{123}$; that is, $a = 0.123123123 \cdots$. Then $1000a = 123.123123 \cdots$. Hence $1000a - a = 123.123123 \ldots - 0.123123 \cdots$. Thus $999a = 123$. Hence $\frac{999a}{999} = \frac{123}{999}$. Thus $a = \frac{123}{999} = \frac{41}{333}$. Hence a is a rational number.

Example 29. Let $a = 0.1\overline{23}$; that is, $a = 0.1232323 \cdots$. Then $1000a = 123.2323 \cdots$. Also $10a = 1.2323 \cdots$. Thus $990a = 122$. Hence $\frac{990a}{990} = \frac{122}{990}$. Thus $a = \frac{122}{990} = \frac{61}{495}$. Hence a is a rational number.

Example 30. Let $a = 35.67\overline{2}$; that is, $a = 35.67222 \cdots$. Then $1000a = 35672.222 \cdots$. Also $100a = 3567.222 \cdots$. Thus $900a = 32,105$. Hence $a = \frac{32,105}{9,000}$. Thus $a = \frac{6,421}{1,800}$. Hence a is a rational number.

Conversely, there is a theorem which states that every rational number can be represented by a terminating decimal or a repeating decimal. The proof of this theorem is based on long division. For example, $\frac{1}{4} = 0.25$, $\frac{5}{11} = 0.454545 \cdots$, and $\frac{1}{7} = 0.142857\ 142857\ 142857 \cdots$. Hence *the set of rational numbers is the set of numbers which can be represented by terminating or repeating decimals;* and *the set of irrational numbers is the set of numbers with nonterminating, nonrepeating decimal representations.*

For example, the nonterminating, nonrepeating decimal $0.101001000100001 \cdots$ is an irrational number. Other irrational numbers are $\sqrt{3}$, $\sqrt{5}$, $\frac{\sqrt{6}}{2}$, π, $\frac{\pi}{3}$, and e. Although it is simple to prove that numbers like $\sqrt{2}$, $\sqrt{3}$, and $\sqrt{5}$ are irrational, it is difficult to prove that numbers like π and e are irrational. There are other irrational numbers such as $\sqrt[3]{17}$.

DEFINITION 18.   The real number a is said to be an mth *root* of the real number b if and only if $a^m = b$.

For example, 2 is a *fifth* root of 32 because $2^5 = 32$, 3 is a *fourth* root of 81 because $3^4 = 81$, 4 is a *cube* root of 64 because $4^3 = 64$, and $^-4$

is a *cube* root of $^-64$ because $(^-4)^3 = {}^-64$. However, $\sqrt{^-64}$ is not a real number because the square of every real number is nonnegative. Every real number, except 0, has two square roots, three cube roots, four fourth roots, and, in general, m m^{th} roots (not necessarily real numbers). Every positive real number has one positive m^{th} root. Every negative real number has one negative real m^{th} root if m is odd, and no real m^{th} root if m is even. For any positive integer m, the mth root of 0 is 0.

DEFINITION 19.   (a) The positive m^{th} root of the positive real number a is called *the principal m^{th} root of a* and is denoted by $\sqrt[m]{a}$ or $a^{\frac{1}{m}}$.

(b) The negative m^{th} root of the negative real number a is called *the principal m^{th} root of a* and is denoted by $\sqrt[m]{a}$ or $a^{\frac{1}{m}}$.

Exercise 2.5

I. Apply Theorems 9 and 10 and Definition 15 to simplify each of the following.

(1) $\dfrac{5^5 \times 5^2}{5^3}$

(2) $\dfrac{6^6 \times 6^3}{6^4}$

(3) $\dfrac{2^2 \times 2^2 \times 3^2}{(2^5 \times 3^4)}$

(4) $\dfrac{3^4 \times 3^2 \times 4^3}{(3^6 \times 4^5)}$

(5) $\dfrac{8^0 \times 5 \times 6^2}{(5^2 \times 6)}$

(6) $\dfrac{7^0 \times 6 \times 8^3}{(6^3 \times 8^2)}$

(7) $[2\pi^2(\sqrt{2})^3] \times [2^4\pi^3]$

(8) $[2^2\pi^3(\sqrt{3})^5] \times [2^3\pi^2]$

(9) $\dfrac{a^3b^2c}{a^4b^2c^5}$

(10) $\dfrac{a^2bc^5}{a^7b^4c}$

II. Simplify each of the following.

(1) 8^0

(2) 6^0

(3) $(8\sqrt{2})^0$

(4) $(5\sqrt{3})^0$

(5) $(^-8)^0$

(6) $(^-6)^0$

(7) $^-8^0$

(8) $^-6^0$

(9) $8(\sqrt{2})^0$

(10) $5(\sqrt{3})^0$

III. Simplify each of the following.

(1) $(^-\sqrt{2})^2$

(2) $^-(\sqrt{3})^2$

(3) $^-(\sqrt{2})^2$

(4) $^-(\sqrt{3})^2$

(5) $(a\sqrt{5})^3$

(6) $(b\sqrt{7})^2$

(7) $b(\sqrt{7})^2$

(8) $a(\sqrt{5})^3$

(9) $(1.5a + 3.7b)^0$

(10) $(3.9a - 3.7b)^0$

IV. Apply Theorems 11 and 12 to each of the following.

(1) $(6ab)^3$

(2) $(5ac)^2$

(3) $(bcd)^4$

(4) $(ack)^3$

(5) $\left(\frac{2 \times 6 \times a}{3 \times 7 \times b}\right)^5$

(6) $\left(\frac{9.1a}{2.9b}\right)^6$

(7) $\left(\frac{\pi r^2}{\pi ab}\right)^2$

(8) $\left(\frac{2\pi r}{\pi r^2}\right)^2$

(9) $\left(\frac{4\pi r^3}{3a}\right)^2$

(10) $\left(\frac{4\pi r^2}{ab}\right)^3$

V. Express each of the following without a negative exponent.

(1) 2^{-3}

(2) 5^{-2}

(3) 4^{-2}

(4) 3^{-3}

(5) $2a^{-3}$

(6) $3b^{-2}$

(7) $(2a)^{-3}$

(8) $(3b)^{-2}$

(9) $(2 + a)^{-2}$

(10) $2 + a^{-2}$

VI. Express each of the following rational numbers in the form $\frac{a}{b}$.

(1) 5.7565656 . . .

(2) 7.3424242 . . .

(3) 0.050414141 . . .

(4) 0.505636363 . . .

(5) 11.121212 . . .

(6) 16.171717 . . .

(7) 17.161161161 . . .

(8) 16.171171171 . . .

(9) 3.333 . . .

(10) 5.555 . . .

VII. (1) Prove that the open sentence $r^2 = 3$ cannot be converted to a true sentence by replacement of the variable by a rational number.

(2) Prove that the open sentence $r^2 = 4$ *can* be converted to a true sentence by replacement of the variable by a rational number. If, as in (1), you try to prove that the open sentence $r^2 = 4$ cannot be converted to a true sentence by replacement of the variable by a rational number, where does the proof fail?

(3) Prove that the open sentence $r^2 = 6$ cannot be converted to a true sentence by replacement of the variable by a rational number.

VIII. Express each of the following principal mth roots as an integer. (Assume that a is a positive integer.)

(1) $\sqrt{16}$

(2) $\sqrt[3]{27}$

(3) $\sqrt[3]{-27}$

(4) $\sqrt[6]{64}$

(5) $\sqrt[5]{-32}$

(6) $\sqrt[4]{16}$

(7) $\sqrt[3]{-125}$

(8) $\sqrt{a^4}$

(9) $\sqrt{a^2}$

(10) $\sqrt[3]{a^3}$

IX. (1) Explain why the definition of a^0 is consistent with the theorems which express the laws of exponents.

(2) Explain why $a \neq 1$ and $b \neq 1$ in the proof of Theorem 14.

2.6   Order Relation in $(R, +, \times)$

Now we recall that the real number a is less than the real number b if and only if there exists a positive real number k such that $a + k = b$. Symbolically, $a < b$ if and only if $a + k = b$ for some positive real number k. For example, $3 < 7$ because $3 + 4 = 7$, and $4 < 7$ because $4 + 3 = 7$. However, $4 \not< 4$ because $4 + 0 = 4$, and $4 \not< 3$ because $4 + {}^-1 = 3$; the real numbers 0 and $^-1$ are *not* positive. The relation $<$ between real numbers is called an *order relation*. Recall that the real number system possesses the following *order* properties.

1. If a and b are any real numbers, then $a < b$, or $a = b$, or $b < a$ (but only one).
   (The real number a is said to be *positive* if and only if $0 < a$, and is said to be *negative* if and only if $a < 0$.)
2. If a, b, and c are any real numbers and $a < b$, then $a + c < b + c$.
3. If a and b are any real numbers, and c is any positive real number, and if $a < b$, then $ac < bc$.
4. If a and b are any real numbers, and c is any negative real number, and if $a < b$, then $bc < ac$.
5. If a, b, and c are any real numbers such that $a < b$ and $b < c$, then $a < c$.

The first order property, usually called the *trichotomy property*, is intuitively obvious. The second order property is a mathematical statement of the fact that the order of any inequality is preserved if a given real number is added to both members of the inequality. For example, since $5 < 7$ it follows that $5 + 3 < 7 + 3$ and $5 + {}^-2 < 7 + {}^-2$. The third order property is a statement of the fact that the order of any inequality is preserved if both members of the inequality are multiplied by a given *positive* real number. For example, since $5 < 7$, it follows that $5 \times 3 < 7 \times 3$ and $5 \times \sqrt{2} < 7 \times \sqrt{2}$. The fourth order property is a statement of the fact that the order of any inequality is *reversed* if both members of the inequality are multiplied by a given negative real number. For example, since $5 < 7$, it follows that $7 \times {}^-3 < 5 \times {}^-3$ and $7 \times {}^-\sqrt{3} < 5 \times {}^-\sqrt{3}$. The fifth order property is the familiar *transitive property*. Since $5 < 7$ and $7 < 8$, it follows from the transitive property that $5 < 8$.

Property 4 actually follows from property 3 and such properties as the sign property. However, it is included for emphasis.

Properties 1 through 5 could have been phrased in terms of the order relation $>$. Since $a < b$ if and only if $b > a$, it is merely a matter of replacing "<" by ">." For this reason, we shall restrict our attention to the relation <. Whenever we study the real number system as an ordered system, we usually indicate the order relation < by speaking of the *ordered real number system* $(R, +, \times, <)$. The real number system $(R, +, \times, <)$ is an example of an abstract system known as an *ordered field*. In the following definition, precise meaning is given to the term *ordered field*.

DEFINITION 20.   A mathematical system $(F, +, \times, <)$ is said to be an *ordered field* if and only if the system possesses the properties *F*1 through *F*11 and *O*1 through *O*5.

*F*1.   If a and b are any elements of F, then $a + b$ is a unique element of F (*closure property for addition*).

*F*2.   If a, b, and c are any elements of F, then $(a + b) + c = a + (b + c)$ (*associative property for addition*).

*F*3.   There exists a unique element 0 of F such that $a + 0 = a$ for any element of F (*identity property for addition*).

*F*4.   If a is any element of F, then there exists a unique element ^-a of F such that $a + \ ^-a = 0$ (*inverse property for addition*).

*F*5.   If a and b are any elements of F, then $a + b = b + a$ (*commutative property for addition*).

*F*6.   If a and b are any elements of F, then $a \times b$ is a unique element of F (*closure property for multiplication*).

*F*7.   If a, b, and c are any elements of F, then $(a \times b) \times c = a \times (b \times c)$ (*associative property for multiplication*).

*F*8.   There exists a unique element 1 of F such that $a \times 1 = a$ for any element a of F (*identity property for multiplication*).

*F*9.   If a is any nonzero element of F, then there exists a unique element $\frac{1}{a}$ of F such that $a \times \frac{1}{a} = 1$ (*inverse property for multiplication*).

*F*10.   If a and b are any elements of F, then $a \times b = b \times a$ (*commutative property for multiplication*).

*F*11.   If a, b, and c are any elements of F, then $a(b + c) = ab + ac$ (*distributive property*).

*O*1.   If a and b are any elements of F, then exactly one of the following is true:

$$a < b,$$
$$a = b, \qquad (trichotomy\ property)$$
$$b < a.$$

*O*2.   If a, b, and c are any elements of F such that $a < b$, then $a + c < b + c$.

*O*3. If a, b, and c are any elements of F such that $0 < c$ and $a < b$, then $ac < bc$.

*O*4. If a, b, and c are any elements of F such that $c < 0$ and $a < b$, then $bc < ac$.

*O*5. If a, b, and c are any elements of F such that $a < b$ and $b < c$, then $a < c$ (*transitive property*).

If two rational numbers $\frac{a}{b}$ and $\frac{c}{d}$ are expressed in lowest terms, we can prove from the definition and properties of order between real numbers that $\frac{a}{b} < \frac{c}{d}$ if and only if $ad < bc$. For example, $\frac{3}{5} < \frac{5}{7}$ because $3 \times 7 < 5 \times 5$.

It is easy to prove that $(R_a, +, \times, <)$ is an ordered field. However, since $(I, +, \times)$ is not a field, we see that $(I, +, \times, <)$ is not an ordered field. It is a simple exercise to prove that $(I, +, \times, <)$ possesses properties *O*1 through *O*5. In the exercises you are asked to prove that *F*9 is the only ordered field property which $(I, +, \times, <)$ does not possess.

Letting $E = \{\ldots, {}^-6, {}^-4, {}^-2, 0, 2, 4, 6, \ldots\}$ (the set of even integers), we may prove that $(E, +, \times, <)$ possesses properties *F*1 through *F*7, *F*10, *F*11, and *O*1 through *O*5. Thus $(E, +, \times, <)$ possesses the order properties *O*1 through *O*5 but is *not* an ordered field.

By the sign property for multiplication we know that ${}^-a \times {}^-b = ab$ for any real numbers a and b. In particular, the product of two negative real numbers is a positive real number. That is, if $r < 0$ and $s < 0$, then $0 < rs$ (*rs* is positive). Also, if $r < 0$ and $0 < s$, then $rs < 0$ (*rs* is negative). Moreover, if $0 < r$ and $0 < s$, then $0 < rs$ (*rs* is positive). In other words, *the product of two negative real numbers is a positive real number; the product of a negative real number and a positive real number is a negative real number; and the product of two positive real numbers is a positive real number.*

Actually, these properties are consequences of the order properties *O*1 through *O*5. For example, to prove that the product of two negative real numbers, r and s, is a positive real number, we employ property *O*4 with $r = a$, $0 = b$, and $s = c$, as follows:

$$r < 0 \text{ and } s < 0$$
$$0 \times s < r \times s \quad \text{(by } O4)$$
$$0 < rs.$$

Similarly, to prove that the product of a positive real number r and a negative real number s is a positive real number, we employ property *O*4 with $0 = a$, $r = b$, and $s = c$, as follows:

$$0 < r \text{ and } s < 0$$
$$r \times s < 0 \times s \quad \text{(by } O4)$$
$$rs < 0.$$

The proof that the product of two positive real numbers, r and s, is a positive real number is similar and follows from $O3$.

These three consequences of the order properties may be restated, in condensed form, as follows:

For all real numbers a, b, and c,

$0 < ab$ if and only if $0 < a$ and $0 < b$ or $a < 0$ and $b < 0$;

$ab < 0$ if and only if $0 < a$ and $b < 0$ or $a < 0$ and $0 < b$.

The fact that the system of integers possesses all of the order properties but not all of the field properties leads us to suspect that the order properties are *not* consequences of the field properties. The student who is familiar with *modular number systems* already knows that there are fields which are not ordered fields. In Chapter 10 we shall actually study those modular number systems which are fields but which do not possess the order properties. In Chapter 7 we shall see another example of a field which is not ordered; namely, the *complex number system*. These examples (called *counterexamples*) will constitute *proof* that the order properties are not consequences of the field properties.

Recall that every positive real number has two square roots, one positive and the other negative. For example, the two square roots of 16 are 4 and $^-4$, and the two square roots of $\frac{4}{9}$ are $\frac{2}{3}$ and $\frac{-2}{3}$. On the *number line*, 4 and $^-4$ are equidistant from 0, and $\frac{2}{3}$ and $\frac{-2}{3}$ are equidistant from 0, as illustrated in Figure 2.2.

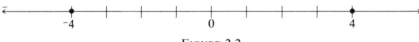

$$^-4 \qquad 0 \qquad 4$$

FIGURE 2.2

We recognize the fact that 4 and $^-4$ are equidistant from 0 by saying that the *absolute value* of 4 is equal to the *absolute value* of $^-4$ and writing $|4| = |^-4|$.

DEFINITION 21.   The *absolute value* of the real number a is equal to

(a) ^-a if a is negative.

(b) 0 if a is 0,

(c) a if a is positive.

We denote the absolute value of a by $|a|$. For example, $|^-3| = ^-(^-3)$ $= 3$, $|0| = 0$, $|7| = 7$, $|\sqrt{2}| = \sqrt{2}$, $|\frac{-2}{3}| = \frac{2}{3}$, $|5 + ^-7| = 2$, and $|5 - \sqrt{25}| = 0$. The absolute value of a is the distance on the number line between the point a and the point 0. Thus $|^-\pi| = $ distance between $^-\pi$ and 0; that is, $|^-\pi| = \pi$. Similarly, $|\pi|$ (distance between π and 0) $= \pi$.

Recall that $\sqrt{9} = 3$, the principal square root. That is, $\sqrt{(3)^2} = 3$ and $\sqrt{(-3)^2} = 3 = {}^-(-3)$. Similarly, $\sqrt{16} = \sqrt{4^2} = \sqrt{(-4)^2} = 4 = {}^-(-4)$. In general, $\sqrt{a^2} = {}^-a$ if $a < 0$, $\sqrt{a^2} = 0$ if $a = 0$, and $\sqrt{a^2} = a$ if $0 < a$. That is, $\sqrt{a^2} = |a|$ for every real number a. Hence $\sqrt{x}$ is nonnegative for every nonnegative real number x.

The following theorem is a statement of some of the important properties of *absolute value*.

THEOREM 15. *If a and b are any real numbers, then*

(a) $|a \times b| = |a| \times |b|$,
(b) $|a + b| \le |a| + |b|$.

It follows from Theorem 15 (a) that $\left|\frac{a}{b}\right| = \frac{|a|}{|b|}$ for any real number a and any nonzero real number b. For example, $\left|\frac{2}{-\pi}\right| = \frac{|2|}{|-\pi|} = \frac{2}{\pi}$ and $\left|\frac{2-x}{\sqrt{2}}\right| = \frac{|2-x|}{|\sqrt{2}|} = \frac{|2-x|}{\sqrt{2}}$. Theorem 15 (b), called the *triangle inequality*, states that the absolute value of the sum of two real numbers, a and b, *is less than or equal to* the sum of the absolute value of a and the absolute value of b. The following examples illustrate the triangular inequality.

Example 1. $|3 + 5| = |3| + |5| = 3 + 5 = 8$.

Example 2. $|3 + {}^-5| = |{}^-2| = 2$, and $|3| + |{}^-5| = 3 + 5 = 8$. Hence $|3 + {}^-5| < |3| + |{}^-5|$.

Example 3. $|{}^-3 + {}^-5| = |{}^-8| = 8$, and $|{}^-3| + |{}^-5| = 3 + 5 = 8$. Hence $|{}^-3 + {}^-5| = |{}^-3| + |{}^-5|$.

In Examples 1 and 3, $|a + b| = |a| + |b|$ and hence $|a + b| \le |a| + |b|$. In example 2, $|a + b| < |a| + |b|$ and hence $|a + b| \le |a| + |b|$.

Exercise 2.6

I. (1) Prove that $(R, +, \times, <)$ is an ordered field.
  (2) Prove that $(R_a, +, \times, <)$ is an ordered field.

II. (1) Prove that $(I, +, \times, <)$ possesses all properties of an ordered field except $F9$.
  (2) Prove that $(E, +, \times, <)$ possesses all properties of an ordered field except $F8$ and $F9$.
  (3) Let O = the set of odd integers. Which ordered field properties does $(O, +, \times, <)$ possess?
  (4) Let I^+ = the set of positive integers = $\{1, 2, 3, \ldots\}$. Which ordered field properties does $(I^+, +, \times, <)$ possess?

(5) Let I^- = the set of negative integers = $\{^-1,\ ^-2,\ ^-3,\ \ldots\}$. Which ordered field properties does $(I^-,\ +,\ \times,\ <)$ possess?

III. (1) Give an example in which $\frac{a}{b} < \frac{c}{d}$ but $ad \not< bc$ if b and d are not restricted to be positive integers.

(2) Prove that the product of two positive real numbers is a positive real number. (*Hint.* Use Property $O3$.)

IV. (1) Prove: If the symbol "<" is replaced by the symbol ">" in the statement of Properties $O1$ through $O5$, the resulting properties are valid in an ordered field.

(2) Prove that $a < b$ if and only if $^-b < {}^-a$ for all real numbers a and b.

(3) Prove that every negative real number is less than every positive real number.

V. Compute each of the following.

(1) $|^-5|$

(2) $|2 + {}^-5|$

(3) $|^-3(7 + {}^-7)|$

(4) $|2 + \sqrt{3}|$

(5) $|\sqrt{3} - 2|$

(6) $|^-\sqrt{5}|$

(7) $|\frac{^-2}{7}|$

(8) $|\frac{^-5 + 3}{^-2 \sqrt{7}}|$

(9) $\sqrt{10^2}$

(10) $\sqrt{(^-9)^2}$

(11) $\sqrt{(^-3)^2 + (^-4)^2}$

(12) $\sqrt{(^-3)^2 \times 4^2}$

2.7 Density of Real Numbers

Recall that the set C_0 possesses the *well-ordering property*. That is, if A is any nonempty subset of C_0, then there is one and only one element a_0 which is the smallest (or least) element of A. For example, if $A = \{5, 3, 7\}$, then $a_0 = 3$. However, if $A = C_0$, then $a_0 = 0$. The sets I, R_a, and R do not possess the well-ordering property. To prove this fact for I, for example, we note merely that $I^- \subset I$ and that I^- does not contain a least element; that is, the set $\{^-1,\ ^-2,\ ^-3,\ \ldots\}$ does not contain a least element. To prove that R_a does not possess the well-ordering property, with respect to the natural ordering $(<)$, we observe that $B = \{r: (0 < r) \wedge (r \in R_a)\}$ is a nonempty subset of R_a which does not have a least element. No matter what element r_0 we may *assume* to be the least element of B, we can compute a smaller one. For example, if we assume 0.001 to be the least element of B, we see that 0.0005 is even smaller. In general, if r_0 is assumed to be the least element of B, we see that the average (arithmetic mean) of 0 and r_0 is even less than r_0; that is, $0 < \frac{r_0}{2}$ and $\frac{r_0}{2} < r_0$. This contradiction proves that B does not contain a least element. Hence R_a does not possess the well-ordering property. The proof that R does not possess the well-ordering property is similar.

We may employ the above technique to prove that between every pair of points on the number line (corresponding to two different real numbers) there is another point. For example, between the points corresponding to the real numbers $\sqrt{2}$ and π is the point corresponding to the real number $\frac{(\sqrt{2} + \pi)}{2}$. Similarly, between 6.8 and 6.9 is 6.85. These are illustrated in Figures 2.3 and 2.4, respectively.

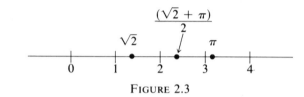

FIGURE 2.3

FIGURE 2.4

It follows readily that there are *infinitely many* points between any two different points on the number line (and hence that there are infinitely many real numbers between any two different real numbers). Thus it appears that the real numbers "fill up" the number line. The proof of this fact actually depends on an important property known as the *Dedekind property*, which is independent of the preceding properties.

DEDEKIND PROPERTY

If $A \cap B = \varnothing$, $A \cup B = R$, $A \neq \varnothing$, $B \neq \varnothing$, and each element of A is less than every element of B, then A contains a largest or B contains a least element.

If we assume that there is a one-to-one correspondence between the set of points on the number line and the set of real numbers, then the Dedekind property assures us that the real numbers "fill up" the number line. That is, there are no "holes" or "gaps" in the number line.

The Dedekind property, which is not an algebraic property, is *not* a consequence of the ordered field properties. In fact, although the rational number system is an ordered field, the rational number system does not possess the Dedekind property. To prove this, let A be the set of all rational numbers whose squares are less than 2, and let B be the set of all rational numbers whose squares are greater than 2. Then

$A \cap B = \varnothing$, $A \cup B = R_a$, $A \neq \varnothing$, $B \neq \varnothing$, and each element of A is less than every element of B. But A does not contain a largest element and B does not contain a smallest element.

Another property of real numbers, closely related to the Dedekind property, is the *Archimedean property*. The Archimedean property is especially useful in geometric constructions. In the language of real numbers it may be stated as follows.

ARCHIMEDEAN PROPERTY

If a and b are any positive real numbers such that $a < b$, then there exists a (positive) integer k such that $b < ak$.

For example, if $a = 0.17$ and $b = 169$, then k may be chosen as 1000. Obviously, any number larger than 1000 may be used for k. Is there a positive integer smaller than 1000 which will satisfy the Archimedean property?

Since the real numbers completely "fill up" the number line, the reader may be tempted to conclude that there is no further need for extension of the number system. However, in Chapter 6 we shall see the need for a more inclusive number system. In Chapter 7 we shall actually develop that larger number system, called the *complex number system*. In the meantime, we shall continue the study of the real number system with particular applications to problems of algebra.

Exercise 2.7

I. Compute the least element of each of the following subsets of C_0.

(1) $A = \{0, 1, 2, 3\}$ (4) $D = \{5, 10, 15, \ldots\}$
(2) $B = \{0, 2, 4, \ldots\}$ (5) $E = \{2, 4, 6, \ldots\}$
(3) $C = \{17\}$ (6) $F = \{10, 3, 9, 5\}$

II. Illustrate the Archimedean property in each of the following. Compute the *smallest* integer k such that $b < ak$.

(1) $a = 3.1$, $b = 97$ (4) $a = 0.1$, $b = 27$
(2) $a = \frac{1}{7}$, $b = \frac{22}{7}$ (5) $a = 0.05$, $b = 50,000$
(3) $a = \frac{1}{7}$, $b = 22$ (6) $a = 0.003$, $b = 30,000$

III. (1) Let $A = \{r\colon r < 7\}$ and $B = \{s\colon 7 \leq s\}$.
    Prove that A and B satisfy the statement of the Dedekind property. Compute the largest element of A *or* the smallest element of B.

   (2) Let $A = \{r\colon r \leq 7\}$ and B $\{s\colon 7 < s\}$.
    Prove that A and B satisfy the statement of the Dedekind prop-

erty. Compute the largest element of A *or* the smallest element of B.

(3) Let $A = \{r: r \leq {}^-5\}$ and $B = \{s: {}^-5 < s\}$.

Prove that A and B satisfy the statement of the Dedekind property. Compute the largest element of A *or* the smallest element of B.

(4) Let $A = \{r: r < {}^-5\}$ and $B = \{s: {}^-5 \leq s\}$.

Prove that A and B satisfy the statement of the Dedekind property. Compute the largest element of A *or* the smallest element of B.

(5) Let $A = \{r: r < \frac{2}{5}\}$ and $B = \{s: \frac{2}{5} < s\}$. Does the Dedekind property apply? Why?

(6) Let $A = \{r: r \leq 6.7\}$ and $B = \{s: 6.7 \leq s\}$. Does the Dedekind property apply? Why?

CHAPTER 3

Linear Equations
and Linear Inequalities
in One Variable

3.1 Classical Terminology

In your previous studies you have converted open sentences to true sentences by replacement of the variables by elements of the set under consideration; i.e., by elements of the universal set. For example, you have converted the open sentence $2v - 3 = 7$ to the true sentence $2(5) - 3 = 7$ by replacement of the *variable* v by the positive integer 5. You have undoubtedly referred to open sentences of the type $2x - 3 = 7$ as *equations*. Other words with which you are probably familiar are *expression, term,* and *coefficient*. In this section we formally define all of these words and several others.

DEFINITION 1. A symbol is said to be a *variable* if and only if it represents any member of the universal set.

For example, if the universal set is the set of all real numbers, the symbol x in the open sentence $3x + 2 = 14$ is a variable. In particular, since x represents a real number, it is frequently called a *real variable*. Henceforth, in this text, unless otherwise specified, all variables are real variables.

If x is a variable, then $x + 3$ is also a variable. Similarly $3x + 4 - \frac{2}{3x} + \frac{-7}{5}$ is also a variable. It is convenient to refer to such variables as *expressions* or *phrases*.

DEFINITION 2.   An *expression* (or *phrase*) is a numeral, variable, or combination of numerals and variables.

The following examples illustrate Definition 2.

Example 1.   0 is an expression.

Example 2.   3 is an expression.

Example 3. x is an expression.

Example 4. $\frac{2}{3} + {}^-x$ is an expression.

Example 5. $\frac{1}{2} + \frac{4}{5x} + \frac{-2x}{3y}$ is an expression.

Example 6. $\left(\frac{1}{2}\right)\left(\frac{5}{12}\right)({}^-3x + y - 2z)$ is an expression.

Example 7. $3x + 3y + 3z$ is an expression.

Example 8. $\frac{({}^-4 + 0)5 + 3x}{y - t}$ is an expression.

Example 9. ${}^-16t^2 + 25t + 100$ is an expression.

Example 10. $\frac{xy}{z^2}$ is an expression.

We say that the expression $\frac{2}{3} + {}^-x$ in Example 4 contains two terms, $\frac{2}{3}$ and ${}^-x$. The expression of Example 5 contains the three terms $\frac{1}{2}$, $\frac{4}{5x}$, and $\frac{-2x}{3y}$, whereas the expression of Example 6 contains the single term $\left(\frac{1}{2}\right)\left(\frac{5}{12}\right)({}^-3x + y - 2z)$. The expression of Example 7 contains three terms. Similarly, the expression of Example 9 contains three terms. However, the expression of Example 8 has only the one term, $\frac{({}^-4 + 0)5 + 3x}{y - t}$, and the expression of Example 10 has only one term.

DEFINITION 3.   The *terms* of the expression $v_1 + v_2 + \ldots + v_k$ are $v_1, v_2, \ldots,$ and v_k.

Notice that each of the terms $v_1, v_2, \ldots, v_k$ may, itself, be an expression containing more than one term.

Example 11. $v_1 + v_2 + v_3$ contains 3 terms.

Example 12. $(x + y) + (2x + {}^-3y) + {}^-(2t + 3u + {}^-5y) + {}^-2$ contains 4 terms.

Example 13. $5w + 5x + 5y + 5z$ contains 4 terms.

Example 14. $5(w + x + y + z)$ contains 1 term.

Example 15. $5x + 2y + 5y + z$ contains 4 terms.

Example 16. $(5x + 2y) + (5y + z)$ contains 2 terms.

The above examples illustrate the fact that the number of terms in an expression depends on the *punctuation* in the expression.

DEFINITION 4. The *coefficient* of the variable v in the term av of an expression is a.

In Example 4 the coefficient of the variable x is $^{-}1$. In Example 7, the coefficient of each variable is 3. In Example 9, the coefficient of the variable t^2 is $^{-}16$ and the coefficient of the variable t in the term $25t$ is 25. In Example 10, the coefficient of the variable $\frac{xy}{z^2}$ is 1, the coefficient of the variable xy is $\frac{1}{z^2}$, the coefficient of the variable $\frac{y}{z^2}$ is x, the coefficient of the variable $\frac{x}{z^2}$ is y, etc.

Now we shall study special types of expressions. The terminology and computational techniques employed here will be useful throughout your mathematical studies. Any expression may be classified according to the number of terms it contains.

DEFINITION 5. A *monomial* is an expression consisting of exactly one term.

DEFINITION 6. A *binomial* is an expression consisting of exactly two terms.

DEFINITION 7. A *multinomial* is an expression consisting of more than one term.

Example 17. $\frac{3x^2}{2t}$ is a monomial.

Example 18. $5(2 + {}^{-}3xt)$ is a monomial.

Example 19. $10 + {}^{-}15xt$ is a binomial.

Example 20. $2x({}^{-}4 + t) + \frac{-7}{y}$ is a binomial.

Example 21. $ax^2 + bx + c$ is a multinomial.

Example 22. $2 + {}^{-}x + \frac{6y}{z} + 2t$ is a multinomial.

Example 23. $5 + 7x$ is a multinomial.

We see that any binomial is a multinomial. If we agree that the terms of any multinomial are numbered from left to right, we may say that the first term of the multinomial in Example 21 is ax^2, the second term is bx, and the third term is c.

Now we wish to formulate a mathematical model of the following physical problem: If the sum of three consecutive integers is 15, what is the first integer? A mathematical model of this physical problem is $\{x: x + (x + 1) + (x + 2) = 15\}$, in which the variable x represents the first integer. In the classical approach to the same physical problem, one would require the *solution* or *root of the equation* $x + (x + 1) + (x + 2) = 15$. We introduce the second model because of its almost universal usage. As the reader will recall from high school algebra, an *equation* is a statement of equality, as illustrated in the following examples.

Example 24. $6 + 3 = 9$ is an equation.

Example 25. $1 + 2 = 7$ is an equation.

Example 26. $x^2 - 2 = 0$ is an equation.

Example 27. $2x = 2x - 3$ is an equation.

Example 28. $x + 3x = 4x$ is an equation.

Example 29. $x + (x + 1) + (x + 2) = 15$ is an equation.

Example 30. $3x + 3 = 15$ is an equation.

The equation of Example 24 is a true sentence, whereas the equation of Example 25 is a false sentence. The equations of Examples 26 through 30 are open sentences which cannot be classified as true or false. However, each of these equations can be converted to a sentence by the method of quantification or by the method of replacement of the variable. To convert an open sentence to a true sentence by the replacement method, we must replace the variable by some element of the universal set. For example, the open sentence $3x + 3 = 15$ can be converted to a *true* sentence by replacement of the variable x by the real number 4. If we replace x by any *other* real number, the open sentence $3x + 3 = 15$ is converted to a *false* sentence. We say that the *solution set* of $3x + 3 = 15$ is $\{4\}$. If we replace the variable x in the equation $x + 3x = 4x$ by *any* real number, that open sentence is converted to a *true* sentence. We say that the *solution set* of the equation $x + 3x = 4x$ is the universal set R (the set of reals). If we replace the variable in the open sentence $2x = 2x - 3$ by *any* real number, that open sentence is converted to a *false* sentence. We say that the *solution set* of the equation $2x = 2x - 3$ is the null set, $\varnothing$. In general, we define the solution set of any open sentence as follows.

DEFINITION 8.   The subset S of the universal set is said to be the *solution set* of an open sentence p_x if and only if replacement of the variable x in p_x by any element of S converts the open sentence p_x to a true sentence and replacement of the variable x in p_x by any element of $\tilde{S}$ converts the open sentence p_x to a false sentence:

In the following section we shall learn to compute the solution sets of some open sentences. In your previous studies when you converted open sentences to true sentences, you were computing subsets of their solution sets. In most cases, these subsets were actually the solution sets.

The following definition relates the classical words *solution* and *root* to the *solution set* of an equation.

DEFINITION 9.   Any element of the solution set of an equation is called a *solution* (or *root*) of the equation.

For example, a solution (or root) of the equation $3x + 3 = 15$ is 4. We frequently *write*, "$x = 4$," and *say*, "4 is a solution of $3x + 3 = 15$." The words *solve the equation* mean *compute the solution set of the equation*.

Exercise 3.1

I. Identify the coefficient of the variable in each of the following expressions.

(1) $3x$ (6) $\left(\frac{-2}{3}\right)x$
(2) $\left(\frac{-5}{3}\right)y$ (7) $3t$
(3) $\sqrt{2}t$ (8) $\left(\frac{2}{3} + \frac{-5}{4}\right)s$
(4) ^-5z (9) $\left(\frac{-2}{3} + 4\right)y$
(5) $17w$ (10) $10t$

II. Identify the coefficient of the variable x in each of the following expressions.

(1) ^-3x (6) $\left(\frac{2a}{3}\right)x$
(2) $(^-3 + a)x$ (7) $axyz$
(3) ^-3ax (8) $^-(2 + a)x$
(4) $abcx$ (9) $(ab^2 + {}^-c)x$
(5) $(a + b + c)x$ (10) $0x$

III. Identify each of the following expressions as monomial or multinomial.

(1) $2 + {}^-3x$ (6) $5 + 2x + 6y$

(2) $^-3 + 2x + 7y + z$ (7) $x^2 + {}^-3x + 4$

(3) $\frac{(2/3x + 4)}{(5x^2 + 5x^3)}$ (8) $3 + {}^-2t + t^2 + 7t^3 + {}^-8t^4$

(4) $\frac{(4 + 2x + 5)}{(6t + {}^-2/3y)}$ (9) $0 + 4y + 8z$

(5) x (10) $4y + 8z$

IV. Identify each binomial in Exercise III.

V. Tell which of the following are equations.

(1) $3y = 3$

(2) $2 = \frac{1}{3}$

(3) $ab = ba$

(4) $\frac{3}{4} < \frac{7}{8}$

(5) $4x \div \frac{6}{3}$

(6) $3x = 2x + 1$

(7) The sun is larger than the earth.

(8) $3x - 2 + 1$

(9) $2(x + 5) = 2x + 5$

(10) $2(x + 5) = 2x + 10$

(11) $2(x)(3) = 5$

(12) $2(x + 5) = 2x + 3$

(13) $z + 3 + \frac{2}{3z}$

(14) $|3x + 5| = 3x$

(15) $x^2 + 2x + 1 = 0$

(16) $x^2 + 2x + 1$

(17) $x^2 - 9 = (x - 3)(x + 3)$

(18) $x^2 - 9 = 0$

(19) $\sqrt{x + 4} = 4$

(20) $\sqrt{x + 4}$

VI. Tell which of the equations in Exercise V above are open sentences.

VII. Guess the solution set of each of the following equations.

(1) $x + {}^-1 = 0$ (6) $\sqrt{x} = 2$

(2) $2x = 2$ (7) $x^2 = 4$

(3) $2x = 0$ (8) $3x = \frac{1}{2}$

(4) $2x + 2 = 4$ (9) $3x = 1$

(5) $4x + 1 = x + 4$ (10) $12x = 4$

3.2 Addition and Multiplication of Expressions

Before studying equations and inequalities we shall consider the techniques involved in the combinations and expansions of expressions by the operations of addition and multiplication. Skills in these techniques will be useful in the computation of the solution set of an equation or inequality. The field properties and properties derivable from them are quite useful. In every example, the variable represents any real number; i.e., *the universal set is the set of reals.*

The following examples illustrate addition of expressions.

Example 1. $4x + 3x = (4 + 3)x = 7x.$

Example 2. $4x + (3x + {}^-7x) = 4x + 3x + {}^-7x = (4 + 3 + {}^-7)x = 0x = 0.$

Example 3. $(7xy + 3xy + {}^-4xy) + ({}^-10xy + 20xy + xy + {}^-2xy)$
$= (7 + 3 + {}^-4)xy + ({}^-10 + 20 + 1 + {}^-2)xy = 6xy + 9xy = (6 + 9)xy$
$= 15xy.$

Example 4. $(4x + 5y) + {}^-7x = 4x + 5y + {}^-7x = 4x + {}^-7x + 5y$
$= (4 + {}^-7)x + 5y = {}^-3x + 5y.$

Example 5. $2x + 4y + \sqrt{5}x = 2x + \sqrt{5}x + 4y = (2 + \sqrt{5})x + 4y.$

Example 6. $({}^-2x + 3) + y - 2(11x - 5 + 4y) = {}^-2x + 3 + y$
$+ {}^-2(11x - 5 + 4y) = {}^-2x + 3 + y + {}^-22x + 10 + {}^-8y = ({}^-2 + {}^-22)x$
$+ (1 + {}^-8)y + (3 + 10) = {}^-24x + {}^-7y + 13.$

Example 7. $\left(\frac{-1}{3}\right) + \left(\frac{-7}{3}\right)x + \left(\frac{4}{5}\right)xy + 3 + \left(\frac{1}{5}\right)xy = \left(\frac{-7}{3}\right)x + \left(\frac{4}{5}\right)xy + \left(\frac{1}{5}\right)xy$
$+ 3 + \frac{-1}{3} = \left(\frac{-7}{3}\right)x + \left(\frac{4}{5} + \frac{1}{5}\right)xy + \left(\frac{9}{3} + \frac{-1}{3}\right) = \left(\frac{-7}{3}\right)x + xy + \frac{8}{3}.$

Example 8. $2.13x - 5.26x - 7.45y - 6.35y - 2.15 = (2.13 + {}^-5.26)x$
$+ ({}^-7.45 - 6.35)y + {}^-2.15 = {}^-3.13x + {}^-13.80y + {}^-2.15.$

Example 9. $\sqrt{3}x + \sqrt{2}y + 2.1x - 6x^2 = \sqrt{3}x + 2.1x + \sqrt{2}y - 6x^2$
$= (\sqrt{3} + 2.1)x - 6x^2 + \sqrt{2}y.$

Example 10. $\frac{-2}{3} - \left(\frac{4}{5}\right)x + \left(\frac{7}{3}\right)y + \left(\frac{3}{10}\right)x = \frac{-2}{3} + \left(\frac{-4}{5}\right)x + \left(\frac{3}{10}\right)x + \left(\frac{7}{3}\right)y$
$= \frac{-2}{3} + \left(\frac{-8}{10} + \frac{3}{10}\right)x + \left(\frac{7}{3}\right)y = \frac{-2}{3} + \left(\frac{-5}{10}\right)x + \left(\frac{7}{3}\right)y = \frac{-2}{3} + \left(\frac{-1}{2}\right)x + \left(\frac{7}{3}\right)y.$

The following examples illustrate the technique of multiplication of expressions.

Example 11. $x(x + 1) = xx + x1 = x^2 + x.$

Example 12. $x^2(x^3 + {}^-3x^4) = x^2(x^3) + x^2({}^-3x^4) = x^5 + {}^-3x^6.$

Example 13. $({}^-4x^3 + {}^-3x^2)x^4 = {}^-4x^3(x^4) + {}^-3x^2(x^4) = {}^-4x^7 + {}^-3x^6.$

Example 14. $(x + {}^-1)\ (x + 3) = (x + {}^-1)x + (x + {}^-1)3$
$= x^2 + {}^-1x + 3x + {}^-3 = x^2 + 2x - 3.$

Example 15. $(x + y)\ (x - y) = (x + y)\ (x + {}^-y)$
$= (x + y)x + (x + y)^-y = x^2 + xy + x({}^-y) + y({}^-y)$
$= x^2 + xy + {}^-xy + {}^-y^2 = x^2 + {}^-y^2 = x^2 - y^2.$

Example 16. $(2x + 7)\ ({}^-1x^2 + 5x) = (2x + 7)^-1x^2 + (2x + 7)5x$
$= 2x({}^-1x^2) + 7({}^-1x^2) + 2x(5x) + 7(5x) = {}^-2x^3 + {}^-7x^2 + 10x^2 + 35x$
$= {}^-2x^3 + 3x^2 + 35x.$

Example 17. $(x + 3)\ (x + 2y) = (x + 3)x + (x + 3)2y$
$= x^2 + 3x + 2xy + 6y.$

Example 18. $(3x + 5)\ (x^3 + {}^-3x^2y + 6)$
$= (3x + 5)\ (x^3) + (3x + 5)\ ({}^-3x^2y) + (3x + 5)6$
$= 3x^4 + 5x^3 + {}^-9x^3y + {}^-15x^2y + 18x + 30.$

Example 19. $4 + {}^-4(x + 3)5 + {}^-5 = 4 + ({}^-4)\ (5)\ (x + 3) + {}^-5$
$= 4 + {}^-20(x + 3) + {}^-5 = (4 + {}^-5) + {}^-20(x + 3) = {}^-1 + {}^-20x + {}^-60$
$= {}^-20x + {}^-61.$

Example 20. $(x + y)^2 = (x + y)\ (x + y) = (x + y)x + (x + y)y$
$= x^2 + yx + xy + y^2 = x^2 + 2xy + y^2.$

Example 21. $(x + y + z)^2 = (x + y + z)\ (x + y + z)$
$= (x + y + z)x + (x + y + z)y + (x + y + z)z$
$= x^2 + xy + xz + xy + y^2 + yz + xz + yz + z^2$
$= x^2 + y^2 + z^2 + 2xy + 2xz + 2yz.$

Example 22. ${}^-2xy(3x + {}^-4y + 5z + {}^-7)$
$= {}^-2xy(3x) + ({}^-2xy)\ ({}^-4y) + ({}^-2xy)\ (5z) + ({}^-2xy)\ ({}^-7)$
$= {}^-6x^2y + 8xy^2 + {}^-10xyz + 14xy.$

Example 23. $(x - y)\ (x^2 + xy + y^2)$
$= (x - y)x^2 + (x - y)xy + (x - y)y^2$
$= (x + {}^-y)x^2 + (x + {}^-y)xy + (x + {}^-y)y^2$
$= x^3 + {}^-x^2y + x^2y + {}^-xy^2 + xy^2 + {}^-y^3 = x^3 + {}^-y^3 = x^3 - y^3.$

Example 24. $(x - a)^2 = (x + {}^-a)^2 = (x + {}^-a)\ (x + {}^-a)$
$= (x + {}^-a)x + (x + {}^-a)\ ({}^-a) = x^2 + {}^-ax + {}^-ax + ({}^-a)\ ({}^-a)$
$= x^2 + {}^-2ax + a^2 = x^2 - 2ax + a^2.$

Although the techniques in this section are probably familiar to you from high school algebra, they are included as review of high school algebraic manipulations and as applications of the important field properties. You should justify each step in each of the above examples as an application of one of the field properties, or a consequence of the field properties, or a definition. We justify Example 24 as follows:

$(x - a)^2 = (x + {}^-a)^2$ (by definition of subtraction),

$(x + {}^-a)^2 = (x + {}^-a)(x + {}^-a)$ (by definition of exponent),

$(x + {}^-a)(x + {}^-a) = (x + {}^-a)x + (x + {}^-a)^-a$ (by the distributive property),

$(x + {}^-a)x + (x + {}^-a)^-a = x^2 + {}^-ax + {}^-ax + ({}^-a)({}^-a)$ (by DP and commutative property for multiplication),

$x^2 + {}^-ax + {}^-ax + ({}^-a)({}^-a) = x^2 + {}^-2ax + a^2$ (by DP, definition of addition, and sign property for multiplication),

$x^2 + {}^-2ax + a^2 = x^2 - 2ax + a^2$ (by definition of subtraction).

Exercise 3.2

I. Justify each step in Examples 2, 3, 7, 9, 10, 12, 14, 16, 19, 21, 22, and 23.

II. Reduce each of the following expressions to a simpler expression.

(1) $23ax + 2ax + {}^-25ax$

(2) $(\frac{1}{2})x + (\frac{3}{4})x + (\frac{3}{2})x + {}^-x$

(3) $\sqrt{2}x + 3y + 5\sqrt{2}x$

(4) $101x + {}^-3c + {}^-99x + 3c$

(5) $\sqrt{5} + \sqrt{9} + \sqrt{x} + {}^-3\sqrt{5} + 4\sqrt{9}$

(6) $2.1x + (\frac{3}{-2})y + 1.1x + 2x + (\frac{-4}{3})y$

(7) $\frac{27}{5} + \frac{z}{3} + \frac{-3}{5} + \frac{-3}{4} + \frac{1}{5}$

(8) $2 + x + y + 3 - x$

(9) $2 + 7x + {}^-5x$

(10) $2xy + {}^-3xz + 4zy + tyz + 2xz$

III. Combine or expand each of the following expressions as indicated. The final answer should not contain any parentheses or brackets.

(1) $3 + 2x(2 + {}^-5)5 + {}^-3$

(2) $3x + 2x(2 + 5x)4 + {}^-3$

(3) $5[2 + 3({}^-2 + x)({}^-4x) + 2(x + {}^-3)]$

(4) $3 + 9x + 7 + {}^-6x + {}^-4(x + {}^-3)$

(5) ${}^-4 + (7x + 3) + {}^-2(x + 5) + (3 + 2x)7 + (3 + 3x) + 7$

(6) $2x + 4x + (3x + 5 + x)4 + {}^-3(x + 1) + 3$

(7) $0x + x + 2x + 3x + 4x + 5$

(8) $1(x + 2) + 2(x + 1) + 3(x + 5)$

(9) $6 + {}^-6(x + 3 + {}^-5x + {}^-3)$

(10) $6 + ({}^-6x + 3 + {}^-5x + {}^-3)$

(11) $(6 + {}^-6)(x + 3 + {}^-5x + {}^-3)$

(12) $(6 + {}^-6)(x) + 3({}^-5x + {}^-3)$

(13) $6 + {}^-6x[3({}^-5x + {}^-3)]$

(14) $6 + ({}^-6x + 3)({}^-5x) + {}^-3$

(15) $6 + {}^-6(x + 3) + {}^-({}^-5x + {}^-3)$

(16) $6 + {}^-6(x + 3) + {}^-(5x + {}^-3)$

(17) $6 + ({}^-6x + 3) + ({}^-5x + {}^-3)$

(18) $(6 + {}^-6)(x + 3) + ({}^-5x + {}^-3)$

(19) $(6 + {}^-6)(x + 3 + {}^-5x) + {}^-3$

(20) $(6 + {}^-6x) + 3 + {}^-5x + {}^-3$

(21) $(6 + {}^-6x + 3)({}^-5x + {}^-3)$

(22) $(6 + {}^-6x)(3 + {}^-5x + {}^-3)$

(23) $(6 + {}^-6x + 3)({}^-5x) + {}^-3$

(24) $6 + {}^-6[x(3 + {}^-5x + {}^-3)]$

(25) ${}^-(6 + {}^-6x) + 3 + 5x - {}^-3$

(26) $(x + {}^-3)(4 + 7x)$

(27) $(x + 2y)(3x + {}^-5y)$

(28) $(2x - 3)(x + y + 3)$

(29) $(x + y + z)[4 + 2(y + 3x)]$

(30) $\left[\left(\frac{2}{3}\right)x + \frac{4}{5}\right]({}^-15x + 45)$

(31) $(x + 2y + 3z)^2$

(32) $(x - 2y - 3z)^2$

(33) $(a + x)^3$

(34) $(a - 2x)^3$

(35) $(x - 2a)(x + 2a)$

(36) $(x - 2)(x^2 + 2x + 4)$

(37) $(x + 2)(x^2 - 2x + 4)$

(38) $(x + y)(x^2 - xy + y^2)$

(39) $(x + 2y)(x^2 - 2xy + y^2)$

(40) $x^2yz^3(x^2 + yz - z^2 - xz - 2xy)$

3.3   Linear Equations

In this section we shall define *linear equation* in one variable and develop a method for computing its solution set. As the linear equation serves as a mathematical model for many physical problems, its solution set serves as the model for the solutions of these physical problems. After you have learned to solve any linear equation in one variable, you will be able to solve many different physical problems, without having to learn a set of different techniques for the different problems.

The following example illustrates the method of computing the solution set of an equation in one variable.

Example 1. Compute the solution set of the equation $5x + 12 = 0$.*

For all x,
$$(5x + 12 = 0) \rightarrow (5x + 12 + {}^-12 = 0 + {}^-12),$$
$$(5x + 12 + {}^-12 = 0 + {}^-12) \rightarrow (5x = {}^-12),$$
$$(5x = {}^-12) \rightarrow \left(\left[\tfrac{1}{5} \right] 5x = \left[\tfrac{1}{5} \right] \left[{}^-12 \right] \right),$$
$$\left(\left[\tfrac{1}{5} \right] 5x = \left[\tfrac{1}{5} \right] \left[{}^-12 \right] \right) \rightarrow \left(x = \tfrac{-12}{5} \right).$$
Hence for all x,
$$(5x + 12 = 0) \rightarrow \left(x = \tfrac{-12}{5} \right).$$
Conversely for all x,
$$\left(x = \tfrac{-12}{5} \right) \rightarrow \left(5x = 5 \left[\tfrac{-12}{5} \right] \right),$$
$$\left(5x = 5 \left[\tfrac{-12}{5} \right] \right) \rightarrow (5x = {}^-12),$$
$$(5x = {}^-12) \rightarrow (5x + 12 = {}^-12 + 12),$$
$$(5x + 12 = {}^-12 + 12) \rightarrow (5x + 12 = 0).$$
Hence, for all x,
$$\left(x = \tfrac{-12}{5} \right) \rightarrow (5x + 12 = 0).$$
Thus for all x,
$$(5x + 12 = 0) \leftrightarrows \left(x = \tfrac{-12}{5} \right).$$
Thus $\{x: 5x + 12 = 0\} \overset{J}{=} \left\{ x: x = \tfrac{-12}{5} \right\} = \left\{ \tfrac{-12}{5} \right\}.$

You probably recall from your study of high school algebra that you solved the above linear equation as follows:

$$5x + 12 = 0,$$
$$5x = {}^-12,$$
$$x = \tfrac{-12}{5}.$$

The method you used is a shorthand method for the solution in Example 1. In fact, the shorthand method is an abbreviation for the following sequence of steps:

$$\text{for all } x, \; 5x + 12 = 0$$
$$\leftrightarrows 5x = {}^-12$$
$$\leftrightarrows x = \tfrac{-12}{5}.$$

The important point in the latter argument is that each step is reversible, as shown by the double arrow, $\leftrightarrows$. That is, each step in the computation

---

* The meanings of the symbols, "$\rightarrow$" and "$\leftrightarrows$," in this example, as well as other symbols used in this text, are included in the "Table of Symbols."

is of the form $p \leftrightarrows q$. Every replacement for x which converts the open sentence $5x + 12 = 0$ to a true sentence also converts the open sentence $x = \frac{-12}{5}$ to a true sentence. Conversely, every replacement which converts the open sentence $x = \frac{-12}{5}$ to a true sentence also converts $5x + 12 = 0$ to a true sentence. In general, the open sentence p_x is *equivalent to* the open sentence q_x if and only if they have the same solution set.

The following example illustrates that certain manipulations on an equation may reduce that equation to one which is *not* equivalent to the original equation.

Example 2.   Compute the solution set of $x(x - 1) = 3(x - 1)$.

$$x(x - 1) = 3(x - 1)$$
$$\tfrac{1}{x-1} \times x(x - 1) = \tfrac{1}{x-1} \times 3(x - 1)$$
$$x = 3.$$

The solution set of $x = 3$ is $\{3\}$. However, the solution set of $x(x - 1) = 3(x - 1)$ is $\{3, 1\}$. Thus $x = 3$ is *not* equivalent to $x(x - 1) = 3(x - 1)$. The reason that the derived equation, $x = 3$, is not equivalent to the original equation, $x(x - 1) = 3(x - 1)$, is that we eliminated the possibility that x could be equal to 1 when we multiplied by $\frac{1}{x-1}$.

As the following theorem shows, we can be certain that any step which involves only addition of any expression to both members of an equation yields an equation equivalent to the given equation. Also any step involving multiplication of both members of an equation by a nonzero real number yields an equation equivalent to the given equation.

THEOREM 1.   (*a*) *If u_1 and u_2 are any expressions and u is any expression, then the equation $u_1 = u_2$ is equivalent to the equation $u_1 + u = u_2 + u$.*

(*b*) *If u_1 and u_2 are any expressions and r is any nonzero real number, then the equation $u_1 = u_2$ is equivalent to the equation $u_1 r = u_2 r$.*

Proof. (*a*) For all variables in u_1, u_2, and u,
$(u_1 = u_2) \rightarrow (u_1 + u = u_2 + u)$.
Conversely, for all variables in u_1, u_2, and u,
$(u_1 + u = u_2 + u) \rightarrow (u_1 + u + {}^-u = u_2 + u + {}^-u)$
$(u_1 + u + {}^-u = u_2 + u + {}^-u) \rightarrow (u_1 = u_2)$.
Hence $u_1 = u_2$ is equivalent to $u_1 + u = u_2 + u$.

(*b*) Left as an exercise. $\diamondsuit$

The following examples further illustrate the method of computing the solution set of an equation by use of Theorem 1.

Example 3. Compute the solution set of $5x + 7 = 0$.

$$5x + 7 = 0$$
$$5x + 7 + {}^-7 = 0 + {}^-7$$
$$5x = {}^-7$$
$$\left(\tfrac{1}{5}\right)(5x) = \left(\tfrac{1}{5}\right)({}^-7)$$
$$x = \tfrac{-7}{5}.$$

Thus the solution set is $\left\{\tfrac{-7}{5}\right\}$.

Example 4. Solve the equation $3x + 2 = 6 - x$.

$$3x + 2 = 6 - x$$
$$3x + 2 + (x + {}^-2) = 6 - x + (x + {}^-2)$$
$$4x = 4$$
$$x = 1.$$

Example 5. Compute the solution set of the equation $2x - 5 = 3 - {}^-2x$.

$$2x - 5 = 3 - {}^-2x$$
$$2x - 5 = 3 + 2x$$
$$2x - 5 + ({}^-2x + 5) = 3 + 2x + ({}^-2x + 5)$$
$$0 = 8.$$

Thus $\{x: 2x - 5 = 3 - {}^-2x\} = \{x: 0 = 8\} = \varnothing$.
Hence the solution set is empty; i.e., there is no replacement which converts $2x - 5 = 3 - {}^-2x$ to a true sentence.

Example 6. Solve the equation $\left(\tfrac{3}{4}\right)x + \tfrac{2}{5} = \tfrac{1}{2} + \left(\tfrac{7}{10}\right)x$.

To simplify the computation, we multiply both members by the least common denominator: $[4, 5, 2, 10] = 20$.

Thus $20\left[\left(\tfrac{3}{4}\right)x + \tfrac{2}{5}\right] = 20\left[\tfrac{1}{2} + \left(\tfrac{7}{10}\right)x\right]$

$$20\left(\tfrac{3}{4}\right)x + 20\left(\tfrac{2}{5}\right) = 20\left(\tfrac{1}{2}\right) + 20\left(\tfrac{7}{10}\right)x$$
$$15x + 8 = 10 + 14x$$
$$15x + 8 + ({}^-8 + {}^-14x) = 10 + 14x + ({}^-8 + {}^-14x)$$
$$x = 2.$$

Example 7. Compute the solution set of $2x - 5 = {}^-5 + 2x$.

$$2x - 5 = {}^-5 + 2x$$
$$2x - 5 + ({}^-2x + 5) = {}^-5 + 2x + ({}^-2x + 5)$$
$$0 = 0$$

Thus $\{x: 2x - 5 = {}^-5 + 2x\} = \{x: 0 = 0\} = R$; i.e., every real number is a root of $2x - 5 = {}^-5 + 2x$.

The equations in Examples 1, 3, 4, and 6 are called *linear equations in one variable.*

DEFINITION 10.   An equation is said to be a *linear equation* in *one variable* if and only if it can be reduced to the form $ax + b = 0$, where $a \neq 0$, by means of Theorem 1.

Although the equations in Examples 5 and 7 resemble linear equations, at first glance, they are *not* linear equations. Examples 1, 3, 4, and 6 illustrate the fact that any linear equation has exactly one root. The following theorem asserts that this is true. As the proof is similar to Example 1, it is omitted.

THEOREM 2.   *The solution set of the linear equation* $ax + b = 0$ *is the set* $\left\{\frac{-b}{a}\right\}$.

Exercise 3.3

I. Compute the solution set of each of the following linear equations. Check by replacement of the variable.

(1) $3x + 18 = 0$

(2) $3x + {}^-18 = 0$

(3) $2x + 5 = 7$

(4) $5x + 2 = 12$

(5) $5x + {}^-2 = 8 + x$

(6) $5x + 2 = x + {}^-3$

(7) $3 + 8x + {}^-4 = {}^-5$

(8) $x + {}^-5 + 3x = 12$

(9) $\left(\frac{1}{4}\right)x + \frac{-6}{5} + {}^-4x = \frac{-8}{3}$

(10) $\left(\frac{1}{3}\right)x + \frac{-4}{5} = \left(\frac{1}{4}\right)x + {}^-8$

II. Solve each of the following equations.

(1) $^-3x = x + 4$

(2) $^-x = 3x + 4$

(3) $\left(\frac{3}{2}\right)x = \frac{4}{5}$

(4) $\frac{3}{4} + 2x + \frac{5}{6} = \frac{11}{5}$

(5) $\left(\frac{2}{3}\right)x + 7 + \left(\frac{-3}{4}\right)x = 8$

(6) $x + \frac{2}{3} + 2x + 5 = 0$

(7) $x(3 + 4) = 3(x + 10)$

(8) $(x + 2)(3 + 7) = \frac{3}{5} + \left(\frac{3}{5}\right)x$

(9) $\left(3\frac{1}{2}\right)x + \left(7\frac{1}{2}\right)x + 11x$

(10) $8x + 3x = 88$

(11) $3x + {}^-4 = 5 + 3x$

(12) $2x = 1 + 2x$

(13) $2x = 1 - 2x$

(14) $\left(\frac{3}{5}\right)x + 2 = 5 + \left(\frac{3}{5}\right)x - 3$

(15) $\left(\frac{1}{2}\right)x + \frac{4}{3} = \frac{1}{3} + \left(\frac{1}{2}\right)x$

(16) $\left(\frac{2}{3}\right)x = \frac{4}{5} + \frac{(2x)}{3}$

(17) $\frac{x}{5} = \frac{2}{3} + \left(\frac{1}{5}\right)x$

(18) $x + 7 = \frac{2(7 + x)}{2}$

(19) $x + 3 = 3 + x$

(20) $x + 3 = 3 - x$

III. (1) Prove Theorem 1(b).

(2) Prove Theorem 2.

IV. Check each of the following equations to determine whether it is linear.

(1) $x + 1 = 1$ (6) $x + 3 = 2 + x$

(2) $x - 1 = 0$ (7) $7 - 2x = {}^-2x + 3$

(3) $3x + 7 = 2$ (8) ${}^-2x + 3 = 3 - 2x$

(4) $x = 3$ (9) $3x - 7 = 4 + 7x$

(5) $x + 3 = 3 + x$ (10) $5 - 6x = 5 - 2x$

3.4 Applications of Linear Equations

Now that we know how to solve the linear equation in one variable, we shall study some applications of linear equations. Although the mathematical models of some physical problems are more easily formulated by arithmetic methods, the models of many physical problems are most easily formulated in terms of open sentences. The following examples illustrate the applications of linear equations in one variable.

Example 1. Compute three consecutive integers whose sum is 15.

We formulate a mathematical model as follows:

Let x represent the first integer. Then $x + 1$ represents the second integer, and $x + 2$ represents the third integer. The universal set is the set of integers. The linear equation whose solution represents the first integer is $x + (x + 1) + (x + 2) = 15$.

We solve as in Section 3.2.

$$x + (x + 1) + (x + 2) = 15$$
$$3x + 3 = 15$$
$$x = 4.$$

Since the possibility exists that the mathematical model was formulated incorrectly, we should check the solution in the *given* problem.

Thus we should check whether the sum of the integers 4, 5, and 6 is equal to 15. We see that $4 + 5 + 6 = 15$, and hence that the solution of the *given* problem is complete and correct.

Example 2. Compute three consecutive integers whose sum is 16.

We formulate a mathematical model as follows:

Let x represent the first integer. Then $x + 1$ represents the second integer, and $x + 2$ represents the third integer. The universal set is the set of integers. We solve as in Section 3.3.

$$x + (x + 1) + (x + 2) = 16$$
$$3x + 3 = 16$$

Since $3 \nmid 13$ and $U = I$, we see that the solution set of $3x = 13$ is the empty set. Thus the sum of three consecutive integers cannot be 16.

Example 3. Barbara has $1.44 in pennies and nickels. She has 6 more pennies than nickels. How many nickels does Barbara have? How many pennies does Barbara have?

We formulate the mathematical model as follows:

Let $U = C_0$ and let x represent the number of nickels. Then $x + 6$ represents the number of pennies. Hence $.05x + .01(x + 6) = 1.44$ (in dollar value). Thus $5x + (x + 6) = 144$ (in penny value).

$$5x + x = 144 - 6.$$
$$6x = 138.$$
$$x = 23.$$
$$x + 6 = 29.$$

Hence Barbara has 23 nickels and 29 pennies.

Again, we check the answer, not in the mathematical model, but in the original physical problem. The dollar value of 23 nickels is $1.15. The dollar value of 29 pennies is $.29. Consequently the dollar value of 23 nickels and 29 pennies is $1.44.

Example 4. Mr. Morris is three times as old as his daughter. In 13 years, he will be twice as old as his daughter. What is Mr. Morris's present age?

We formulate the mathematical model as follows:

Let $U = I^+$, and let x represent the daughter's age. Then $3x$ represents Mr. Morris's age. In 13 years, the daughter's age will be $x + 13$, and Mr. Morris's age will be $3x + 13$.

Since Mr. Morris's age in 13 years, $(3x + 13)$, will be *twice* his daughter's age in 13 years, $(x + 13)$, we see that $3x + 13 = 2(x + 13)$. Hence $3x + 13 = 2x + 26$. Thus $x = 13$ and $3x = 39$.

The daughter's age is 13, and the father's age is 39. As a check we observe that the daughter's age in 13 years will be 26, and the father's age in 13 years will be 52, twice the daughter's age.

Example 5. Anthony leaves Boston for Miami at 9:00 AM and drives at an average speed of 40 mph. Jacob leaves Boston at 10:00 AM and follows Anthony at an average speed of 50 mph. At what time will Jacob overtake Anthony?

We formulate a mathematical model as follows:

Let $U = R^+$ and let t represent the number of hours Anthony has traveled when Jacob overtakes him. Then Jacob has traveled $t - 1$ hours when he overtakes Anthony. Since distance = rate $\times$ number of time units, we see that Anthony travels $40t$ miles and Jacob travels $50(t - 1)$ miles by the time Jacob overtakes Anthony. Since they both travel the same distance, we see that

$$40t = 50(t - 1)$$
$$40t = 50t - 50$$
$$^-50t + 40t = ^-50$$
$$^-10t = ^-50$$
$$t = 5.$$

Hence Jacob overtakes Anthony in 5 hours. That is, Jacob overtakes Anthony at 2:00 PM.

You may have noticed that the problem of Example 5 can be solved by arithmetic methods. Since Anthony has a 40-mile headstart on Jacob at 10:00 AM, Jacob must travel a distance of 40 miles in *addition* to the distance Anthony travels from 10:00 AM. As Jacob's average speed is 50 mph and Anthony's average speed is 40 mph, Jacob travels an additional 10 miles each hour. Hence, *in 4 hours*, Jacob travels an *additional* 40 miles. Thus Jacob overtakes Anthony 4 hours after 10:00 AM (5 hours after 9:00 AM); i.e., at 2:00 PM. While this method may appear easier to you, you should realize that there are many problems which are not so easily solved without the use of linear equations. Furthermore, Example 5 adequately and simply illustrates the application of linear equations, and simple illustrations are no less valid than difficult ones.

Example 6. The perimeter of a rectangular lot is 500 feet. The length of the lot exceeds the width by 50 feet. Compute the width and length of the lot.

We formulate a mathematical model as follows:

Let $U = R^+$ and let x represent the width of the lot. Then $x + 50$ represents the length of the lot. The perimeter is represented by $x + (x + 50) + x + (x + 50)$. However, the perimeter is 500 feet. Thus the width of the lot is the solution of the linear equation $x + (x + 50) + x + (x + 50) = 500.$

$$4x + 100 = 500$$
$$4x = 400$$
$$x = 100.$$

Hence the width is 100 feet, and the length is 150 feet.
As a check, we note that $100 + 150 + 100 + 150 = 500$.

Whenever you encounter a physical problem, you should not expect to be able to read it once and immediately formulate a mathematical model for its solution. Rather, you should expect to read it once for the gist of the problem, reread it for better understanding, and then reread it in parts, formulate the model in parts, and finally unite all parts of the model and solve. In the following exercises you will have plenty of opportunity to test your skill in this respect. Remember that the exercises are not necessarily the most practical ones but those whose mathematical models are easily formulated. The skills you acquire in this section will help you to solve the more practical problems which will be introduced later in this text and which you may encounter in your other studies.

Exercise 3.4

I. Formulate a mathematical model for each of the following problems, and solve.

(1) Compute three consecutive integers whose sum is 105.
(2) Compute three consecutive integers whose sum is 411.
(3) Compute three consecutive odd integers whose sum is 141.
(4) Compute three consecutive odd integers whose sum is 351.
(5) Compute three consecutive odd integers whose sum is 360.
(6) Compute three consecutive even integers whose sum is 361.
(7) Tommy has $2.17 in pennies and nickels. He has 7 more pennies than nickels. How many of each coin does Tommy have?
(8) Carolyn has $1.04 in pennies and nickels. She has 3 times as many pennies as nickels. How many of each coin does Carolyn have?
(9) Joyce has $3.34 in pennies, nickels, and quarters. She has 5 more nickels than pennies, and 5 fewer quarters than pennies. How many of each coin does Joyce have?

(10) Margaret has $10.60 in nickels, dimes, and quarters. She has 7 more dimes than nickels and 3 times as many quarters as nickels. How many of each coin does Margaret have?

(11) Elaine's father is 3 times as old as Elaine is now. In 10 years from now, he will be twice as old as Elaine will be. How old is Elaine now?

(12) Henry's father is twice as old as Henry is now. In 20 years from now, he will be $1\frac{1}{2}$ times as old as Henry will be. How old is Henry now?

(13) Joseph is 20 years younger than his father. In 15 years he will be $\frac{3}{5}$ of his father's age. How old is Joseph now?

(14) Willis leaves New Orleans for Chicago at 6:00 PM and drives at an average speed of 36 mph. Duane leaves New Orleans at 8:00 PM and follows Willis at an average speed of 48 mph. At what time will Duane overtake Willis?

(15) Bobby leaves Dallas for Kansas City at 7:00 AM and drives at an average speed of 30 mph. Leo leaves Dallas at 10:00 AM and follows Bobby at an average speed of 40 mph. At what time will Leo overtake Bobby?

(16) Richard leaves New York for Boston at 12:00 noon and travels at an average speed of 40 mph. Two hours later Ruth leaves New York and travels in the opposite direction at an average speed of 50 mph. At what time are they 170 miles apart?

(17) Robert leaves Lafayette for Little Rock at 6:00 AM and travels at an average speed of 35 mph. One and a half hours later Donald leaves Lafayette and travels in the opposite direction at an average speed of 40 mph. At what time are they 165 miles apart?

(18) The perimeter of a rectangular lot is 300 feet. The length of the lot is twice the width of the lot. Compute the width and the length.

(19) The perimeter of a rectangular lot is 300 feet. The length of the lot is $1\frac{1}{2}$ times the width of the lot. Compute the width and the length.

(20) A farmer has 1,000 feet of fencing and wishes to fence in a part of his land along a river to restrain his cattle. From experience he knows that his cattle will not enter the river. For this reason he will need only three sides of a rectangular fence. The length of the rectangle (which parallels the river) is to be twice the width of the plot. What are the dimensions of the fenced-in plot?

(21) Compute three consecutive integers such that the sum of the first and the third is equal to 286.

(22) Compute three consecutive integers such that twice the sum of the first and the third is equal to 4 times the second.

(23) Compute three consecutive integers such that the sum of the first and the third is equal to the second.

(24) Compute three consecutive integers such that the sum of the second and the third is equal to the first.

(25) Sylvia and Yvonne leave home on their bikes and travel in opposite directions. Sylvia travels $1\frac{1}{2}$ times as fast as Yvonne. After 3 hours they are 60 miles apart. Compute their rates of speed.

II. (1) The following problem appeared on a test: Jim left Atlanta for Washington, D. C., at 8:00 AM and drove at an average speed of 40 mph. Walter left Atlanta 3 hours later and drove in the opposite direction at an average speed of 50 mph. At what time were Walter and Jim 30 miles apart?

One student wrote the following:

$$40t + 50(t - 3) = 30,$$
$$40t + 50t - 150 = 30,$$
$$90t = 180,$$
$$t = 2.$$

That is, Jim and Walter were 30 miles apart at 10:00 AM. However, we know that Walter did not leave until 11:00 AM and at 10:00 AM Jim was 80 miles from Atlanta. Explain the apparent paradox.

(2) Would the student's mathematical model have been correct if the distance had been 130 miles rather than 30 miles?

3.5   Linear Inequalities

In this section we shall define *linear inequality* in one variable and develop a method for computing its solution set. As the linear inequality serves as a mathematical model for many physical problems, its solution set serves as the model for the solutions of these physical problems. After you have learned to solve any linear inequality in one variable, you will be able to solve many different physical problems, without having to learn a set of different techniques for the different problems.

The following example illustrates a method of computing the solution set of an open sentence which is an inequality. Observe that the *ordered field properties* are employed.

Example 1. Compute the solution set of the inequality $5x + 12 < 0$, and represent the solution set geometrically on the number line.

$$\text{Now } 5x + 12 < 0$$
$$\leftrightarrows 5x + 12 + {}^-12 < 0 + {}^-12 \qquad \text{(by } O2)$$
$$\leftrightarrows 5x < {}^-12$$
$$\leftrightarrows \left(\tfrac{1}{5}\right)(5x) < \left(\tfrac{1}{5}\right)({}^-12) \qquad \text{(by } O3)$$
$$\leftrightarrows x < \tfrac{-12}{5}.$$

Hence $\{x: 5x + 12 < 0\} = \left\{x: x < \tfrac{-12}{5}\right\}$.

The "hollow dot" indicates that $\tfrac{-12}{5}$ is not included in the solution set. The double arrows are included for emphasis. In practice we usually omit them.

Whenever the coefficient of x is negative, you must be careful not to violate property $O4$. The following example illustrates a valid procedure.

Example 2. Compute the solution set of the inequality ${}^-5x + 12 < 0$, and represent the solution set geometrically on the number line.

$$^-5x + 12 < 0$$
$$(^-5x + 12) + {}^-12 < 0 + {}^-12$$
$$^-5x < {}^-12$$
$$\left(\tfrac{-1}{5}\right)({}^-12) < \left(\tfrac{-1}{5}\right)({}^-5x) \qquad \text{(by } O4)$$
$$\tfrac{12}{5} < x.$$

Hence $\{x: {}^-5x + 12 < 0\} = \left\{x: \tfrac{12}{5} < x\right\}$.

The following alternate procedure is based on property $O3$.

Example 3. Compute the solution set of the inequality ${}^-5x + 12 < 0$.

$$^-5x + 12 < 0$$
$$5x + (^-5x + 12) < 5x + 0$$
$$12 < 5x$$
$$\left(\tfrac{1}{5}\right)(12) < \left(\tfrac{1}{5}\right)(5x) \qquad \text{(by } O3)$$
$$\tfrac{12}{5} < x.$$

As in the case of an equation, certain manipulations on an inequality may reduce that inequality to an inequality which is *not* equivalent to the original inequality. The following theorem, which follows directly from the order properties, tells us which manipulations on an inequality yield an equivalent inequality.

THEOREM 3.   (*a*) *If u_1 and u_2 are any expressions and u is any expression, then the inequality $u_1 < u_2$ is equivalent to the inequality $u_1 + u < u_2 + u$.*

(*b*) *If u_1 and u_2 are any expressions and r is any positive real number, then the inequality $u_1 < u_2$ is equivalent to the inequality $u_1 r < u_2 r$.*

(*c*) *If u_1 and u_2 are any expressions and s is any negative real number, then the inequality $u_1 < u_2$ is equivalent to the inequality $u_2 s < u_1 s$.*

The following examples further illustrate the procedure for solving an inequality.

Example 4.   Compute the solution set of the inequality
$\left(\frac{-1}{3}\right)x + \frac{1}{4} < \left(\frac{-1}{6}\right)x + 4$.

To simplify the computation we multiply both members by the least common denominator: $[3, 4, 6, 1] = 12$. Thus

$$12\left[\left(\frac{-1}{3}\right)x + \frac{1}{4}\right] < 12\left[\left(\frac{-1}{6}\right)x + 4\right] \qquad \text{(by } O3\text{)}$$
$$^-4x + 3 < {}^-2x + 48$$
$$^-2x < 45$$
$$\left(\frac{-1}{2}\right)(45) < \left(\frac{-1}{2}\right)({}^-2x) \qquad \text{(by } O4\text{)}$$
$$\frac{-45}{2} < x.$$

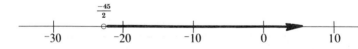

The following example illustrates that the solution set of an inequality may be empty.

Example 5.   Compute the solution set of $3x + 4 < x + 2 + 2x$.

$$3x + 4 < x + 2 + 2x$$
$$3x + 4 < 3x + 2$$
$$3x + 4 + {}^-3x + {}^-4 < 3x + 2 + {}^-3x + {}^-4$$
$$0 < {}^-2$$

Thus $\{x: 3x + 4 < x + 2 + 2x\} = \{x: 0 < {}^-2\} = \varnothing$.

The following example illustrates that the solution set of an inequality may be the entire set of reals.

Example 6. Compute the solution set of $3x < 3x + 2$.

$$3x < 3x + 2$$
$$3x + {}^-3x < 3x + 2 + {}^-3x$$
$$0 < 2$$

Thus $\{x: 3x < 3x + 2\} = \{x: 0 < 2\} = R$.

The inequalities in Examples 1, 2, 3, and 4 are called *linear inequalities in one variable*.

DEFINITION 11.   An inequality is said to be a *linear inequality in one variable* if and only if it can be reduced to the form $ax + b < 0$, where $a \neq 0$, by means of Theorem 3.

Although the inequalities in Example 5 and 6 resemble linear inequalities, at first glance, they are not linear inequalities.

Example 7. Prove that $0 < 7x + 9$ is a linear inequality in one variable.

$$0 < 7x + 9$$
$$0 + ({}^-7x + {}^-9) < (7x + 9) + ({}^-7x + {}^-9)$$
$${}^-7x + {}^-9 < 0$$

It follows from Definition 11 that $0 < 7x + 9$ is a linear inequality.

Exercise 3.5

I. Determine whether each of the following is a linear inequality. In each case, justify your answer by use of Definition 11.

(1) ${}^-3x \cdot 4 < 5$ (11) $x < 7$
(2) $4x \cdot 1 < 2x$ (12) $7 < x$
(3) $x \cdot \frac{3}{2} < 2x + 1$ (13) $3x + 2 = 5x + 2 + {}^-2x$
(4) $0 < {}^-7x + 5$ (14) $2x + 3 = x + 4 + x$
(5) $0 < 3x + 1$ (15) $x < 0$
(6) $2x + 3 < x + 3$ (16) $0 < x$
(7) $2x + 2 < x + 1 + x$ (17) $0 < 5 + 3x$
(8) $2x + 1 < 2x + 2$ (18) ${}^-3 < {}^-1 + 4x$
(9) $2x + 3 < 3$ (19) $x < 2x$
(10) $7x + {}^-2 < {}^-2$ (20) ${}^-5x < 2x$

II. Compute the solution set of each of the following linear inequalities, and represent the solution set geometrically on the number line.

(1) $2x + 5 < {}^-3x$ (3) $0 < 2x + 7$
(2) ${}^-2x + 5 < 3x$ (4) $0 < {}^-2x + 7$

(5) $\left(\frac{-1}{3}\right)x < 0$ (8) $4x + 2 < 5x + 7 + x$

(6) $1 < \left(\frac{3}{4}\right)x + \frac{1}{3}$ (9) $3x + \frac{1}{3} < 2x + 2$

(7) $^-x < ^-7$ (10) $^-3x + 3 < 3$

3.6 Compound Inequalities

In this section we study *compound* inequalities in which the connective is $\vee$ (*or*) or $\wedge$ (*and*). The following examples illustrate the procedure.

Example 1. Compute the solution set of the compound inequality $5x + 12 \leq 0$.

This inequality is really an abbreviation for
$(5x + 12 < 0) \quad \vee \quad (5x + 12 = 0)$.

$$(5x + 12 < 0) \quad \vee \quad (5x + 12 = 0)$$
$$5x < ^-12 \quad \vee \quad 5x = ^-12$$
$$x < \tfrac{-12}{5} \quad \vee \quad x = \tfrac{-12}{5}$$
$$x \leq \tfrac{-12}{5}.$$

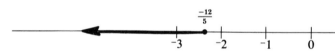

We see that the solution set of $5x + 12 < 0 \ \vee \ 5x + 12 = 0$ is the *union* of the solution set of $5x + 12 < 0$ and of the solution set of $5x + 12 = 0$.

In general, the solution set of $p_x \ \vee \ q_x$ is the *union* of the solution set of p_x and the solution set of q_x; i.e., $\{x: p_x \ \vee \ q_x\} = \{x: p_x\} \cup \{x: q_x\}$.

In actual practice we usually arrange the work as follows:

$$5x + 12 \leq 0$$
$$5x \leq ^-12$$
$$x \leq \tfrac{-12}{5}.$$

The only reason we included the longer method was to elaborate on the details.

Example 2. Compute the solution set of the compound inequality $^-5x + 12 \leq 0$.

$$^-5x + 12 \leq 0$$
$$^-5x \leq ^-12$$
$$\left(\tfrac{-1}{5}\right)(^-12) \leq \left(\tfrac{-1}{5}\right)(^-5x)$$
$$\tfrac{12}{5} \leq x.$$

Example 3. Solve the compound inequality $^-3 < 2x + 7 < 5$.

This inequality is really an abbreviation for the compound inequality $^-3 < 2x + 7 \wedge 2x + 7 < 5$.

The solution set of $^-3 < 2x + 7 \wedge 2x + 7 < 5$ is equal to the *intersection* of the solution set of $^-3 < 2x + 7$ and $2x + 7 < 5$; i.e., $\{x: {}^-3 < 2x + 7 \wedge 2x + 7 < 5\} = \{x: {}^-3 < 2x + 7\} \cap \{x: 2x + 7 < 5\}$.

$$^-3 < 2x + 7 \qquad\qquad 2x + 7 < 5$$
$$^-3 + {}^-7 < 2x \qquad\qquad 2x < {}^-2$$
$$^-5 < x \qquad\qquad\qquad x < {}^-1$$

$\{x: {}^-5 < x\} \cap \{x: x < {}^-1\} = \{x: {}^-5 < x < {}^-1\}$.

In actual practice, we usually arrange the work as follows:

$$^-3 < 2x + 7 < 5$$
$$^-3 + {}^-7 < 2x < 5 + {}^-7$$
$$^-10 < 2x < {}^-2$$
$$^-5 < x < {}^-1.$$

Example 4. Compute the solution set of the compound inequality $2 < {}^-5x + 3 \leq 15$.

$$2 < {}^-5x + 3 \leq 15$$
$$2 + {}^-3 < {}^-5x \leq 15 + {}^-3$$
$$^-1 < {}^-5x \leq 12$$
$$\left(\tfrac{-1}{5}\right)(12) \leq \left(\tfrac{-1}{5}\right)({}^-5x) < \left(\tfrac{-1}{5}\right)({}^-1) \qquad \text{(by } O4\text{)}$$
$$\tfrac{-12}{5} \leq x < \tfrac{1}{5}.$$

Example 5. Compute the solution set of the compound inequality $|2x + 3| < 1$.

Now $|2x + 3| < 1 \leftrightarrows {}^-1 < 2x + 3 < 1$.

$$^-1 < 2x + 3 < 1$$
$$^-1 + {}^-3 < 2x < 1 + {}^-3$$
$$^-4 < 2x < {}^-2$$
$$^-2 < x < {}^-1.$$

Example 6. Compute the solution set of the compound inequality $3 \leq |{-5x} - 4|$.

Now $3 \leq |{-5x} - 4| \leftrightarrows [(3 \leq {-5x} - 4) \vee ({-5x} - 4 \leq {-3})]$
$3 \leq {-5x} - 4 \vee {-5x} - 4 \leq {-3}$
$5x \leq {-3} - 4 \cdot \vee 3 - 4 \leq 5x$
$5x \leq {-7} \vee {-1} \leq 5x$
$x \leq \frac{-7}{5} \vee \frac{-1}{5} \leq x$ (by $O3$)
Hence $\{x : 3 \leq |{-5x} - 4|\} = \{x : x \leq \frac{-7}{5} \vee \frac{-1}{5} \leq x\}$
$\qquad\qquad\qquad\qquad = \{x : x \leq \frac{-7}{5}\} \cup \{x : \frac{-1}{5} \leq x\}.$

The above examples illustrate the solution of compound inequalities. Notice that no new ideas are involved in this section. If you know how to solve a linear equation and a linear inequality, then you can solve any of the above types of compound inequalities. Of course you need to know the definition of *absolute value* and the following facts:

$$\{x : p_x \vee q_x\} = \{x : p_x\} \cup \{x : q_x\},$$
$$\{x : p_x \wedge q_x\} = \{x : p_x\} \cap \{x : q_x\}.$$

Exercise 3.6

Compute the solution set of each of the following inequalities and represent the solution set geometrically on the number line.

(1) $5x + 1 \leq 6$

(2) $6x + 1 \leq 5$

(3) $-2x + 2 \leq 3$

(4) $-6x + 5 \leq 7$

(5) $x + 1 \leq 3x + 2 + {-2x}$

(6) $5x + 2 \leq 7x + 5 + {-2x}$

(7) $x + 2 \leq 3x + 1 + {-2x}$

(8) $5x + 5 \leq 7x + 2 + {-2x}$

(9) $4 \leq {-5x} + 9 \leq 14$

(10) $3 \leq {-7x} + 2 \leq 5$

(11) $2x + 2 \leq 4x + 5 + {-2x} + {-4}$

(12) $3x + 3 \leq 6x + 7 + {-3x} + {-6}$

(13) $|x| \leq 5$

(14) $|2x| \leq 6$

(15) $(x \leq 5) \vee (7 \leq x)$

(16) $(x \leq 5) \vee (7 < x)$

(17) $(x \leq 5) \wedge (3 < x)$

(18) $(x \leq 5) \wedge (7 < x)$

(19) $(x \leq 5) \vee (3 < x)$

(20) $(x = 8) \wedge (x = 10)$

(21) $(x = 8) \vee (x = 10)$

(22) $(x = 8) \vee (x < 7)$

(23) $(x < 5) \wedge (2 \leq x)$

(24) $(x < 5) \wedge (15 < x)$

(25) $(x < 5) \vee (15 < x)$

(26) $3 \leq |x| + 6$

(27) $5 \leq |x| - 2$

(28) $|2x + 1| < 3$

(29) $4 \leq |5x + 1|$

(30) $|{-3x} + 1| \leq 1$

(31) $-3 < |x + 2|$

(32) $|2x - 3| \leq 4$

(33) $|1 - 2x| \leq 1$

(34) $|x + 3| < 2$

(35) $|2 - 5x| < 7$

(36) $3 \leq |5x - 4|$

3.7 Application of Linear Inequalities

Now that we know how to solve linear inequalities in one variable we shall study some applications of linear inequalities. The following examples illustrate the applications.

Example 1. James is 5 years older than Betty, and the sum of their ages is less than 65. What is James's maximum possible age?

Let U be the set of positive integers.

Let the variable x represent Betty's age. Then $x + 5$ represents James's age and $x + (x + 5)$ represents the sum of their ages. Hence $x + (x + 5) < 65$. Thus $2x < 60$. Hence $x < 30$. Betty's age is less than 30, and James's age is less than 35. James's maximum possible age is 34.

Example 2. If there were three times as many students in a fifth grade class as there are now, there would be at least 42 more students than there are now. What is the minimum number of students in the class?

Let U be the set of positive integers.

Let x represent the number of students in the class. Then $3x$ represents the number of students in the projected class.

$$x + 42 \leq 3x,$$
$$42 \leq 2x,$$
$$21 \leq x.$$

Hence there at least 21 students in the class.

Example 3. Compute the smallest counting number such that the sum of one-third of it and $\frac{3}{4}$ of it is larger than 39.

Let x represent the counting number. Then $\left(\frac{1}{3}\right)x + \left(\frac{3}{4}\right)x$ is larger than 39; i.e., $39 < \left(\frac{1}{3}\right)x + \left(\frac{3}{4}\right)x$.

$$39 < \frac{4 + 9}{12}\, x,$$
$$39 < \left(\frac{13}{12}\right)x,$$
$$\left(\frac{12}{13}\right)(39) < \left(\frac{12}{13}\right)\left(\frac{13}{12}\right)x,$$
$$36 < x.$$

Hence the smallest counting number satisfying the given conditions is 37.

Example 4. In 6 months in one job Mr. Rayburn earned at least \$7,000 and the following 6 months in another job he earned \$8,000. What were his minimum average monthly earnings?

Let x represent his average monthly earnings. Then $\frac{(7000 + 8000)}{12} \leq x$. Hence $\frac{15,000}{12} \leq x$; i.e., $1250 \leq x$. Thus Mr. Rayburn's minimum average monthly earnings were \$1,250.

Example 5. Mr. Landry has between $30,000 and $45,000 to build a house. The type of house his wife wants costs $15 per sq. ft. Compute the range of the area of his new house.

Let x represent the number of square feet in the house he will build. Then $15x$ represents the cost of the house. Thus $30,000 \leq 15x \leq 45,000$. Hence $2,000 \leq x \leq 3,000$. Thus the area of Mr. Landry's new house is from 2,000 to 3,000 sq. ft.

The simple examples above serve merely to illustrate the method employed in the formulation of a mathematical model of a physical problem. There are many more practical applications of inequalities in linear programming, probability, calculus, etc. Later we shall consider some of these applications in more detail. The skills you acquire in this section will help you to solve the more practical problems when you encounter them.

Exercise 3.7

Formulate a mathematical model for each of the following problems, and compute the solution set.

(1) Jim had a certain number of marbles and received twice this number more as a present. After he lost one marble he had at least 59 marbles left. What is the smallest number of marbles Jim could have had in the beginning?

(2) Joan's age is five years more than three times Mary Jane's age and Joan's age is more than 31. What is Mary Jane's minimum possible age?

(3) On a three-day hike Ann, Jessie, and Inez walked twice as far the second day as the first, and four miles the third day. If the total distance was no more than 22 miles, what is the maximum distance they could have walked the first day?

(4) Sally has more than $1.05 in pennies and nickels, and has three times as many pennies as nickels. What is the smallest number of nickels Sally could have?

(5) Mr. and Mrs. Barron want to build a house with a floor area between 1800 sq. ft. and 2400 sq. ft. The type of house they want will cost $12 per sq. ft. Compute the price range of their new house.

(6) One mathematics class contains 10 more students than a second class. If four students resign from the larger class and $\frac{1}{4}$ of the students resign from the smaller class, there are fewer than 76

students left in the two classes combined. What is the maximum number of students in the smaller class before resignations?

(7) A family vacation budget allowed four times as much for food as for camping expenses and five times as much for travel as for camping expenses. If the total budget is at most $450, what is the maximum amount allotted to travel?

(8) Janice sold tickets for a school play. She sold twice as many adult tickets at 50 cents each as student tickets at 25 cents each. After she lost $3, she had less than $15.75 left from the sale of tickets. What is the maximum number of tickets of each type that she sold?

(9) If the steam pressure of a boiler is increased by 50%, the greater pressure is at least 27,000 pounds per square inch. What is the minimum pressure on the boiler before the increase?

(10) Maggie's father is five times as old as Maggie. In four years the sum of the their ages will be less than 56 years. What is Maggie's maximum possible present age?

CHAPTER 4

Functions and Graphs

4.1 Cartesian Product and the Coordinate Plane

In your previous study of *sets*, you have studied the binary operators $\cup$, $\cap$, and $\times$ between any two sets A and B. Recall that $A \cup B = \{x: x \in A \vee x \in B\}$, $A \cap B = \{x: x \in A \wedge x \in B\}$, and $A \times B = \{(a, b): a \in A \wedge b \in B\}$. You have learned that the ordered pair (a, b) is, in general, different from the ordered pair (b, a) and $A \times B \neq B \times A$ unless $A = \varnothing$, $B = \varnothing$, or $A = B$. The following examples will help you to review the *Cartesian product* $A \times B$ of two sets A and B and to distinguish it from union and intersection.

Example 1. $A = \{1, 3, 5\}$, $B = \{1, 2\}$.
$A \times B = \{(1, 1), (1, 2), (3, 1), (3, 2), (5, 1), (5, 2)\}$,
$A \cup B = \{1, 2, 3, 5\}$,
$A \cap B = \{1\}$.

Example 2. $A = \{2, 4\}$, $B = \{2, 4, 6, 8\}$.
$A \times B = \{(2, 2), (2, 4), (2, 6), (2, 8), (4, 2), (4, 4),$
$\qquad\qquad (4, 6), (4, 8)\}$,
$A \cup B = \{2, 4, 6, 8\}$,
$A \cap B = \{2, 4\}$.

Example 3. $A = \{1\}$, $B = \{4, 5, 6\}$.
$A \times B = \{(1, 4), (1, 5), (1, 6)\}$,
$A \cup B = \{1, 4, 5, 6\}$,
$A \cap B = \varnothing$.

Example 4. $A = \varnothing$, $B = \{0, 1, 4\}$.
$A \times B = \varnothing$,
$A \cup B = \{0, 1, 4\}$,
$A \cap B = \varnothing$.

Recall that R is the set of all real numbers. Then $R \times R = \{(x, y):$ $x \in R \wedge y \in R\}$; i.e., $R \times R$ is the set of all ordered pairs of real numbers. Analogous to the manner in which we established a one-to-one correspondence between the set of reals and the set of points on the number line, we establish a one-to-one correspondence between the set $R \times R$ and the set of points in a plane which we call the *coordinate plane*. First we let X and Y be two perpendicular lines and label their point of intersection *Origin*. These lines are called the *X-axis* and the *Y-axis*, respectively. According to established convention, we let the *X-axis* be horizontal and the *Y-axis* be vertical. The points on X to the *right* of *Origin* are labeled so that they correspond to the positive reals, and the points to the *left* of *Origin* are labeled so that they correspond to the negative reals. Similarly, the points on Y *above Origin* correspond to the positive reals, and the points on Y *below Origin* correspond to the negative reals. The coordinate plane is shown in Figure 4.1.

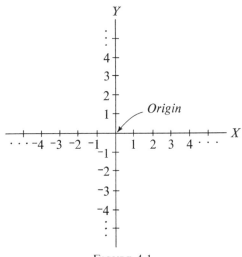

FIGURE 4.1

We establish a one-to-one correspondence between $R \times R$ and the coordinate plane as follows:

The *ordered pair* (3, 5) corresponds to the *point* in the coordinate plane 3 units to the *right* of *Origin and* 5 units above *Origin*. This point is labeled (3, 5) in Figure 4.2. The *ordered pair* (3, ⁻5) corresponds to the *point* 3 units to the *right* of *Origin* and 5 units *below Origin*. This point is labeled (3, ⁻5) in Figure 4.2. The *ordered pair* (⁻3, 5) corresponds to the *point* 3 units to the *left* of *Origin* and 5 units *above Origin*. This point is labeled (⁻3, 5) in Figure 4.2. The *ordered pair* (⁻3, ⁻5) corresponds to the *point* 3 units to the left of *Origin* and 5 units *below Origin*. This point is labeled (⁻3, ⁻5) in Figure 4.2. The *ordered pair*

(0, 0) corresponds to the point 0 units to the right of *Origin* and 0 units above *Origin*. Thus this point is *Origin* and is labeled (0, 0) as shown in Figure 4.2.

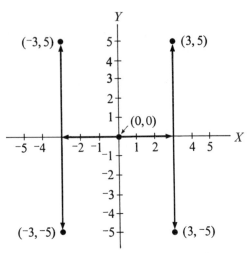

FIGURE 4.2

In general, if *a* and *b* are nonnegative reals, (*a*, *b*) correspond to the unique point *a* units to the *right* of (0, 0) and *b* units *above* (0, 0). The pairs (*a*, ⁻*b*), (⁻*a*, *b*), and (⁻*a*, ⁻*b*) correspond to points located in a similar manner. Conversely, any point in the coordinate plane may be made to correspond to an ordered pair of real numbers. The point located *a* units to the *right* or *left* of (0, 0) and *b* units *above* or *below* (0, 0) corresponds to the unique ordered pair (*a*, *b*).

Thus *there is a one-to-one correspondence between the set of all ordered pairs of reals and the set of all points in the coordinate plane.* Each ordered pair corresponds to a unique point in the coordinate plane, no two ordered pairs correspond to the same point, each point in the coordinate plane correspond to a unique ordered pair, and no two points of the coordinate plane correspond to the same ordered pair. Hence we may label a point by the ordered pair to which it corresponds. For example, the point which corresponds to the ordered pair (*x*, *y*) may be labeled "(*x*, *y*)." For this reason we shall frequently refer to the point labeled "(*x*, *y*)" as *the point* (*x*, *y*). This procedure should cause no confusion or ambiguity.

DEFINITION 1. The members *x* and *y* of the ordered pair (*x*, *y*) are called the *coordinates* of the ordered pair. The first member *x* is called the *first coordinate*, and the second member *y* is called the *second coordinate*.

For example, the first coordinate of the point (3, ⁻5) is 3 and the second coordinate is ⁻5. Whenever the universal set is $X \times Y$, the first *coordinate* is called the *x-coordinate* and the second coordinate is called the *y-coordinate*.

A physical interpretation of this one-to-one correspondence is as follows. Let (0, 0) represent the main intersection of a city whose blocks are square. The ordered pair (3, ⁻5), for example, corresponds to the street corner (intersection) which one reaches by beginning at (0, 0) and walking *East* 3 blocks and then *South* 5 blocks. The arrows in Figure 4.2 show the paths taken. Conversely, the corner 3 blocks *East* and 5 blocks *South* of the main intersection corresponds to the ordered pair (3, ⁻5).

The following concept is a generalization of the labeling of points on the number line.

DEFINITION 2.   The *graph* of a set of ordered pairs of real numbers is the set of points in the coordinate plane which correspond to the ordered pairs.

To *sketch the graph* or to *graph* a set of ordered pairs of real numbers is to locate (approximately) the set of points corresponding to the ordered pairs and to *label* these points by means of heavy dots or coordinates (or both). The concept of the *graph* is a *mathematical* one, whereas the *sketch of a graph* is a *physical model* of a *mathematical concept*. Conversely, the *graph* is a *mathematical model* of the *physical sketch* of the graph.

In actual practice, there are many possible sketches of a graph. The particular sketch that one makes depends upon the accuracy with which he locates points corresponding to the ordered pairs. In this text we refer to *the sketch* even though we have not located the unique ideal graph.

Example 5.   The graph of (⁻5, ⁻2) is the point in the coordinate plane 5 units to the left of (0, 0) and 2 units below (0, 0). The sketch of the graph is shown in the accompanying figure.

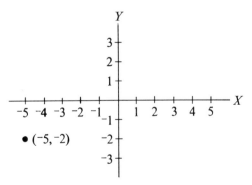

Example 6. The graph of (0, ⁻3) is the point in the coordinate plane 0 units to the right (or left) of (0, 0) and 3 units below (0, 0). The sketch of the graph is shown in the accompanying figure.

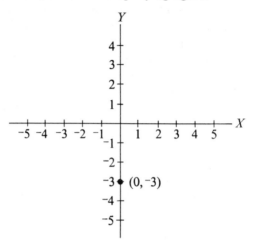

Example 7. The graph of {(⁻5, ⁻2), (0, ⁻2), (0, 0), (⁻5, 0)} is the union of the graphs of (⁻5, ⁻2), (0, ⁻2), (0, 0), and (⁻5, 0). The sketch of the graph is shown in the accompanying figure.

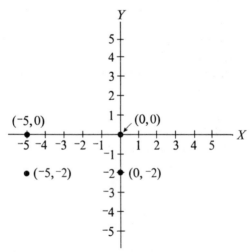

Example 8. The graph of {(3, 5), (3, ⁻5), (⁻3, 5), (⁻3, ⁻5)} is the union of the graphs of (3, 5), (3, ⁻5), (⁻3, 5), and (⁻3, ⁻5). The sketch of the graph is shown in the accompanying figure.

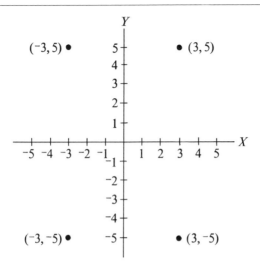

Exercise 4.1

I. Compute $A \times B$ for each of the following pairs of sets.

(1) $A = \{2\}$, $B = \{0\}$
(2) $A = \{2\}$, $B = \{0, 1, 2, 3\}$
(3) $A = \{^-1, 0, 1\}$, $B = \{1, 2\}$
(4) $A = \varnothing$, $B = \{1, 3\}$
(5) $A = \{0, 1, 2, \ldots\}$, $B = \{0, 1\}$
(6) $A = \{0, 1, 2, \ldots\}$, $B = \{0, 1, 2, \ldots\}$
(7) $A = \{0\}$, $B = R$
(8) $A = \{1\}$, $B = R$
(9) $A = \{$Tom, Dick, Harry$\}$, $B = \{$Mary, Jane$\}$
(10) $A = \{$Bea, Gloria, Sharon$\}$, $B = \{110, 115, 120\}$

II. Compute $B \times A$ for each pair of sets in I above.

III. (1) Compute $A \cap B$ for each pair of sets in I above.
(2) Compute $A \cup B$ for each pair of sets in I above.

IV. *Describe* the graph of each of the following sets of ordered pairs of reals.

(1) $\{(2, 3)\}$ (6) $\{(2, 0)\}$
(2) $\{(^-2, ^-3)\}$ (7) $\{(0, ^-3)\}$
(3) $\{(^-2, 3)\}$ (8) $\{(2, 0), (0, ^-3), (2, ^-3)\}$
(4) $\{(2, ^-3)\}$ (9) $A \times B$ where $A = R$ and $B = R$
(5) $\{(0, 3)\}$ (10) $A \times B$ where $A = R$ and $B = \{0\}$

V. Sketch the graph of each set in Exercise IV.

VI. Compute $X \times Y \times Z$ in each of the following cases.

(1) $X = \{0, 1, 2\}$, $Y = \{3\}$, $Z = \{5, 6\}$
(2) $X = \{0\}$, $Y = \{1, 2\}$, $Z = \{3, 4, 5\}$
(3) $X = \{\ \}$, $Y = \{1, 2\}$, $Z = \{3, 4, 5\}$
(4) $X = C_0$, $Y = \{1\}$, $Z = \{2\}$
(5) $X = C_0$, $Y = C_0$, $Z = C_0$
(6) $X = I$, $Y = I$, $Z = I$
(7) $X = \{\text{Diane, Sally}\}$, $Y = \{1\}$, $Z = \{\text{book}\}$
(8) $X = \{^{-}1, ^{-}2\}$, $Y = \{0\}$, $Z = \{^{-}3\}$

4.2 Functions

One of the most useful concepts in mathematics is the concept of a *function*. The physical world abounds with examples of functions. One of the important tasks of a scientist is the formulation of a mathematical model for a given physical problem such that the relationship between two physical objects is determined by the mathematical relationship between the two corresponding mathematical entities. For example, a physicist formulates a mathematical model to express the relationship between the distance a body has moved and the time it has been in motion. Similarly, a psychologist expresses the relationship between the I.Q. of a student and the predicted performance in college. Finally, by means of a mathematical model a manufacturer expresses the relationship between his net profit and the quantity of articles he manufactures.

Observe that there are two sets involved in each of the above examples. In the first example, one set is the set of elements representing *time* (in seconds or other convenient units), and the other set is the set of elements representing *distance* (in feet or other convenient units). In the second example, one set is a set of positive numbers representing *I.Q.'s*, and the other set is a set of nonnegative numbers representing *grade-point averages*. In the third example, one set is a set of positive integers representing the *number of articles manufactured*, and the other set is a set of numbers representing the *profit*. In each of these examples, the investigator is interested in a *rule of correspondence* which assigns to each element of one set some element of the second set. In the first example, to the time the rule assigns a distance; in the second example, to the I.Q., the rule assigns a grade-point average; and in the third example, to the number of articles the rule assigns a net profit.

The above examples are only three of the many examples in which each element of one set is associated with (or assigned to) some element of a second set. For this reason mathematicians study the important concept of *function*.

DEFINITION 3.   A *function from a set A to a set B* is a rule of correspondence from A to B which assigns to each element of A exactly one element of B.

According to Definition 3, both a *rule* and a *set A* are necessary to define a *function from A to B*. In practice, we usually speak of a *function* (rather than a *function from A to B*) whenever the set *A* is understood from the context.

In each of the above examples the rule formulated by the investigator is a function. The following example further illustrates Definition 3.

Example 1.   Consider a rule which assigns to each person a weight in pounds as shown in the accompanying figure.

This rule defined on the set *A* (the set of all persons) is certainly a function; each person has exactly one weight (no one has two different weights). If we denote the weight of any person x by $w(x)$, we can illustrate the rule as shown.

$$
\begin{array}{ccl}
\text{Al} & \longrightarrow & w(\text{Al}) \\
\text{Bill} & \longrightarrow & w(\text{Bill}) \\
\text{Carl} & \longrightarrow & w(\text{Carl}) \\
\text{Doris} & \longrightarrow & w(\text{Doris}) \\
& \bullet\ \bullet\ \bullet\ \bullet & \\
a & \longrightarrow & w(a)
\end{array}
$$

By the rule of correspondence (the weighing machine), to the person a is assigned his weight $w(a)$.

As in Example 1, in order to indicate that element of *B* to which a given element of *A* corresponds, we introduce a special notation for *function.* For this purpose we employ the **bold-faced** letter **f**, write **f**: $A \to B$ (or simply **f** when there is no ambiguity) to mean that the function **f** from A to B assigns to each element of A a unique element of B, and write $\mathbf{f}(a)$ to represent that element of B which is assigned to the element a of A. The symbol $\mathbf{f}(a)$ is read **f** *of a*. The following examples illustrate the notation for function.

Example 2. Consider the rule which assigns to each element of A a unique element of B as in the accompanying figure.

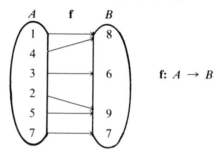

f: $A \to B$

According to our notation, we write

$$\mathbf{f}(1) = 8$$
$$\mathbf{f}(4) = 8$$
$$\mathbf{f}(3) = 6$$
$$\mathbf{f}(2) = 9$$
$$\mathbf{f}(5) = 9$$
$$\mathbf{f}(7) = 7$$

Observe that a function may assign the same element of B to more than one element of A.

Example 3. Consider the function in the accompanying figure.

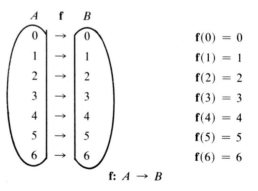

$$\mathbf{f}(0) = 0$$
$$\mathbf{f}(1) = 1$$
$$\mathbf{f}(2) = 2$$
$$\mathbf{f}(3) = 3$$
$$\mathbf{f}(4) = 4$$
$$\mathbf{f}(5) = 5$$
$$\mathbf{f}(6) = 6$$

f: $A \to B$

Observe that $A = B$ in this example and that $\mathbf{f}(a) = a$ for every a in A.

Example 4.   Consider the function in the accompanying figure.

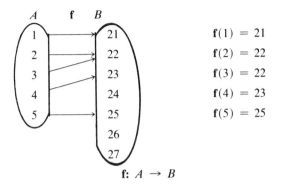

$$f(1) = 21$$
$$f(2) = 22$$
$$f(3) = 22$$
$$f(4) = 23$$
$$f(5) = 25$$

f: $A \to B$

Observe that some elements of B are not assigned to elements of A.

Example 5.   Consider the rule in the accompanying figure.

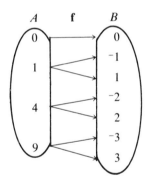

By Definition 3, this rule of correspondence is *not* a function, because 4 is assigned to two different elements of B.

DEFINITION 4.   (a) The set A of the function **f:** $A \to B$ is called the *domain of* **f.**

(b) The element $f(a)$ which a function **f:** $A \to B$ assigns to the element a is called the *image of a under* **f** (or *the value of* **f** *at a*).

(c) The set of all images under a function **f:** $A \to B$ is called the *range of* **f.**

In Example 2, the domain of **f** is the set $\{1, 4, 3, 2, 5, 7\}$ and the range of **f** is $\{8, 6, 9, 7\}$. In Example 3, the domain of **f** is $\{0, 1, 2, 3, 4, 5, 6\}$, and the range of **f** is also $\{0, 1, 2, 3, 4, 5, 6\}$. In Example 4, the domain of **f** is $\{1, 2, 3, 4, 5\}$, the range of **f** is $\{21, 22, 23, 25\}$, and the

image of 4 under **f** is 23. Observe that the range in this case is *not* the
set *B*. In fact, we are usually not interested in specifying the range but
only in specifying a set which contains the range as a subset.

We frequently employ letters other than **f** to represent functions. The
following example is a function with which your are already familiar.

Example 6.   Consider the function in the accompanying figure.

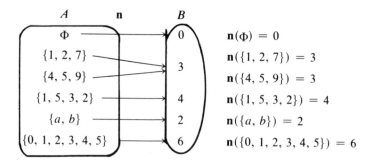

Observe that the elements of the set *A* are sets. The domain is *A* and
the range is *B*. The image of $\varnothing$ is 0, the image of $\{1, 2, 7\}$ is 3, the image
of $\{4, 5, 9\}$ is 3, the image of $\{1, 5, 3, 2\}$ is 4, the image of $\{a, b\}$ is
2, and the image of $\{0, 1, 2, 3, 4, 5\}$ is 6.

In summary, we observe that a function is a general concept, of which
there are many special examples. The domain may be a set of numbers, a
set of people, a set of sets, or any set (finite or infinite). The range is completely determined by the rule of correspondence and the domain and is
a subset of *B* which may be a proper subset of *B*. A function may be
visualized as a machine; the elements of the range constitute the output.
A simple example is the ordinary scale of Example 1. In general, the
machine may appear as in Figure 4.3.

FIGURE 4.3

Exercise 4.2

I. Determine which of the following rules of correspondence are functions.

(1)   A   B   (2) A   B   (3) A   B

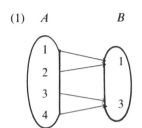   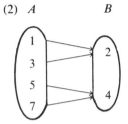   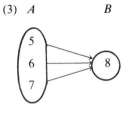

(4)   A   B   (5) A   B   (6) A   B

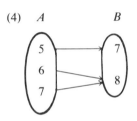   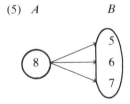   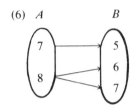

(7)   A   B   (8) A   B   (9) A   B

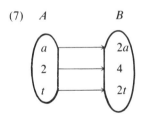   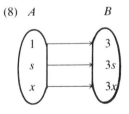   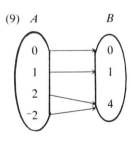

(10)   A   B   (11) A   B   (12) A   B

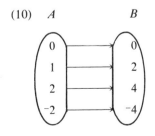   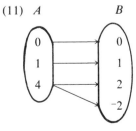   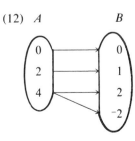

(13) 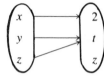 (14) 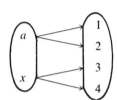 (15)

(16)  (17) 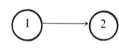 (18)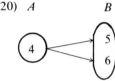

(19) 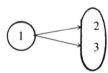 (20)

II. (1) Compute the domain and range of each *function* in Exercise I.
    (2) Compute $f(1)$ for each function in Exercise I whose domain contains 1 as an element.

III. If the domain and range of a function are interchanged, is the resulting correspondence necessarily a function?

IV. Determine which of the following are functions with the domain equal to the set of all U.S. citizens.

    (1) $f(x)$ is the father of x.
    (2) $m(x)$ is the mother of x.
    (3) $g(x)$ is the grandfather of x.
    (4) $u(x)$ is the uncle of x.
    (5) $s(x)$ is the son of x.
    (6) $d(x)$ is the daughter of x.
    (7) $h(x)$ is the husband of x.
    (8) $w(x)$ is the wife of x.
    (9) $b(x)$ is the brother of x.

(10) $c(x)$ is the cousin of x.
(11) $i(x)$ is x.
(12) $p(x)$ is the paternal grandfather of x.

4.3   Function Defined by an Open Sentence and a Set of Real Numbers

In this section we shall study functions whose domains are subsets of the reals and whose ranges also are subsets of the reals. The rules of correspondence (the functions) will be given by open sentences. The following examples illustrate this type of function.

Example 1.   Let $y = x + 1$ and $A = \{-3, -2, -1, 0, 1, 2, 3\}$. Then $y = x + 1$ is a function which assigns a real number to each element of A as follows:

$$\begin{array}{ccc}
-3 & \to & -2 \\
-2 & \to & -1 \\
-1 & \to & 0 \\
0 & \to & 1 \\
1 & \to & 2 \\
2 & \to & 3 \\
3 & \to & 4.
\end{array}$$

That is, using the standard notation for a function, we may write

$$\begin{array}{l}
\mathbf{f}(-3) = -2 \\
\mathbf{f}(-2) = -1 \\
\mathbf{f}(-1) = 0 \\
\mathbf{f}(0) = 1 \\
\mathbf{f}(1) = 2 \\
\mathbf{f}(2) = 3 \\
\mathbf{f}(3) = 4.
\end{array}$$

Since each real number x of the domain corresponds to the real number $x + 1$ of the range, we can write the function as $\mathbf{f}(x) = x + 1$.

Example 2.   Let $y = x^2$ and $A = \{-3, -2, -1, 0, 1, 2, 3\}$. Then $y = x^2$ is a function which assigns a real number to each element of A as follows:

$$\begin{array}{ccc}
-3 & \to & 9 \\
-2 & \to & 4 \\
-1 & \to & 1 \\
0 & \to & 0 \\
1 & \to & 1 \\
2 & \to & 4 \\
3 & \to & 9.
\end{array}$$

Again, using the standard notation for function, we write

$$\mathbf{f}(^-3) = 9$$
$$\mathbf{f}(^-2) = 4$$
$$\mathbf{f}(^-1) = 1$$
$$\mathbf{f}(0) = 0$$
$$\mathbf{f}(1) = 1$$
$$\mathbf{f}(2) = 4$$
$$\mathbf{f}(3) = 9.$$

Since each real number x of the domain corresponds to the real number x^2 of the range, we write $\mathbf{f}(x) = x^2$.

In general, $y = $ *expression in x* is a function from A to the reals R if and only if exactly one real number y is assigned to each real number x of the domain. Observe that the domain in Examples 1 and 2 is a proper subset of the reals. Usually we do not restrict the domain in this manner. Unless we specify otherwise, it will be understood that the domain is the set of reals, or it will be clear from the problem what set the domain is. For this reason we frequently speak of the function without specifying the domain.

The following examples further illustrate the concept of function.

Example 3. $y = x^2 + 3$ is a function.

The expression in x is $x^2 + 3$. To each real number a is assigned the real number $a^2 + 3$. We may write $\mathbf{f}(x) = x^2 + 3$. The domain of $\mathbf{f}(x) = x^2 + 3$ is the set of reals, and the range is a proper subset of the reals; namely, range $= \{y: 3 \leq y\}$.

$$\mathbf{f}(0) = 0^2 + 3 = 3$$
$$\mathbf{f}(1) = 1^2 + 3 = 4$$
$$\mathbf{f}(2) = 2^2 + 3 = 7$$
$$\mathbf{f}(^-1) = (^-1)^2 + 3 = 4$$
$$\mathbf{f}(^-2) = (^-2)^2 + 3 = 7$$
$$\mathbf{f}(^-3) = (^-3)^2 + 3 = 12, \text{ etc.}$$

Example 4. $y = 3$ is a function.

The expression is 3, a constant. To each real number a is assigned the real number 3. We may write $\mathbf{f}(x) = 3$. The domain of $\mathbf{f}(x) = 3$ is the set of reals, and the range is $\{3\}$.

$$\mathbf{f}(^-1) = 3$$
$$\mathbf{f}(0) = 3$$
$$\mathbf{f}(1) = 3$$
$$\mathbf{f}(2) = 3, \text{ etc.}$$

This function is frequently called a *constant* function.

Example 5. $y = \sqrt{x}$ is a function.

The expression in x is $\sqrt{x}$. To each nonnegative real number a is assigned the nonnegative real number $\sqrt{a}$. We may write $\mathbf{f}(x) = \sqrt{x}$. The domain of $\mathbf{f}(x) = \sqrt{x}$ is the set of nonnegative reals, and the range is also the set of *nonnegative* reals.

$$\mathbf{f}(0) = 0$$
$$\mathbf{f}(1) = 1$$
$$\mathbf{f}(2) = \sqrt{2}$$
$$\mathbf{f}(3) = \sqrt{3}$$
$$\mathbf{f}(4) = 2, \text{ etc.}$$

Example 6. $y = \frac{1}{(x + 1)}$ is a function.

The expression in x is $\frac{1}{(x + 1)}$. To each real number a (except $a = {}^-1$) is assigned the real number $\frac{1}{(a + 1)}$. We may write $\mathbf{f}(x) = \frac{1}{(x + 1)}$. The domain of $\mathbf{f}(x) = \frac{1}{(x + 1)}$ is the set of all real numbers except $^-1$. The reason $^-1$ is *not* included in the domain is that $\mathbf{f}(^-1) = \frac{1}{(-1 + 1)} = \frac{1}{0}$, which is not defined.

$$\mathbf{f}(0) = \frac{1}{(0 + 1)} = 1$$
$$\mathbf{f}(1) = \frac{1}{(1 + 1)} = \frac{1}{2}$$
$$\mathbf{f}(2) = \frac{1}{(2 + 1)} = \frac{1}{3}$$
$$\mathbf{f}(^-3) = \frac{1}{(-3 + 1)} = \frac{1}{-2} = \frac{-1}{2}, \text{ etc.}$$

In the study of functions the following definition is useful.

DEFINITION 5.   (a) The variable x which represents any element of the domain is called the *independent variable.*

(b) The variable y which represents that element of the range corresponding to the variable x is called the *dependent variable.*

The term *independent* is used because the variable x may be *any* member of the domain. Since the variable y corresponding to x *depends* on x, y is called the *dependent* variable. You should remember that x and y are variables and that the choice of letters is arbitrary. Thus if r represents any element of the domain and s represents the corresponding element of the range, the function $y = x + 1$ of Example 1 may be written $s = r + 1$.

Exercise 4.3

I. Name the domain of each of the following functions.

(1) $\mathbf{f}(x) = x$

(2) $\mathbf{f}(x) = {}^-x$

(3) $\mathbf{f}(u) = {}^-2u + 1$

(4) $\mathbf{f}(u) = 2u - 1$

$$(5) \ \mathbf{f}(v) = v^2 - 2 \qquad\qquad (8) \ \mathbf{f}(x) = x^3 + 1$$
$$(6) \ \mathbf{f}(v) = 2v^2 - 1 \qquad\qquad (9) \ \mathbf{f}(t) = t^2 + 1$$
$$(7) \ \mathbf{f}(x) = x^3 - 1 \qquad\quad (10) \ \mathbf{f}(t) = t^2 - 1$$

II. Name the independent variable and the dependent variable of each function in Exercise I.

III. Compute $\mathbf{f}(^-4)$ for each function in Exercise I.

IV. Compute $\mathbf{f}(4)$ for each function in Exercise I.

V. Compute $\mathbf{f}(0)$ for each function in Exercise I.

VI. The following function is defined on the set $\{1, 2, 3, 4\}$: to each element x of $\{1, 2, 3, 4\}$ the element $3x$ is assigned.

    (1) Write the function as an open sentence.
    (2) List the domain of the function.
    (3) List the range of the function.

VII. Name the range of the function in Example 6.

VIII. Compute $\frac{\mathbf{f}(0)}{\mathbf{f}(^-4)}$ for each function in Exercise I.

IX. Compute $\mathbf{f}(x + h)$ for each function in Exercise I.

X. Compute $\frac{\mathbf{f}(x + h) - \mathbf{f}(x)}{h}$ for each function in Exercise I.

4.4 Graphs of Functions

In the remainder of this chapter we shall confine our attention to the study of functions of the type discussed in Section 4.3. In Section 4.1 we defined the graph of a set of ordered pairs of real numbers. In this section we shall study the *graph of a function* $y = \mathbf{f}(x)$. By this we mean the graph of the set of all ordered pairs of real numbers determined by the function. That is, *the graph of the function* $y = \mathbf{f}(x)$ really means the graph of $\{(x, y): y = \mathbf{f}(x)\}$.

In fact, some mathematicians define the function $\mathbf{f}$ as $\{(x, y): y = \mathbf{f}(x)\}$. From this point of view, the function is identified with its graph.

Since it is frequently impossible to show the entire sketch of the graph of a function, we usually show a partial sketch and call it *the sketch* or *the graph*.

The following examples illustrate the method of sketching the graph of a function.

Example 1. Sketch the graph of $y = x + 1$.

Since $y = x + 1$ is a function, we write $f(x) = x + 1$ and compute some images as follows:

$$f(^-2) = {}^-2 + 1 = {}^-1$$
$$f(^-1) = {}^-1 + 1 = 0$$
$$f(0) = 0 + 1 = 1$$
$$f(1) = 1 + 1 = 2$$
$$f(2) = 2 + 1 = 3.$$

It is convenient to display the computation in a table which shows some of the ordered pairs.

x	$f(x)$
$^-2$	$^-1$
$^-1$	0
0	1
1	2
2	3

The graph of these ordered pairs is shown in the accompanying figure.

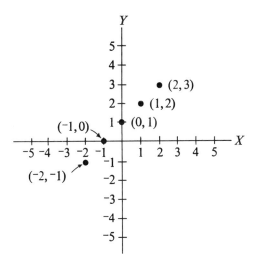

The graph of the function is shown below.

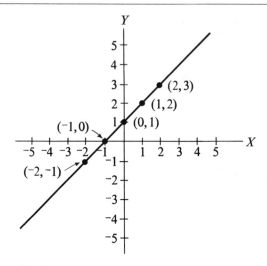

The computed points are labeled for emphasis. As we mentioned previously, we have shown only a part of the sketch. The graph actually extends indefinitely far in both directions.

Example 2.   Sketch the graph of $y = x^2$.

A partial table and the graph are shown in the accompanying figures.

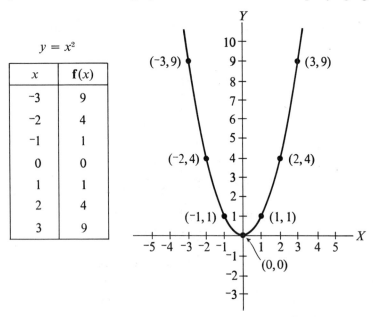

$y = x^2$	
x	$f(x)$
$^-3$	9
$^-2$	4
$^-1$	1
0	0
1	1
2	4
3	9

Example 3.   Sketch the graph of the function $f(x) = x^2 + 3$.

A partial table and the graph are shown in the accompanying figures.

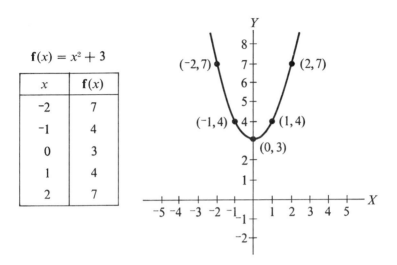

$f(x) = x^2 + 3$	
x	**f**(*x*)
⁻2	7
⁻1	4
0	3
1	4
2	7

Example 4.   Sketch the graph of the function $y = 3$.

The function $f(x) = 3$ assigns to each real number *x* the real number 3. A table and the graph are shown in the accompanying figures.

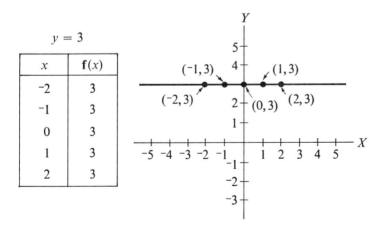

$y = 3$	
x	**f**(*x*)
⁻2	3
⁻1	3
0	3
1	3
2	3

The graph is a straight line parallel to the *X*-axis.

Example 5. Sketch the graph of the function $\mathbf{f}(x) = \sqrt{x}$.

Observe that neither x nor $\mathbf{f}(x)$ can be negative. A table and the graph are shown in the accompanying figures.

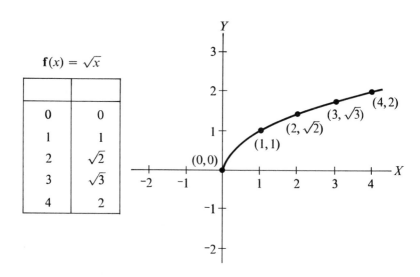

$\mathbf{f}(x) = \sqrt{x}$

0	0
1	1
2	$\sqrt{2}$
3	$\sqrt{3}$
4	2

Exercise 4.4

I. Sketch the graph of each of the following functions.

(1) $\mathbf{f}(x) = 3x$
(2) $\mathbf{f}(x) = 2x$
(3) $\mathbf{f}(x) = x^2 - 2$
(4) $\mathbf{f}(x) = x^2 + 2$
(5) $\mathbf{f}(x) = x^3 + 1$

(6) $\mathbf{f}(x) = x^3 - 1$
(7) $\mathbf{f}(x) = \left(\frac{1}{2}\right)x^2$
(8) $\mathbf{f}(x) = 2x^2$
(9) $\mathbf{f}(x) = 3\sqrt{x}$
(10) $\mathbf{f}(x) = 2\sqrt{x}$

II. Sketch the graph of each of the following functions.

(1) $\mathbf{f}(x) = 2$
(2) $\mathbf{f}(x) = {}^-3$
(3) $\mathbf{f}(x) = 0$
(4) $\mathbf{f}(x) = {}^-1$
(5) $\mathbf{f}(x) = |x|$

(6) $\mathbf{f}(x) = 2|x|$
(7) $\mathbf{f}(x) = |x + 2|$
(8) $\mathbf{f}(x) = |x| + 2$
(9) $\mathbf{f}(x) = \dfrac{1}{(x + 1)}$
(10) $\mathbf{f}(x) = \dfrac{2}{(x - 2)}$

4.5   Linear Functions

In this section we shall study an important subset of the class of functions — the set of *linear functions*. In the preceding sections of this chapter we considered several examples of linear functions. In the exercise you will be asked to prove that $y = ax + b$ is actually a function.

DEFINITION 6.   The function $y = ax + b$ is called a *linear function*.

Example 1. $y = 3x + 1$ is a linear function, in which $a = 3$ and $b = 1$.

The function may be written $\mathbf{f}(x) = 3x + 1$. The sketch is shown in the accompanying figure.

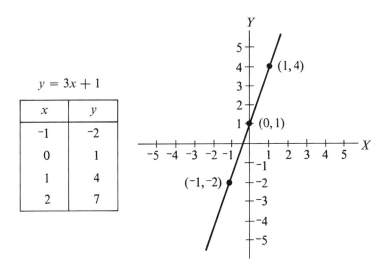

$y = 3x + 1$

x	y
⁻1	⁻2
0	1
1	4
2	7

Recall that the graph of the solution set of the function $y = 3x + 1$ is the graph of the function. That is, the graph of $y = 3x + 1$ is the graph of $\{(x, y): y = 3x + 1\}$.

Example 2. $y = 3x - 5$ is a linear function, in which $a = 3$ and $b = {}^-5$.

The function may be written $\mathbf{f}(x) = 3x + {}^-5$. The sketch is shown in the accompanying figure.

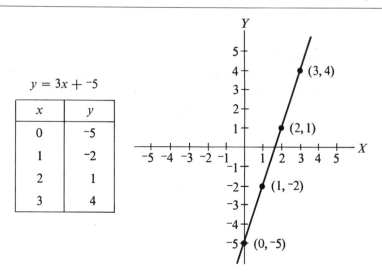

$$y = 3x + {}^-5$$

x	y
0	⁻5
1	⁻2
2	1
3	4

Example 3. $\mathbf{f}(x) = 3x + 10$ is a linear function, in which $a = 3$ and $b = 10$.

The sketch is shown in the accompanying figure.

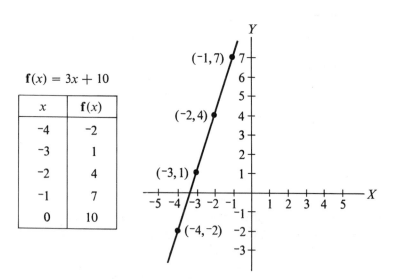

$$\mathbf{f}(x) = 3x + 10$$

x	$\mathbf{f}(x)$
⁻4	⁻2
⁻3	1
⁻2	4
⁻1	7
0	10

Example 4. $\mathbf{g}(x) = {}^-2x$ is a linear function, in which $a = {}^-2$ and $b = 0$.

The sketch is shown in the accompanying figure.

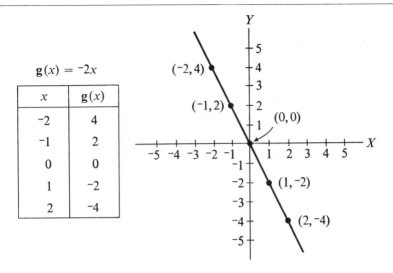

g(x) = -2x

x	g(x)
-2	4
-1	2
0	0
1	-2
2	-4

Example 5. $g(x) = {}^-3$ is a linear function, in which $a = 0$ and $b = {}^-3$.
The sketch is shown in the accompanying figure.

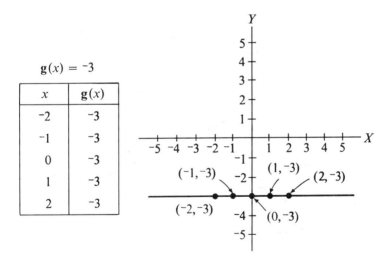

g(x) = -3

x	g(x)
-2	-3
-1	-3
0	-3
1	-3
2	-3

Observe that the graph of each of the above linear functions is a straight line. The reason for the qualifying adjective *linear* in Definition 6 is that the graph of any *linear* function is a straight *line*. The following theorem is a generalization of the observations in each of the above examples.

THEOREM 1. *The solution set of the open sentence $ax + by = c$, in which $b \neq 0$, is equal to the solution set of the linear function $y = \left(\frac{-a}{b}\right)x + \frac{c}{b}$.*

Proof. $ax + by = c \leftrightthreetimes by = {}^-ax + c$

$$\leftrightthreetimes y = \frac{({}^-ax + c)}{b}$$
$$\leftrightthreetimes y = \left(\frac{-a}{b}\right)x + \frac{c}{b}$$

$\left. \right\} b \neq 0$

Hence $\{(x, y): ax + by = c \ \wedge \ b \neq 0\} =$

$$\{(x, y): \left[y = \left(\frac{-a}{b}\right)x + \frac{c}{b}\right] \wedge \ (b \neq 0)\}. \diamondsuit$$

According to Theorem 1, the open sentence $ax + by = c$ generates a linear function, provided $b \neq 0$. Hence the graph of $ax + by = c$ is a straight line. The following examples illustrate Theorem 1.

Example 6. Sketch the graph of the linear function determined by the open sentence $3x + 7y = 6$.

$$3x + 7y = 6$$
$$7y = {}^-3x + 6$$
$$y = \left(\frac{-3}{7}\right)x + \frac{6}{7}$$

Thus the linear function is $y = \left(\frac{-3}{7}\right)x + \frac{6}{7}$. The sketch of the graph is shown in the accompanying figure.

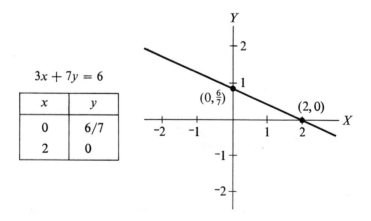

$3x + 7y = 6$

x	y
0	6/7
2	0

Example 7. Sketch the graph of the linear function determined by the open sentence $6x + 14y = {}^-7$.

$$6x + 14y = {}^-7$$
$$14y = {}^-6x + {}^-7$$
$$y = \left(\tfrac{-6}{14}\right)x + \tfrac{-7}{14}$$
$$y = \left(\tfrac{-3}{7}\right)x + \tfrac{-1}{2}$$

Thus the linear function is $y = \left(\tfrac{-3}{7}\right)x + \tfrac{-1}{2}$. The sketch of the graph is shown in the accompanying figure.

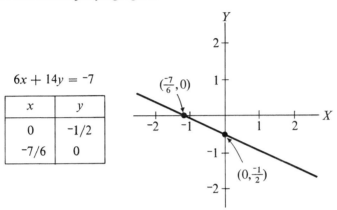

Observe that the coefficients of x in Examples 1, 2, and 3 are all equal and the lines in these examples are parallel. Because of these considerations we make the following definition.

DEFINITION 7.   The *slope* of the linear function $y = ax + b$ is the real number a.

For example, the slope of each of the linear functions of Examples 1, 2, and 3 is 3, the slope of the linear function of Example 4 is $^-2$, the slope of the linear function of Example 5 is 0, and the slope of each of the linear functions of Example 6 and 7 is $\tfrac{-3}{7}$.

The concept of slope of a linear function has a geometric interpretation. If we know that the slope of a linear function is a, we can immediately conclude that an increase of one unit in the variable x is accompanied by a change of $|a|$ units in the variable y. The following examples illustrate the geometric interpretation.

Example 8.   The slope of the linear function $y = 2x - 1$ is 2. The sketch is shown in the accompanying figure.

Observe that an *increase* of 1 unit in the x-coordinate is accompanied by an *increase* of 2 units in the y-coordinate. For this reason we say that the slope of the *line* is equal to 2.

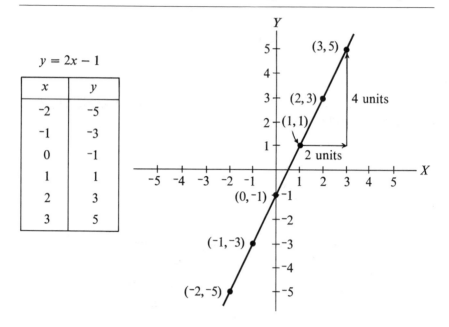

$y = 2x - 1$

x	y
-2	-5
-1	-3
0	-1
1	1
2	3
3	5

Example 9. The slope of the linear function $y = {}^-x$ is $^-1$. The sketch is shown in the accompanying figure.

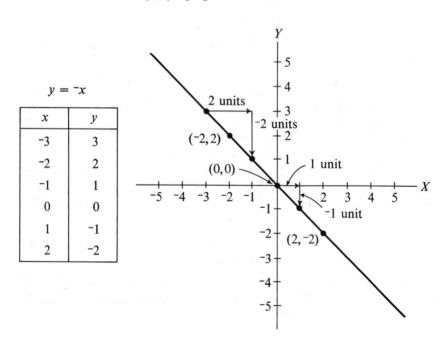

$y = {}^-x$

x	y
-3	3
-2	2
-1	1
0	0
1	-1
2	-2

An *increase* of 1 unit in the *x*-coordinate is accompanied by a *decrease* of 1 unit in the *y*-coordinate.

Example 10.   The slope of the linear function $y = \left(\frac{1}{5}\right)x$ is $\frac{1}{5}$. The sketch is shown in the accompanying figure.

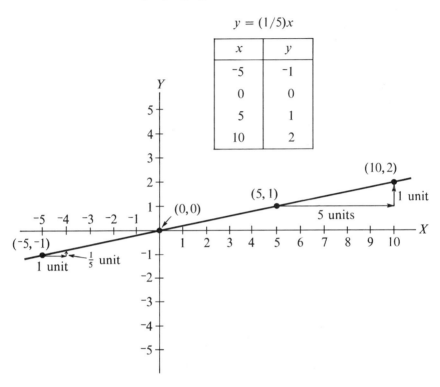

$y = (1/5)x$

x	y
$^-5$	$^-1$
0	0
5	1
10	2

An *increase* of 1 unit in the *x*-coordinate is accompanied by an *increase* of $\frac{1}{5}$ unit in the *y*-coordinate.

From the above examples we observe that the line is almost horizontal whenever the slope is nearly 0, and almost vertical whenever the absolute value of the slope is large. If the slope is positive, an *increase* in the *x*-coordinate is accompanied by an *increase* in the *y*-coordinate. If the slope is negative, an *increase* in the *x*-coordinate is accompanied by a *decrease* in the *y*-coordinate.

Exercise 4.5

I. Decide which functions of Exercise 4.3 are linear functions.

II. Sketch the graph and compute the slope of each of the following linear functions.

(1) $y = x$

(2) $y = \left(\frac{1}{2}\right)x$

(3) $y = {}^{-}5x$

(4) $y = {}^{-}10x$

(5) $y = 5x - 3$

(6) $y = 10x - 2$

(7) $y = \left(\frac{-1}{2}\right)x + 3$

(8) $y = \left(\frac{1}{4}\right)x - 4$

(9) $y = 6$

(10) $y = 0$

III. Determine the linear function $y = ax + b$ defined by each of the following open sentences, and compute its slope.

(1) $2x + 3y = 7$

(2) $^{-}2x + 3y = {}^{-}1$

(3) $x - y = 3$

(4) $x - 4y = {}^{-}3$

(5) $10x - y = 2$

(6) $x + 10y = 2$

(7) $x + 5y = 0$

(8) $5x - y = 0$

(9) $^{-}4x + 2y = 5$

(10) $^{-}3x + 2y = 5$

IV. Sketch the graph of each function in Exercise III.

V. Sketch the graph of each of the following sets.

(1) $\{(x, y): y = x\} \cup \{(x, y): y = \left(\frac{1}{2}\right)x\}$

(2) $\{(x, y): y = x\} \cap \{(x, y): y = \left(\frac{1}{2}\right)x\}$

(3) $\{(x, y): 10x - y = 2\} \cup \{(x, y): x + 10y = 2\}$

(4) $\{(x, y): 10x - y = 2\} \cap \{(x, y): x + 10y = 2\}$

(5) $\{(x, y): [y = 3x + 1] \lor [y = \left(\frac{-1}{3}\right)x]\}$

(6) $\{(x, y): [y = 3x + 1] \land [y = \left(\frac{-1}{3}\right)x]\}$

(7) $\{(x, y): x = 0 \lor y = 0\}$

(8) $\{(x, y): x = 0 \land y = 0\}$

(9) $\{(x, y): 2x - 3y = 5\} \cup \{(x, y): 2x - 3y = {}^{-}5\}$

(10) $\{(x, y): 2x - 3y = 5\} \cup \{(x, y): 6x - 9y = 15\}$

VI. Prove that $y = ax + b$ is actually a function.

(*Hint.* Prove $x_1 = x_2 \rightarrow ax_1 + b = ax_2 + b$ for *all* real numbers x_1, x_2, a, and b.)

VII. Each of the following sets has exactly one element. Compute that element.

(1) $\{(x, y): 2x + 3y = 6 \ \wedge \ x = 0\}$
(2) $\{(x, y): 2x - 3y = 6 \ \wedge \ x = 0\}$
(3) $\{(x, y): y = 3x + 5 \ \wedge \ x = 0\}$
(4) $\{(x, y): y = {}^-2x - \frac{3}{4} \ \wedge \ x = 0\}$
(5) $\{(x, y): y = {}^-3x \ \wedge \ x = 0\}$

The y-coordinate of each of the points $(0, y)$ is called the *y-intercept* of the linear function (or the y-intercept of the line).

VIII. Each of the following sets has exactly one element. Compute that element.

(1) $\{(x, y): 2x + 3y = 6 \ \wedge \ y = 0\}$
(2) $\{(x, y): 2x - 3y = 6 \ \wedge \ y = 0\}$
(3) $\{(x, y): y = 3x + 5 \ \wedge \ y = 0\}$
(4) $\{(x, y): y = {}^-2x - \frac{3}{4} \ \wedge \ y = 0\}$
(5) $\{(x, y): y = {}^-3x \ \wedge \ y = 0\}$

The x-coordinate of each of the points $(x, 0)$ is called the *x-intercept* of the linear function (or the x-intercept of the line).

4.6 Quadratic Functions

In this section we shall study another important subset of the class of functions — the set of *quadratic functions*. In Sections 4.3 and 4.4 we considered several examples of quadratic functions. In the exercises you will be asked to prove that $y = ax^2 + bx + c$ is actually a function. As the universal set is the set of reals, the coefficients a, b, and c are *real* numbers.

DEFINITION 8. The function $y = ax^2 + bx + c$, in which $a \neq 0$, is called a *quadratic function*.

Example 1. $y = x^2$ is a quadratic function, in which $a = 1$, $b = 0$, and $c = 0$.

The function may be written $\mathbf{f}(x) = x^2$. The sketch of the graph is shown in the accompanying figure.

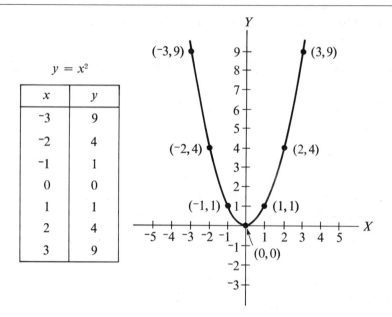

$y = x^2$

x	y
⁻3	9
⁻2	4
⁻1	1
0	0
1	1
2	4
3	9

Example 2. $y = {}^-x^2$ is a quadratic function, in which $a = {}^-1$, $b = 0$, and $c = 0$.

The function may be written $\mathbf{g}(x) = {}^-x^2$. The sketch of the graph is shown in the accompanying figure.

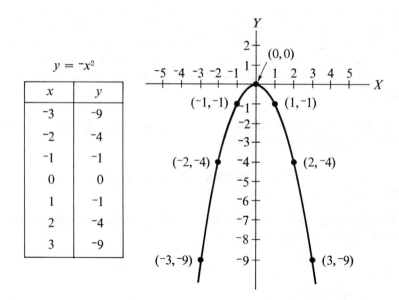

$y = {}^-x^2$

x	y
⁻3	⁻9
⁻2	⁻4
⁻1	⁻1
0	0
1	⁻1
2	⁻4
3	⁻9

Example 3. $y = 2x^2 - 8x$ is a quadratic function, in which $a = 2$, $b = {}^-8$, and $c = 0$.

The sketch is shown in the accompanying figure.

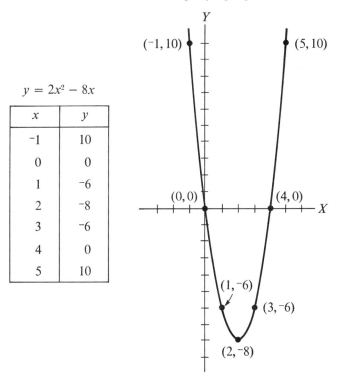

$y = 2x^2 - 8x$

x	y
⁻1	10
0	0
1	⁻6
2	⁻8
3	⁻6
4	0
5	10

Example 4. $y = {}^-x^2 + 3x + 1$ is a quadratic function, in which $a = {}^-1$, $b = 3$, and $c = 1$.

The sketch is shown in the accompanying figure.

$y = {}^-x^2 + 3x + 1$

x	y
⁻1	⁻3
0	1
1	3
2	3
3	1
4	⁻3

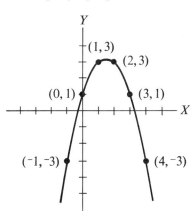

Example 5. $y = x^2 + 3x + 4$ is a quadratic function, in which $a = 1$, $b = 3$, and $c = 4$.

The sketch is shown in the accompanying figure.

$y = x^2 + 3x + 4$

x	y
$^-4$	8
$^-3$	4
$^-2$	2
$^-1$	2
0	4
1	8

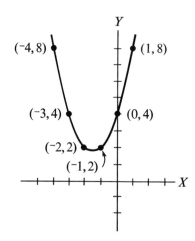

Example 6. $y = ^-2x^2 + x + ^-3$ is a quadratic function in which $a = ^-2$, $b = 1$, and $c = ^-3$.

The sketch is shown in the accompanying figure.

$y = ^-2x^2 + x + ^-3$

x	y
$^-2$	$^-13$
$^-1$	$^-6$
0	$^-3$
1	$^-4$
2	$^-9$

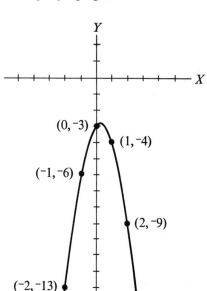

The graph of any quadratic function is called a *parabola*. The orientation of the parabola depends on the coefficients a, b, and c. If a is *negative*, the parabola opens *downward* as in Examples 2, 4, and 6. If a is *positive*, the parabola opens *upward* as in Examples 1, 3, and 5. If a is negative, there is a highest point on the parabola, and if a is positive, there is a lowest point on the parabola. This point is known as the *vertex* of the parabola. These ideas are very important in the applications of quadratic functions.

For example, the mathematical model of the path of a projectile is a parabola. The maximum height attained by the projectile corresponds to the y-coordinate of the vertex of the parabola. Moreover, the mathematical models of many problems of the physical and biological sciences, economics, psychology, social studies, etc. involve quadratic functions.

In order to determine the approximate location of the vertex of the parabola in Example 6, it is necessary to compute several points "between" the points $(0, {}^-3)$ and $(1, {}^-4)$. A more efficient method of determining the vertex *exactly* and on sketching the graph rapidly will be studied in Chapter 5.

Exercise 4.6

I. (1) Decide which functions in Exercise 4.3 are quadratic functions.
   (2) Decide which functions in Exercise 4.4 are quadratic functions.

II. Sketch the graph of each of the following quadratic functions.

(1) $y = 2x^2 + 1$ (6) $y = {}^-5x^2 + 3x$
(2) $y = 2x^2 - 1$ (7) $y = {}^-x^2 - x + 1$
(3) $y = {}^-2x^2 + 1$ (8) $y = {}^-x^2 + x - 1$
(4) $y = {}^-2x^2 - 1$ (9) $y = x^2 + 5x - 6$
(5) $y = {}^-3x^2 + 5x$ (10) $y = x^2 - 5x + 6$

III. Estimate the vertex of each parabola in Exercise II.

IV. Sketch the graph of the quadratic function defined by each of the following open sentences.

(1) $y = {}^-2x^2 - 5$ (6) $y = x^2 + 3x + 2$
(2) $y = {}^-5x^2 - 2$ (7) $y - 3x^2 - 5x + 2 = 0$
(3) $y = 4x^2 + 4x + 1$ (8) $y - 3x^2 - x + 2 = 0$
(4) $y = 4x^2 - 4x + 1$ (9) $y - x^2 - x - 1 = 0$
(5) $y = x^2 - 3x + 2$ (10) $y + x^2 + x + 1 = 0$

V. Estimate the vertex of each parabola in Exercise IV.

VI. Sketch the graph of each of the following sets.

(1) $\{(x, y): y = 3x\} \cup \{(x, y): y = x^2\}$

(2) $\{(x, y): y = 3x\} \cap \{(x, y): y = x^2\}$

(3) $\{(x, y): y = 3x\} \cup \{(x, y): y = {}^-x^2\}$

(4) $\{(x, y): y = 3x\} \cap \{(x, y): y = {}^-x^2\}$

(5) $\{(x, y): y = {}^-x^2 + 1 \lor x + y = 1\}$

(6) $\{(x, y): y = {}^-x^2 + 1 \land x + y = 1\}$

(7) $\{(x, y): y = x^2 - 1 \lor x - y = 1\}$

(8) $\{(x, y): y = x^2 - 1 \land x - y = 1\}$

(9) $\{(x, y): y = x^2 + x - 6 \lor y = 0\}$

(10) $\{(x, y): y = x^2 + x - 6 \land y = 0\}$

(11) $\{(x, y): y = x^2 - x - 6 \land y = 0\}$

(12) $\{(x, y): y = x^2 + 5x + 6 \land y = 0\}$

(13) $\{(x, y): y = 6x^2 - x - 2 \land y = 0\}$

(14) $\{(x, y): y = 6x^2 + x - 2 \land y = 0\}$

(15) $\{(x, y): y = 6x^2 - x - 2 \land x = 0\}$

(16) $\{(x, y): y = 6x^2 + x - 2 \land x = 0\}$

(17) $\{(x, y): y = 6x^2 - x + 2 \land x = 0\}$

(18) $\{(x, y): y = x^2 - x - 6 \land x = 0\}$

(19) $\{(x, y): y = 100x^2 + 16x - 15 \land x = 0\}$

(20) $\{(x, y): y = x^2 + 4 \land x = 0\}$

VII. Prove that $y = ax^2 + bx + c$ is actually a function.

4.7 Linear Inequalities

While linear functions have extensive applications, recent developments in mathematics and industry have caused the study of linear inequalities to gain importance. In the next chapter we shall study the
applications of linear inequalities to industry. In this section we shall
study the techniques of sketching the graphs of linear inequalities.

DEFINITION 9. The open sentences $ax + by < c$ and $ax + by \leq c$,
in which $a \neq 0$ or $b \neq 0$, are called *linear inequalities* in two variables.

The linear inequality $ax + by \leq c$, in which $a \neq 0$ or $b \neq 0$, is
sometimes called a *weak* linear inequality; similarly, $ax + by < c$ is
sometimes called a *strong* linear inequality.

We shall speak of *the graph of the linear inequality* $ax + by \leq c$ to
mean the *graph of its solution set*; i.e., the graph of $\{(x, y): ax + by \leq c\}$. To sketch the graph of the linear inequality $ax + by \leq c$, or of
$ax + by < c$, we first sketch the graph of the linear function $ax + by = c$
and then determine whether the graph of $\{(x, y): ax + by < c\}$ lies
above or below the graph of $ax + by = c$. The following examples illustrate the procedure.

Example 1.   Sketch the graph of $y < x$.

Since $y < x \leftrightarrows {}^-x + y < 0$ for all x and y, we see that $y < x$ is a linear inequality, in which $a = {}^-1$, $b = 1$, and $c = 0$. The sketch of the linear function $y = x$ is shown in the accompanying figure (a).

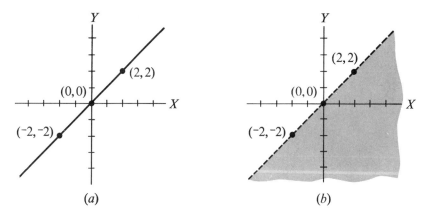

(a) (b)

Since $y < x$ in the linear inequality and $y = x$ in the linear function, the graph of the inequality lies *below* the graph of the function. Conversely, any point of the plane below the graph of the linear function is a point of the graph of the linear inequality. Thus the graph of the linear inequality is the set of all points of the coordinate plane which lie below the graph of the linear function. The point (x, y) lies below the point (x, x) of the linear function if and only if $y < x$. The graph of the linear inequality $y < x$ is shown in the accompanying figure (b). The line is *not* part of the graph of the inequality.

Example 2.   Sketch the graph of $3x + 2 \leq y$.

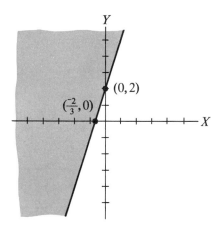

Since $3x + 2 \leq y$ is equivalent to $3x - y \leq {}^-2$, the inequality is indeed a linear inequality. In this case the graph of the inequality is the set of points of the coordinate plane which lie *above* or *on* the graph of the function $y = 3x + 2$. The sketch is shown in the accompanying figure. The line is part of the graph.

Example 3.   Sketch the graph of $y < {}^-3$.

The inequality $y < {}^-3$ is of the form $ax + by < c$, in which $a = 0$, $b = 1$, and $c = {}^-3$. The sketch of the graph is shown in the accompanying figure. The horizontal line is *not* part of the graph.

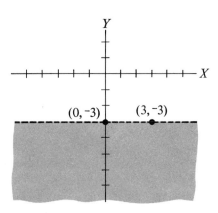

Example 4.   Sketch the graph of $5 < y$.

The inequality $5 < y$ is equivalent to the linear inequality $0x + {}^-1y < {}^-5$. The sketch of the graph is shown in the accompanying figure. The horizontal line is *not* part of the graph.

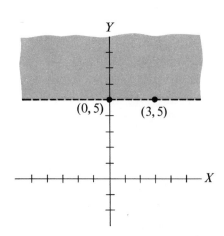

Example 5.   Sketch the graph of the inequality $x \leq 3$.

The inequality is of the form $ax + by \leq c$, in which $a = 1$, $b = 0$, and $c = 3$. The sketch is shown in the accompanying figure. The vertical line is part of the graph.

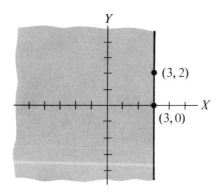

Example 6.   Sketch the graph of the compound inequality

$x < 3 \ \wedge \ ^-5 < x$.

The compound open sentence $^-5 < x \ \wedge \ x < 3$ is usually written as $^-5 < x < 3$. Since $\{(x, y): x < 3 \ \wedge \ ^-5 < x\} = \{(x, y): x < 3\}$ $\cap \ \{(x, y): ^-5 < x\}$, it follows that the graph of the given compound inequality is the intersection of the graph of $\{(x, y): x < 3\}$ and the graph of $\{(x, y): ^-5 < x\}$. The sketch is shown in the accompanying figure. The two vertical lines are *not* part of the sketch.

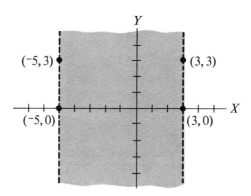

Example 7.   Sketch the graph of the compound inequality

$3 \leq x \ \lor \ x \leq {}^-5$.

Since $\{(x, y): 3 \leq x \ \lor \ x \leq {}^-5\} = \{(x, y): 3 \leq x\} \ \cup \ \{(x, y): x \leq {}^-5\}$, it follows that the graph of the given compound inequality is the union of the graph of $\{(x, y): 3 \leq x\}$ and the graph of $\{(x, y): x \leq {}^-5\}$. The sketch is shown in the accompanying figure. The two vertical lines are parts of the graph.

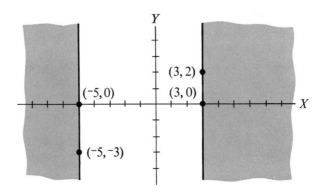

Example 8.   Sketch the graph of the compound inequality

$3 \leq y \ \land \ y \leq x$.

The sketch is shown in the accompanying figure. Notice that the two lines are parts of the graph.

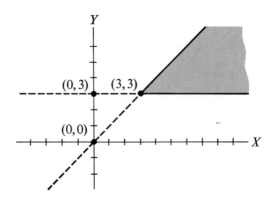

Example 9.   Sketch the graph of the compound inequality

$x < y + 1 \;\; \vee \;\; {}^-3x + 3 < y.$

The sketch is shown in the accompanying figure. Neither dotted line is part of the graph.

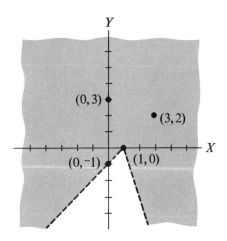

Example 10.   Sketch the graph of the compound inequality

$0 < x \;\; \wedge \;\; 0 \leq y.$

The sketch is shown in the accompanying figure. Notice that the positive half of the X-axis is part of the graph but that the Y-axis is not.

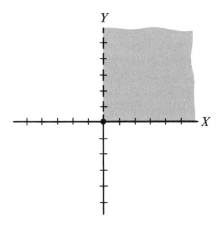

Exercise 4.7

I. Sketch the graph of each of the following inequalities. Recall that, unless otherwise restricted, the domain and the range are the reals.

(1) $x < 0$

(2) $y < {}^-x$

(3) ${}^-4x + 3 \leq y$

(4) $y < {}^-x \wedge {}^-1 < y$

(5) $y < x \wedge \left(\frac{1}{2}\right)x < y$

(6) ${}^-1 < x \leq 4$

(7) $1 < y \vee y < {}^-1$

(8) $1 < y \wedge y < {}^-1$

(9) $y \leq x \wedge \left(\frac{1}{2}\right)x < y \wedge 1 < x < 3$

(10) $y < x \wedge \left(\frac{1}{2}\right)x < y \wedge y < 3$

(11) $y = {}^-3x + 2 \wedge 1 < y < 2$

(12) $y \leq {}^-3x + 2 \vee 3x + 2 \leq y$

(13) $y \leq {}^-3x + 2 \wedge 3x + 2 \leq y$

(14) $\left(\frac{2}{3}\right)x - \left(\frac{4}{5}\right)y < \frac{1}{7}$

(15) $(1 < y \vee y < {}^-1) \wedge (x < {}^-1 \vee 1 < x)$

(16) $(1 < y \vee y < {}^-1) \vee (x < {}^-1 \vee 1 < x)$

II. Which inequalities of Exercise I are *linear inequalities*?

4.8 Applications of Functions

Most of the functions considered in the previous sections have been purely mathematical. In this section we shall study some physical phenomena of nature and give mathematical models of these phenomena. These models will be functions. Thus, as in our previous studies, the study of functions enables us to better understand nature and the world in which we live. The following examples illustrate the application of linear and quadratic functions.

Example 1. In physics, it is frequently necessary to convert a speed expressed in miles per hour to the corresponding speed in feet per second. The formula for the conversion is $v = \left(\frac{22}{15}\right)u$, in which u represents the speed in miles per hour and v represents the speed in feet per second. The sketch of the graph of the linear function $v = \left(\frac{22}{15}\right)u$ is shown in the accompanying figure.

$v = (22/15)u$

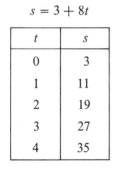

u	v
0	0
15	22
30	44
45	66
60	88
75	110
90	132

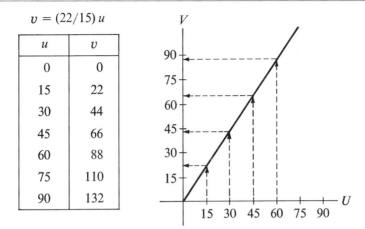

Example 2. Phil is 3 miles west of his home. At 1:00 PM he starts a four-hour journey west on his bicycle at an average speed of 8 miles per hour. The formula which expresses the distance west of his home at any time between 1:00 PM and 5:00 PM is $s = 3 + 8t$, in which t represents the duration of his trip (in hours) and s represents the distance from home. Thus $s = 3 + 8t$ is a function with domain equal to $\{t: 0 \leq t \leq 4\}$. The sketch of the graph is shown in the accompanying figure. Observe from the graph that Phil is 35 miles west of home at 5:00 PM.

$s = 3 + 8t$

t	s
0	3
1	11
2	19
3	27
4	35

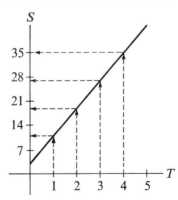

To avoid too tall a sketch, we have employed a scale on the *S-axis* different from that on the *T-axis*. Although the slope of the line appears to be affected by the different scales, it is actually not.

Example 3. You are familiar with the fact that an increase in the volume of a gas results in a decrease in the pressure. The physical law of gases which states this phenomenon is known as *Boyle's Law*. Letting v represent the volume and p the pressure of a gas enclosed in a container (for example, a cylinder or tire), we may state Boyle's Law mathematically by the formula $p = \frac{k}{v}$, in which $0 < v$. Of course, the variable v may represent any positive real number, limited by the physical properties of the container, and k is a real number, known as the *gas constant*, which depends on the particular gas in the container. The formula $p = \frac{k}{v}$ is a function whose domain is R^+. The sketch is shown in the accompanying figure for a gas constant equal to 10.

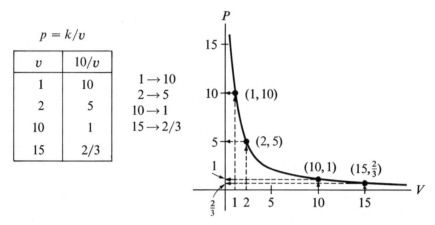

$p = k/v$

v	$10/v$
1	10
2	5
10	1
15	2/3

$1 \rightarrow 10$
$2 \rightarrow 5$
$10 \rightarrow 1$
$15 \rightarrow 2/3$

In particular, observe that a volume of 2 units corresponds to a pressure of 5 units. In the sketch this is indicated by the vertical line segment from the point $(2, 0)$ to the point $(2, 5)$ and the horizontal line segment from the point $(2, 5)$ to the point $(0, 5)$. Thus the number 2 corresponds to the number 5.

Example 4. The president of a canning industry wishes to produce a can which will contain a certain number of cubic inches of peas. He knows that the dimensions of the can will determine how much tin will be used in its manufacture. In the interest of economy he wishes to use the minimum amount of tin possible and still have a can of the desired volume. The amount of tin used, in square inches, is equal to the sum of the area of the top, area of the bottom, and area of the side.

If we denote the length of the radius of the base by r and the height of the can by h, we see that the area of the top is πr^2 square inches, the area of the bottom is πr^2 square inches, and the area of the side is $2\pi rh$ square inches. Thus the total amount of tin used in the can is $\pi r^2 + \pi r^2 + 2\pi rh$ square inches. Designating this area (of tin) by s, we see that the total amount of tin used is given by $s = 2\pi r^2 + 2\pi rh$. Moreover, the volume v is $\pi r^2 h$. Hence $h = \frac{v}{\pi r^2}$. Thus

$$s = 2\pi r^2 + 2\pi rh,$$
$$s = 2\pi r^2 + 2\pi r \left(\frac{v}{\pi r^2}\right),$$
$$s = 2\pi r^2 + \frac{2v}{r}.$$

If the manufacturer desires a can whose volume is 20π cubic inches, then he replaces the variable v by the real number 20π. The resulting equation is $s = 2\pi r^2 + \frac{40\pi}{r}$. The sketch of the graph of $s = 2\pi r^2 + \frac{40\pi}{r}$ is shown in the accompanying figure.

$$s = 2\pi r^2 + \frac{40\pi}{r}$$

r	s
1	42π
2	28π
2.1	27.8π
2.2	27.8π
3	31.3π
4	42π

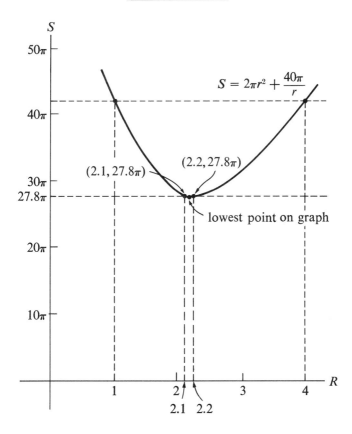

The lowest point on the graph corresponds to the minimum value of *s*. The surface area, and hence the cost of the tin, will be minimum whenever the length of the radius is approximately equal to 2 inches. When $r = 2$ inches, $h = \frac{20\pi}{\pi(2)^2} = \frac{20\pi}{4\pi} = 5$ inches.

Thus the manufacturer saves money by making a can with a radius of 2 inches and a height of 5 inches (if he wants a volume of 20π cubic inches). By the methods of a branch of mathematics known as *calculus*, one may solve the above type of problem more easily and accurately.

Much of mathematics is concerned with the study of functions. Hypotheses are stated and conclusions are derived. The resulting theorems shed much light on the nature of functions. As the theorems are stated in general terms, we may infer the conclusion of any theorem for any particular function which satisfies the hypotheses of the theorem. Thus, for example, an important theorem states certain hypotheses; the conclusion is that any function which satisfies these hypotheses has a maximum value or a minimum value. This theorem, in particular, is used in the solution of the above problem. It must be remembered, however, that not all functions have maximum and minimum values. These functions, of course, would not satisfy the hypotheses of this theorem.

Another theorem, called the *fundamental theorem of algebra*, is stated as follows: $\{x: a_0 + a_1x + a_2x^2 + \cdots + a_nx^n = 0 \wedge n$ is a positive odd integer $\wedge a_n \neq 0\} \neq \emptyset$. For example, the open sentence $x^5 + 2x^4 + 3x^2 + {}^-4 = 0$ satisfies the hypotheses of the above theorem. Hence we can be certain that the solution set is not empty. That is, there is at least one real number x_0 such that the sentence $x_0^5 + 2x_0^4 + 3x_0^2 + {}^-4 = 0$ is true. In other words, the equation $x^5 + 2x^4 + 3x^2 + {}^-4 = 0$ has at least one real root. The fundamental theorem of algebra guarantees that *every* equation of the form $a_0 + a_1x + a_2x^2 + \cdots + a_nx^n = 0$, in which *n* is a positive odd integer and $a_n \neq 0$, has at least one real root.

Exercise 4.8

I. The formula for converting temperature in degrees centigrade to degrees Fahrenheit is $F = \left(\frac{9}{5}\right)C + 32$.

   (1) Sketch the graph of $F = \left(\frac{9}{5}\right)C + 32$, $^-50 \leq C \leq 100$.

   (2) Estimate the centigrade reading corresponding to a Fahrenheit reading of 86°.

   (3) Estimate the temperature at which the two readings are equal.

II. (1) Derive the formula for converting temperature in degrees Fahrenheit to temperature in degrees centigrade.

   (2) Sketch the graph of the linear function derived in (1).

(3) Estimate the Fahrenheit reading corresponding to a centigrade reading of 40°.

(4) Estimate the temperature at which the two readings are equal.

III. Ohm's Law in electricity may be written $e = ir$, in which e represents the voltage, i represents the current, and r represents the resistance. If $r = 100$ ohms, then $e = 100i$. Sketch the graph of the function $e = 100i$, $0 \leq i \leq 10$. (*Hint*. You may choose the scale on the E-axis different from the scale on the I-axis.)

IV. A boy standing on the top of a building 100 feet high throws a ball straight up with a speed of 32 feet per second. The equation describing the motion of the ball is $s = 100 + 32t + {}^{-}16t^2$, in which t represents the time measured in seconds and s represents the height of the ball measured in feet. Sketch the graph of $s = 100 + 32t + {}^{-}16t^2$.

V. In Exercise IV use the sketch to estimate (1) the time when the ball reaches its maximum height, (2) the maximum height reached by the ball, and (3) the time when the ball strikes the ground.

VI. The volume of the region enclosed by a sphere of radius r is $\left(\frac{4}{3}\right)\pi r^3$. Sketch the graph of $v = \left(\frac{4}{3}\right)\pi r^3$. Use the graph to estimate the radius when the volume is 40π units.

VII. The formula for the area of a rectangle is $k = xy$ and the perimeter is $p = 2x + 2y$. If $k = 20$ square units, determine the dimensions x and y which will yield the minimum perimeter. (*Hint*. Solve $20 = xy$ for x and replace the variable x in $p = 2x + 2y$.)

CHAPTER 5

Systems of Linear Equations and Inequalities

5.1 Systems of Linear Equations in Two Variables

In Chapter 4 we learned that the graph of a linear function in two variables is a straight line. For example, the graph of the linear function $y = x + 3$ is the straight line through the two points $(0, 3)$ and $(^-3, 0)$, as shown in Figure 5.1(a). Similarly, the graph of the linear function $y = ^-x$ is the straight line through the two points $(0, 0)$ and $(^-3, 3)$, as shown in Figure 5.1(b).

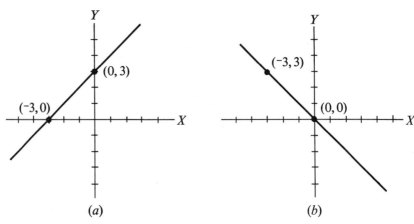

(a)　　　　　　　　　　　　　　(b)

FIGURE 5.1

For convenience both graphs are sketched relative to a common set of axes, as shown in Figure 5.2.

154

Observe that the two straight lines of Figure 5.2 constitute the graph of the set $\{(x, y): (y = x + 3) \lor (y = {}^-x)\}$; i.e., the graph of $\{(x, y): y = x + 3\} \cup \{(x, y): y = {}^-x\}$.

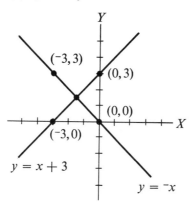

FIGURE 5.2

Frequently we must solve a physical problem whose mathematical model consists of two linear functions $y = a_1x + b_1$ and $y = a_2x + b_2$ and whose desired solution set is the set of all ordered pairs (x, y) which satisfy both equations $y = a_1x + b_1$ and $y = a_2x + b_2$. The desired solution set is $\{(x, y): y = a_1x + b_1 \land y = a_2x + b_2\}$, which is equal to $\{(x, y): y = a_1x + b_1\} \cap \{(x, y): a_2x + b_2\}$; i.e., the intersection of the lines determined by the open sentences $y = a_1x + b_1$ and $y = a_2x + b_2$. In Section 5.3 we shall consider several physical problems which may be solved by means of linear functions. In Section 5.2 we shall discuss the various possible intersections of two linear functions. In the remainder of this section we shall discuss the commonly used procedure for computing the intersection of two linear functions. The following examples illustrate the various methods.

Example 1. Solve the *system of simultaneous linear equations* $\begin{bmatrix} y = 2x + 3 \\ y = x + 5 \end{bmatrix}$; i.e., compute the set of all pairs (x, y) which satisfy both linear equations.

(1) $y = 2x + 3$
(2) $y = x + 5$
(1) $y = 2x + 3$
(2) $2x + 3 = x + 5$
$\quad 2x - x = 5 - 3$
$\quad\quad\quad x = 2$
$\quad\quad\quad y = x + 5$
$\quad\quad\quad y = 2 + 5$
$\quad\quad\quad y = 7$

The solution of the system is $x = 2$, $y = 7$; i.e., the point $(2, 7)$.

In effect, we *substituted* the variable $2x + 3$ of equation (1) for the variable y in equation (2). For this reason, the method of solution is usually called *solution by substitution*. The method of solution by substitution is illustrated again in Example 2.

Example 2. Solve the system of linear equations $\begin{bmatrix} 2x + y = 5 \\ 3x + 2y = 9 \end{bmatrix}$.

(1) $y = 5 - 2x$

(2) $3x + 2(5 - 2x) = 9$

$\quad 3x + 10 - 4x = 9$

$\quad {}^-x = 9 - 10$

$\quad {}^-x = {}^-1$

$\quad x = 1$

(1) $y = 5 - 2x$

$\quad y = 5 - 2(1)$

$\quad y = 5 - 2$

$\quad y = 3$

The solution of the system is $x = 1$, $y = 3$; i.e., the point $(1, 3)$. The following example illustrates the method of *solution by addition.*

Example 3. Solve the system $\begin{bmatrix} 2x + y = 5 \\ x - 2y = {}^-5 \end{bmatrix}$.

(1) $2x + y = 5$

(2) $x - 2y = {}^-5$

(1) $2(2x + y) = 2(5)$

(2) $x - 2y = {}^-5$

(1) $4x + 2y = 10$

(2) $\underline{x - 2y = {}^-5}$

$\quad 5x = 5$

$\quad x = 1$

(1) $2x + y = 5$

$\quad 2(1) + y = 5$

$\quad y = 3$

Thus the solution of the system is $x = 1$, $y = 3$; i.e., the point $(1, 3)$. *Graphically*, the point of *intersection* of the graphs of $2x + y = 5$ and $x - 2y = {}^-5$ is the point $(1, 3)$, as shown in the accompanying sketch. Similar comments may be made about Examples 1 and 2. Example 4 further illustrates the method.

From the sketch in Example 3, we see that the point $(1, 3)$ is the point which lies on both lines $x - 2y = {}^-5$ and $2x + y = 5$. That is, $(1, 3)$ lies on $x - 2y = {}^-5$ *and* $2x + y = 5$. Thus $(1, 3)$ is the only element in the *intersection* of the solution set of $x - 2y = {}^-5$ and the solution set of $2x + y = 5$. Symbolically, $\{(x, y): x - 2y = {}^-5 \wedge 2x + y = 5\} = \{(x, y): x - 2y = {}^-5\} \cap \{(x, y): 2x + y = 5\} = \{(1, 3)\}$. In other words, the intersection of the solution sets of the individual linear equations is the solution set of the *system* of linear equations.

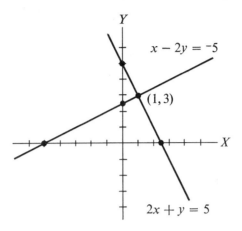

Example 4. Compute the point of intersection of the straight lines $3x + 2y = 4$ and $4x + 3y = 5$.

(1) $3x + 2y = 4$
(2) $4x + 3y = 5$
(1) $^-3(3x + 2y) = {}^-3(4)$
(2) $2(4x + 3y) = 2(5)$
(1) $^-9x + {}^-6y = {}^-12$
(2) $\underline{8x + 6y = 10}$
$\quad\;\; {}^-x = {}^-2$
$\quad\;\; x = 2$
(1) $3x + 2y = 4$
$\quad\;\; 3(2) + 2y = 4$
$\quad\;\; 6 + 2y = 4$
$\quad\;\; 2y = {}^-2$
$\quad\;\; y = {}^-1$

Thus the point of intersection of $3x + 2y = 4$ and $4x + 3y = 5$ is $(2, {}^-1)$. The graph is shown in the accompanying figure.

We summarize this section with the following remarks and a detailed example which shows all steps in the computation of the solution set of a system of linear equations.

To solve a system of simultaneous linear equations in two variables (i.e., to compute the intersection of the two linear functions), we employ the method of substitution or the method of addition. The method of solution guarantees that the set obtained as the solution set is the complete solution set, provided no computational error is made. In order to detect any possible computational errors, it is advisable to check the computed solution by replacing the variables x and y in the original linear equations and proving that the open sentences are converted to true sentences. The coordinates of any point in the solution set *satisfy* the two linear equations. For example, the coordinates 2 and $^-1$ satisfy the linear equations $3x + 2y = 4$ and $4x + 3y = 5$ of Example 4. We see that the solution set of a system of simultaneous linear equations in two variables is the intersection of the solution sets of the individual equations. To *solve* a system of two linear equations in two variables is *to compute the solution set of the system.*

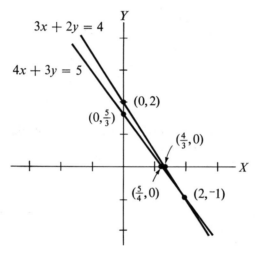

Example 5. Compute the intersection of $\{(x, y): 2x + y = 5\}$ and $\{(x, y): x - 2y = {}^-5\}$.

$$
\begin{aligned}
&\{(x, y): 2x + y = 5\} \cap \{(x, y): x - 2y = {}^-5\} \\
={}& \{(x, y): 2x + y = 5 \ \wedge \ x - 2y = {}^-5\} \\
={}& \{(x, y): y = 5 - 2x \ \wedge \ x - 2y = {}^-5\} \\
={}& \{(x, y): y = 5 - 2x \ \wedge \ x - 2(5 - 2x) = {}^-5\} \\
={}& \{(x, y): y = 5 - 2x \ \wedge \ x - 10 + 4x = {}^-5\} \\
={}& \{(x, y): y = 5 - 2x \ \wedge \ 5x = 5\} \\
={}& \{(x, y): y = 5 - 2x \ \wedge \ x = 1\} \\
={}& \{(x, y): y = 5 - 2(1) \ \wedge \ x = 1\} \\
={}& \{(x, y): y = 3 \ \wedge \ x = 1\} \\
={}& \{(x, y): x = 1 \ \wedge \ y = 3\} \\
={}& \{(1, 3)\}.
\end{aligned}
$$

Thus the intersection of the two solution sets is the set $\{(1, 3)\}$. Hence the intersection of the lines is the point $(1, 3)$.

Exercise 5.1

I. By means of the method of *substitution*, compute the intersection of each of the following pairs of linear functions. Illustrate graphically.

(1) $2x + y = 1$, $y = 3 - x$

(2) $x + y = 3$, $x = y - 2$

(3) $3x + y = 7$, $2x - 3y = 1$

(4) $x - 7y = 11$, $x + 3y = 1$

(5) $x + 2y = 4$, $x + 3y = 1$

(6) $4x + y = {}^-1$, $2x + y = 0$

(7) $x = 2y + 3$, $y = \left(\frac{1}{2}\right)x - \frac{3}{2}$

(8) $x + y = 4$, $\left(\frac{1}{6}\right)x - \left(\frac{1}{2}\right)y = \frac{2}{5}$

(9) $\left(\frac{2}{5}\right)x - \left(\frac{3}{5}\right)y = \frac{4}{5}$, $6y = 4x - 8$

(10) $\left(\frac{2}{5}\right)x + \left(\frac{3}{5}\right)y = \frac{1}{5}$, $4x + 3y = {}^-4$

II. By means of the method of *addition*, compute the intersection of each of the following pairs of functions. Illustrate graphically.

(1) $x + y = 0$, $x - y = 2$

(2) $2x - y = 0$, $2x + y = {}^-4$

(3) $x + 2y = 5$, $3x - y = 1$

(4) $4x + 3y = {}^-1$, $2x - y = 7$

(5) $2x + 4y = 11$, $4x - 3y = 0$

(6) $12x - 18y = {}^-11$, $3x - 2y = 1$

(7) $3x - 5y = 15$, $2x + 3y = 6$

(8) $3x - 6y = 9$, $2x - 4y = 6$

(9) $3x - 9y = 6$, $2x - 6y = 4$

(10) $2x - 4y = 3$, $3x - 6y = 1$

III. Solve each of the following systems of linear equations. Illustrate graphically.

(1) $\begin{bmatrix} 3x + y = 5 \\ x - y = 1 \end{bmatrix}$

(2) $\begin{bmatrix} 5x = y - 5 \\ x + y = {}^-1 \end{bmatrix}$

(3) $\begin{bmatrix} 3x + 5y = 110 \\ 5y - x = 44 \end{bmatrix}$

(4) $\begin{bmatrix} 2x + 4y = 11 \\ 4x - 3y = 0 \end{bmatrix}$

(5) $\begin{bmatrix} 7x - 3y = {}^-1 \\ 3x - 2y = {}^-4 \end{bmatrix}$

(6) $\begin{bmatrix} \left(\frac{2}{3}\right)x + \left(\frac{3}{4}\right)y = \frac{5}{6} \\ 4x + 3y = 4 \end{bmatrix}$

(7) $\begin{bmatrix} 2x - 5 = 0 \\ 5x - 5y = 25 \end{bmatrix}$

(8) $\begin{bmatrix} x + 3y = {}^-1 \\ 5y = 10 \end{bmatrix}$

(9) $\begin{bmatrix} x + \frac{y}{2} + \frac{y}{3} = \frac{1}{6} \\ x - y = 3 \end{bmatrix}$

(10) $\begin{bmatrix} \frac{x}{4} - x - \frac{y}{6} = \frac{-1}{4} \\ x - y = 3 \end{bmatrix}$

5.2   Systems of Linear Equations in Two Variables (*continued*)

In this section we shall continue the study of systems of two linear equations in two variables. In particular, we shall discuss the various possibilities for the solution set of a system and shall learn that the intersection of the solution sets of the linear functions may be empty, infinitely many points, or a single point. Geometrically, the lines corresponding to these cases are parallel, coincident, or intersecting in a single point, respectively. The following examples illustrate the various cases.

Example 1.   Solve the system $\begin{bmatrix} x + 3y = 5 \\ 3x + 9y = 2 \end{bmatrix}$.

The solution set of the system is $\{(x, y): x + 3y = 5 \;\wedge\; 3x + 9y = 2\}$.

$$\{(x, y): x + 3y = 5 \;\wedge\; 3x + 9y = 2\}$$
$$= \{(x, y): {}^-3x + {}^-9y = {}^-15 \;\wedge\; 3x + 9y = 2\}$$
$$= \{(x, y): [({}^-3x + {}^-9y) + (3x + 9y) = ({}^-15 + 2)]$$
$$\wedge \; [3x + 9y = 2]\}$$
$$= \{(x, y): [0 = {}^-13] \;\wedge\; [3x + 9y = 2]\}$$
$$= \{ \; \}.$$

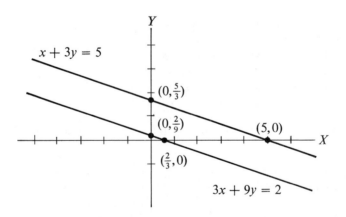

From the sketches of the graphs of the two linear functions $x + 3y = 5$ and $3x + 9y = 2$, we see that the two lines are parallel and hence do not intersect. Thus the fact that the solution set of their intersection is empty should not surprise you. Although it is really impossible to determine exactly from the *sketch* that the two lines are parallel, we can be certain that the two lines are parallel because their slopes are both equal to $\frac{-1}{3}$, as the following computation shows:

$$x + 3y = 5 \qquad\qquad 3x + 9y = 2$$
$$3y = {}^-1x + 5 \qquad\qquad 9y = {}^-3x + 2$$
$$y = \left(\tfrac{-1}{3}\right)x + \tfrac{5}{3} \qquad\qquad y = \left(\tfrac{-3}{9}\right)x + \tfrac{2}{9}$$
$$\qquad\qquad\qquad\qquad y = \left(\tfrac{-1}{3}\right)x + \tfrac{2}{9}$$

Example 2. Solve the system $\begin{bmatrix} 3x - y = 6 \\ {}^-6x + 2y = {}^-12 \end{bmatrix}$.

The solution set of the system is $\{(x, y): 3x - y = 6 \ \wedge \ {}^-6x + 2y = {}^-12\}$.

$$\{(x, y): 3x - y = 6 \ \wedge \ {}^-6x + 2y = {}^-12\}$$
$$= \{(x, y): 3x - y = 6 \ \wedge \ \left(\tfrac{-1}{2}\right)({}^-6x + 2y) = \left(\tfrac{-1}{2}\right)({}^-12)\}$$
$$= \{(x, y): 3x - y = 6 \ \wedge \ 3x - y = 6\}$$
$$= \{(x, y): 3x - y = 6\}.$$

Thus the lines coincide and are really only *one* line. This is illustrated in the accompanying figure.

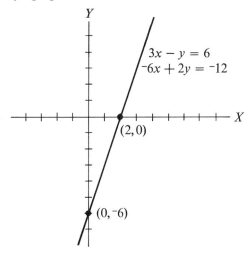

Example 3. Solve the system $\begin{bmatrix} 3x - 2y = 8 \\ x + 3y = {}^-1 \end{bmatrix}$.

The solution set of the system is $\{(x, y): 3x - 2y = 8 \ \wedge \ x + 3y = {}^-1\}$.

(1) $3x - 2y = 8$
(2) $x + 3y = {}^-1$
(1) $3x - 2y = 8$
(2) $\underline{{}^-3x + {}^-9y = 3}$
$\qquad {}^-11y = 11$
$\qquad\quad y = {}^-1$

(2) $x + 3y = {}^-1$

$x + 3({}^-1) = {}^-1$

$x = 2$

Thus the two lines intersect in exactly one point, the point $(2,{}^-1)$. This is illustrated in the accompanying figure.

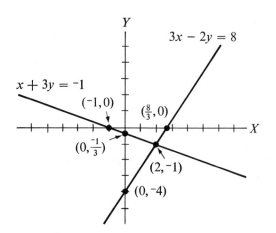

We close this section by summarizing the above results.

1. The solution set of the system $a_1x + b_1y = c_1$, $a_2x + b_2y = c_2$ is the empty set if and only if there exists a real number k such that $a_2 = ka_1$, $b_2 = kb_1$, and $c_2 \neq kc_1$. In this case, the two lines have equal slopes and are parallel, and the system of equations is said to be *inconsistent*.

2. The solution set of the system $a_1x + b_1y = c_1$, $a_2x + b_2y = c_2$ is the infinite set $\{(x, y): a_1x + b_1y = c_1\}$ if and only if there exists a real number k such that $a_2 = ka_1$, $b_2 = kb_1$, and $c_2 = kc_1$. In this case, the two lines have equal slopes, and the system is said to be *consistent* and *dependent*.

3. The solution set of the system $a_1x + b_1y = c_1$, $a_2x + b_2y = c_2$ consists of exactly one point if and only if the slopes of the lines are *not* equal. In this case, the two lines intersect in exactly one point, and the system is said to be *consistent* and *independent*.

It is understood that $a_1 \neq 0$ or $b_1 \neq 0$, and $a_2 \neq 0$ or $b_2 \neq 0$ in each of the above cases. Although the above examples do not constitute proofs of these results, the method of proof is suggested by the examples. Consequently, we do not include the general proofs.

Exercise 5.2

I. Solve each of the following systems of linear equations. Illustrate graphically.

(1) $\begin{bmatrix} 3x - 5y = {}^-19 \\ 6x - y = {}^-20 \end{bmatrix}$

(2) $\begin{bmatrix} x + 3y = 5 \\ 3x - y = 5 \end{bmatrix}$

(3) $\begin{bmatrix} x + 3y = 5 \\ x + 3y = 8 \end{bmatrix}$

(4) $\begin{bmatrix} 3x + 4y = 12 \\ 6x + 8y = 10 \end{bmatrix}$

(5) $\begin{bmatrix} x + 4y = 3 \\ 2x + 8y = 6 \end{bmatrix}$

(6) $\begin{bmatrix} 3x - y = 7 \\ 6x - 2y = 14 \end{bmatrix}$

(7) $\begin{bmatrix} {}^-x = 2y - 4 \\ 2x + 4y = 1 \end{bmatrix}$

(8) $\begin{bmatrix} 2x - 3y = 4 \\ 6y + 4x = 1 \end{bmatrix}$

(9) $\begin{bmatrix} 2x - 3y = 4 \\ 6y = 4x - 8 \end{bmatrix}$

(10) $\begin{bmatrix} 2y = x - 3 \\ y = \left(\frac{1}{2}\right)x - \frac{3}{2} \end{bmatrix}$

(11) $\begin{bmatrix} 2y - 3x + 2 = 0 \\ 5y - 2x + 15 = 0 \end{bmatrix}$

(12) $\begin{bmatrix} y = x + 6 \\ 3x + 2y + 1 = 0 \end{bmatrix}$

(13) $\begin{bmatrix} x = y \\ x = {}^-y \end{bmatrix}$

(14) $\begin{bmatrix} 5x - 4y = 6 \\ 2y - 2.5x = {}^-3 \end{bmatrix}$

(15) $\begin{bmatrix} x - 2y = 3 \\ 4y = 2x + 7 \end{bmatrix}$

II. (1) Which systems in Exercise I are inconsistent?
   (2) Which systems in Exercise I are consistent?
   (3) Which systems in Exercise I are independent?
   (4) Which systems in Exercise I are dependent?

III. Solve each of the following systems of linear equations. Illustrate graphically.

(1) $\begin{bmatrix} x + y = 4 \\ (\frac{1}{6})x = (\frac{1}{2})y + \frac{2}{5} \end{bmatrix}$

(2) $\begin{bmatrix} 2x + 3y = {}^-4 \\ y - 5x = 1 \end{bmatrix}$

(3) $\begin{bmatrix} y = 2x - 4 \\ 2y - x = {}^-5 \end{bmatrix}$

(4) $\begin{bmatrix} 15x = 3y + 2 \\ 10x - 2y = 3 \end{bmatrix}$

(5) $\begin{bmatrix} 7x - 5y = 0 \\ 14x = 10y \end{bmatrix}$

(6) $\begin{bmatrix} 11x = 2y + 7 \\ 4x = 5 - 5y \end{bmatrix}$

(7) $\begin{bmatrix} 3x - 2y - 7 = 0 \\ 6x = 4y + 15 \end{bmatrix}$

(8) $\begin{bmatrix} x + y = 1 \\ 3x = y \end{bmatrix}$

(9) $\begin{bmatrix} x + 3y = 12 \\ 4x = 3y + 3 \end{bmatrix}$

(10) $\begin{bmatrix} 13x + 16y = 7 \\ 15x = 7 - 14y \end{bmatrix}$

IV. (1) Prove each of the three summarizing statements made at the end of the section.

(2) What can you conclude about the solution set of the system $a_1x + b_1y = c_1$, $a_2x + b_2y = c_2$ if $a_1b_2 - a_2b_1 = 0$?

(3) What can you conclude about the solution set of the system $a_1x + b_1y = c_1$, $a_2x + b_2y = c_2$ if $a_1b_2 - a_2b_1 \neq 0$?

5.3 Applications of Systems of Linear Equations in Two Variables

Now that we know how to solve systems of linear equations in two variables, we shall study some applications to physical problems. Although the mathematical models of some physical problems can be formulated by means of linear equations in *one* variable, it is frequently easier to formulate the models by means of linear equations in *two* variables. The following examples illustrate the physical applications of systems of linear equations in two variables.

Example 1. Diana works for a grocer who wants her to mix some coffee which sells for 65¢ per pound with some coffee which sells for 85¢ per pound so that the mixture will weigh 80 pounds and sell for 70¢ per pound. How many pounds of each price coffee should she mix?

Let x represent the number of pounds of 65¢ coffee, and let y represent the number of pounds of 85¢ coffee.

Then $x + y = 80$ (weight), and $.65x + .85y = .70(80)$ (dollar value).

The solution of the mathematical model is the solution of the system
$$\begin{bmatrix} x + y = 80 \\ 65x + 85y = 5600 \end{bmatrix}.$$

(1) $x + y = 80$
(2) $65x + 85y = 5600$
(1) $y = 80 - x$
(2) $13x + 17y = 1120$
$\qquad 13x + 17(80 - x) = 1120$
$\qquad 13x + 1360 - 17x = 1120$
$\qquad ^-4x = ^-240$
$\qquad x = 60$
(1) $y = 80 - x$
$\qquad y = 80 - 60$
$\qquad y = 20.$

Thus Diana should mix 60 pounds of 65¢ coffee and 20 pounds of 85¢ coffee so that the mixture will contain 80 pounds of 70¢ coffee.

As usual, we check the solution in the *original physical problem* rather than in the *mathematical model*. Since she mixes 60 pounds of 65¢ coffee and 20 pounds of 85¢ coffee, the mixture contains 80 pounds of coffee. Since the mixture sells at 70¢ per pound, the total price of the coffee is .70(80) dollars; i.e., $56. The total price of 60 pounds of 65¢ coffee is .65(60); i.e., $39. The total price of 20 pounds of 85¢ coffee is .85(20); i.e., $17. Since $39 + $17 = $56, we conclude that the solution is correct.

Example 2. Susan has $1.44 in pennies and nickels. She has 6 more pennies than nickels. How many nickels does Susan have? How many pennies does Susan have?

Let $U = C_0$ (the set of counting numbers), let x represent the number of nickels, and let y represent the number of pennies.

Then $y = x + 6$ (because she has 6 more pennies than nickels).

Moreover, $.05x + .01y = 1.44$ (the dollar value of all coins).

Thus $5x + y = 144$ (the penny value of all coins).

The solution of the model is the solution of the system $\begin{bmatrix} y = x + 6 \\ 5x + y = 144 \end{bmatrix}.$

(1) $y = x + 6$
(2) $5x + y = 144$
(2) $5x + (x + 6) = 144$
$\quad 6x + 6 = 144$
$\quad 6x = 138$
$\quad\ x = 23$
(1) $y = x + 6$
$\quad y = 23 + 6$
$\quad y = 29$

Hence Susan has 23 nickels and 29 pennies.

We check the solution in the original physical problem rather than in the mathematical model. Since Susan has 23 nickels and 29 pennies, she has 6 more pennies than nickels. The total dollar value of Susan's money is $.05(23) + .01(29)$. Since $.05(23) + .01(29) = \$1.44$, we conclude that the solution is correct.

Example 3.   The sum of the digits of a two-digit number is 13. If the tens digit is subtracted from the units digit, the difference is 3. What is the number?

Let u represent the units digit and t represent the tens digit.
Then $u + t = 13$, and $u - t = 3$.

The solution of the model is the solution of the system $\begin{bmatrix} u + t + 13 \\ u - t = 3 \end{bmatrix}$.

(1) $u + t = 13$
(2) $\underline{u - t = 3}$
$\quad 2u = 16$
$\quad u = 8$
(1) $t = 13 - u$
$\quad t = 13 - 8$
$\quad t = 5$

Hence the units digit is 8 and the tens digit is 5.
Thus the number is 58.
To check we note that $5 + 8 = 13$ and $8 - 5 = 3$. Thus the solution is correct.

Example 4.   Sue and Clarence travel in a motorboat, at maximum speed, 30 miles upstream in 5 hours and return downstream in 3 hours. Compute the maximum speed of the boat in still water and the speed of the current.

Let x represent the speed of the boat in still water, and let y represent the speed of the current.

Then $x - y$ represents the maximum speed upstream, and $x + y$ represents the maximum speed downstream.

Since the product of time and rate is equal to distance, we obtain the system $\begin{bmatrix} 5(x - y) = 30 \\ 3(x + y) = 30 \end{bmatrix}$, which is equivalent to the system $\begin{bmatrix} x - y = 6 \\ x + y = 10 \end{bmatrix}$.

The solution is obviously $x = 8$, $y = 2$.

Hence the maximum speed of the boat in still water is 8 mph, and the speed of the current is 2 mph.

By actual check in the original problem, we see that the solution is correct.

Before you begin the following exercises, you should reread the comments in the last paragraph of Section 3.3.

Exercise 5.3

I. Formulate a mathematical model for each of the following problems, and compute the solution. (Check each solution in the *original* problem.)

(1) Raymond has $2.17 in pennies and nickels. He has 7 more pennies than nickels. How many of each coin does Raymond have?

(2) Norma has $1.04 in pennies and nickels. She has 3 times as many pennies as nickels. How many of each coin does Norma have?

(3) Dianne's father is 3 times as old as Dianne is now. In 6 years from now, he will be $2\frac{1}{3}$ times as old as Dianne will be. How old is Dianne now?

(4) Brenda's father is twice as old as Brenda is now. In 13 years from now, he will be $1\frac{1}{2}$ times as old as Brenda will be. How old is Brenda now?

(5) Vicky is 20 years younger than her mother. In 6 years from now, she will be half her mother's age. How old is Vicky now?

(6) Amy wants to mix enough 45¢ coffee and 60¢ coffee to form a mixture of 90 pounds of 50¢ coffee. How many pounds of each should she mix?

(7) Claudette mixes $12 per ounce perfume with $7 per ounce perfume to form a mixture of 20 ounces worth $9 per ounce. How many ounces of each type should she mix?

(8) Clifton bought 60 pounds of mixed nuts at 45¢ per pound. If the mixture consisted of peanuts and cashews worth 35¢ per pound and 50¢ per pound, respectively, how many pounds of each were in the mixture?

(9) Keith mixes milk of 4% butterfat content with cream of 30%

butterfat content to make 78 quarts of light cream of 18% butter-fat content. How many quarts of milk does he use?

(10) Lurnice mixed two kinds of candy for distribution at a Christmas party. If one candy cost her 50¢ per pound, the other cost her 75¢ per pound, and the 70 pound mixture cost her 60¢ per pound, how many pounds of each kind did she buy?

(11) The sum of the digits of Agnes's age is 12. If the tens digit is subtracted from the units digit, the difference is 6. How old is Agnes?

(12) Twice the tens digit of a two-digit number exceeds the units digit by 12. The tens digit exceeds the units digit by 3. What is the number?

(13) The units digit of a two-digit number exceeds the tens digit by 1. If the digits are interchanged, the resulting number is 6 times the sum of the digits. What is the number?

(14) The sum of the digits of a two-digit number is 15. The tens digit exceeds the units digit by 3. What is the number?

(15) A two digit number is 4 times the sum of its digits, and the units digit is twice the tens digit. What is the number?

(16) Walter and Candy are traveling in a motorboat at maximum speed. A 20-mile trip upstream takes them 5 hours and the return trip downstream takes them 2 hours. Compute the maximum speed of the boat in still water and the speed of the current.

(17) Two planes leave the same airport at 9:00 AM and travel in opposite directions (one travels North and one travels South). If one plane averages 50 mph more than the second plane and the planes are 675 miles apart at 10:30 AM, compute the average speeds of the planes.

(18) Butch and Wayne fly their two seater airplane (at full speed) a distance of 300 miles (with the wind) in 2 hours. The return trip (against the same speed wind) takes them 3 hours. Compute the air speed of the plane and the windspeed.

(19) Alexander and Jude flew (full-speed with the wind) a distance of 270 miles in 2 hours. The return trip (against the same wind at full speed) required 6 hours. Compute the air speed of the plane and the windspeed.

(20) Ursula can type 1.5 times as many words per minute as Edith can. If they begin typing at the same time and type for 20 minutes, the total number of words they type is 3000. How many words per minute does Edith type? How many words per minute does Ursula type?

II. Try to solve each of the following problems, and interpret the results.

(1) Mary Catherine has a total of 15 bills, some $5 bills and some

$2 bills. Altogether she has $50. How many of each bill does Mary Catherine have?
(2) The sum of the digits of a two-digit number is 10. The sum of 3 times the tens digit and 3 times the units digit is 20. Compute the digits of the number.
(3) The sum of the digits of a two-digit number is 10. The sum of 3 times the tens digit and 3 times the units digit is 30. Compute the digits of the number.

III. Why should the solution be checked in the original problem rather than in the mathematical model?

5.4 Systems of Linear Inequalities in Two Variables

In section 4.7 we learned to sketch the graph of any linear inequality in two variables. In addition, we learned to sketch the graph of a compound inequality composed of the conjunction or disjunction of two or more linear inequalities. For example, the graph of the compound inequality $x + y \leq 1 \ \wedge \ x - y \leq 1 \ \wedge \ y \leq 3 \ \wedge \ ^-4 \leq x$ is the shaded region in Figure 5.3, including the line segments of the boundary.

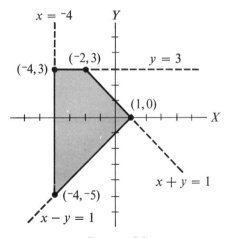

FIGURE 5.3

In this section we shall review sketching the graphs of compound inequalities of the above type and shall introduce concepts which will help us to solve physical problems which involve compound inequalities. In the next section we shall solve some of these physical problems by means of a method called *linear programming*. The following examples will review the ideas involved in the graphing of a compound inequality of the above type.

Example 1. Solve the system of linear inequalities $\begin{bmatrix} 0 \le x \\ x \le 20 \\ 0 \le y \\ y \le 25 \\ x + y \le 30 \\ 10 \le x + y \end{bmatrix}$.

The solution set of the system is $\{(x, y): (0 \le x \le 20) \wedge (0 \le y \le 25) \wedge (10 \le x + y \le 30)\}$, which is equal to $\{(x, y): 0 \le x \le 20\} \cap \{(x, y): 0 \le y \le 25\} \cap \{(x, y): 10 \le x + y \le 30\}$. To sketch the graph of the solution set, we first sketch the graph of each of the inequalities $0 \le x \le 20$, $0 \le y \le 25$, $10 \le x + y \le 30$, as shown in the accompanying figures.

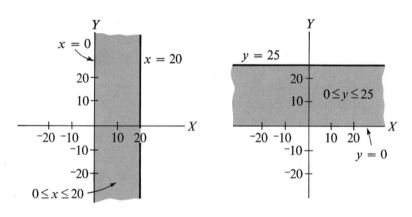

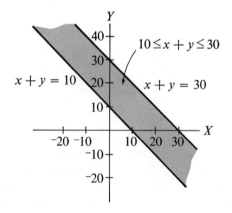

Since the solution set of the system is the intersection of the three sets above, it follows that the graph of the system is the intersection of the three graphs above as shown in the following figure.

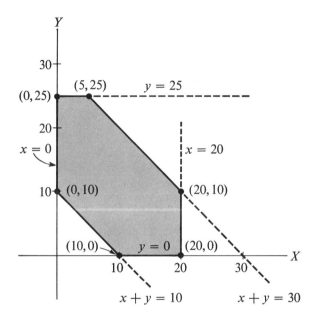

From high school geometry you will recall that the boundary of the graph of the solution set (the boundary of the shaded region) is a convex polygon. For this reason the graph is called a *convex polygonal region*.

Example 2. Solve the system of linear inequalities $\begin{bmatrix} 0 \leq x \\ x \leq 35 \\ 0 \leq y \\ x + y \leq 50 \end{bmatrix}$.

The solution set of the system is $\{(x, y): (0 \leq x \leq 35) \wedge (0 \leq y) \wedge (x + y \leq 50)\}$, which is equal to $\{(x, y): 0 \leq x \leq 35\} \cap \{(x, y): 0 \leq y\} \cap \{(x, y): x + y \leq 50\}$. The sketch of the graph of the solution set is shown in the accompanying figure.

The graph is a convex polygonal region bounded by a convex polygon.

In the next section we shall need to maximize and minimize the value of an expression of the type $ax + by + c$, in which the ordered pairs (x, y) are members of a region whose boundary is a convex polygon. In more advanced mathematics a general theorem is proved which states the conditions under which the maximum value of the linear expression exists. Before we state the theorem (without proof), we shall analyze an example from an intuitive point of view.

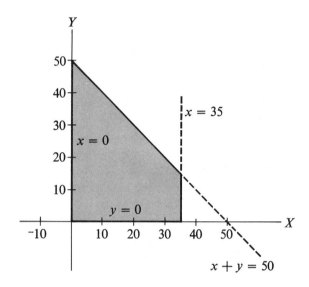

Example 3. Compute an ordered pair of the region of Example 1 for which the value of the expression $2x + 3y$ is maximum.

For convenience, we show the sketch of Example 1 in the accompanying figure. Since we want to maximize the value of $2x + 3y$, we let $2x + 3y = k$, in which k is a real number. For each specific k, the graph of $2x + 3y = k$ is a straight line. For example, the graph of $2x + 3y = 34$ is the straight line with slope $= \frac{-2}{3}$ and x-intercept $= 17$, as shown in the figure. On the other hand, the graph of $2x + 3y = 46$ is the straight line with slope $= \frac{-2}{3}$ and x-intercept $= 23$, as shown in the figure. In fact, for any choice of k, the graph is a straight line with slope $= \frac{-2}{3}$ and thus parallel to the above two lines. Observe that, as k increases, the lines move upward in the figure. Intuitively, the line with slope $= \frac{-2}{3}$ which passes through the point $(5, 25)$ is the line with maximum k which intersects the given region. Since $k = 85$ for this line and $k < 85$ for all other lines which intersect the region and have slope $= \frac{-2}{3}$, and since $(5, 25)$ lies on this line and also *in the region*, we see that, of all ordered pairs in the given region, the ordered pair $(5, 25)$ yields the maximum value of the expression $2x + 3y$. Observe that the point $(5, 25)$ is one of the vertices of the polygon.

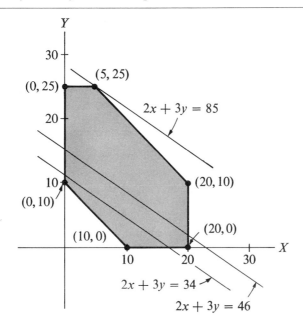

The following theorems, which we state without proof, enable us to solve problems of the type in Example 3 without appealing to intuition.

THEOREM 1.   *If the graph of the solution set of a system of weak linear inequalities is a region of finite area, then the boundary of the region is a convex polygon.*

THEOREM 2.   (*a*) *The maximum value of the expression* $ax + by + c$ ($a \neq 0$ *or* $b \neq 0$) *on a region of the type in Theorem 1 occurs at a vertex of the convex polygon enclosing that region.*

(*b*) *The minimum value of the expression* $ax + by + c$ ($a \neq 0$ *or* $b \neq 0$) *on a region of the type in Theorem 1 occurs at a vertex of the convex polygon enclosing that region.*

In Example 3 we learned that the maximum value of $2x + 3y$ occurs at the vertex $(5, 25)$. To determine the point at which the minimum value occurs, we merely compute the value at each vertex and observe that $2x + 3y$ is minimum at the vertex $(10, 0)$.

Example 4.   Compute an ordered pair of the region of Example 2 for which the value of the expression $2x - y + 4$ is maximum.

By Theorem 1, the boundary of the region is a convex polygon. By Theorem 2, the maximum value of $2x - y + 4$ occurs at one of the vertices. The accompanying table exhibits the value of $2x - y + 4$ at each vertex. By inspection we see that the maximum value of $2x - y + 4$ occurs at the vertex $(35, 0)$. Observe that the minimum value occurs at the vertex $(0, 50)$.

Vertex	Value of $2x - y + 4$
$(0, 0)$	4
$(35, 0)$	74 (maximum)
$(35, 15)$	59
$(0, 50)$	$^-46$ (minimum)

Exercise 5.4

I. Sketch the graph of each of the following systems of linear inequalities.

(1) $\begin{bmatrix} ^-1 \le x \\ 0 \le y \\ 5x + 4y \le 20 \end{bmatrix}$

(2) $\begin{bmatrix} 0 \le x \\ ^-4 \le y \\ 5x + 4y \le 20 \end{bmatrix}$

(3) $\begin{bmatrix} x + 3y \le 12 \\ ^-6 \le 2x - 3y \\ ^-2 \le x + y \\ 2x - y \le 10 \end{bmatrix}$

(4) $\begin{bmatrix} 3x + y \le 12 \\ ^-6 \le 3x - 2y \\ 2 \le x + y \\ x - 2y \le 10 \end{bmatrix}$

(5) $\begin{bmatrix} 3x + 2y \le 6 \\ 6 \le 3x - 2y \\ 6 \le ^-3x + 2y \\ ^-3x - 2y \le 6 \end{bmatrix}$

(6) $\begin{bmatrix} 10 \le 2x - 5y \\ 10 \le ^-2x + 5y \\ 2x + 5y \le 10 \\ ^-2x - 5y \le 10 \end{bmatrix}$

(7) $\begin{bmatrix} ^-3 \le x \le 3 \\ ^-3 \le y \le 3 \end{bmatrix}$

(8) $\begin{bmatrix} 2 \le y \le 8 \\ 2 \le x \le 8 \end{bmatrix}$

II. Compute the maximum value and the minimum value of each of the following expressions on the polygonal region defined in the corresponding part of Exercise I.

(1) $2x - y$
(2) $x + 3y$
(3) $5x + y - 6$
(4) $x - 5y + 7$
(5) $2x + 3y + 10$
(6) $3x - 7y + 10$
(7) $x + 3$
(8) $y - 2$

5.5　Linear Programming

In this section we shall apply the methods of the previous sections to a class of physical problems known as *linear programming* problems, which occur in business and industry. Linear programming, as an application of mathematics, was invented so that problems concerning the allocation of resources could be solved. During World War II it gained prominence. Since the war much research has been done in linear programming and still more research is to be done in the extension of these ideas.

Linear programming is only one of the more recent applications of mathematics. The fact that mathematics now has extensive applications to economics, management, psychology, the social sciences, and the biological sciences as well as to physics, chemistry, and engineering has had an impact on the elementary school, secondary school, and college curricula. Prior to World War II, most applications of mathematics beyond arithmetic were in the physical sciences.

The following example illustrates the method of solving simple linear programming problems.

Example. A manufacturer has two warehouses W_1 and W_2 containing 30 lathes and 35 lathes, respectively. A customer in Lafayette orders 20 lathes and a customer in Baton Rouge orders 25 lathes. The cost of shipping each lathe from each warehouse to each city is shown in the following table.

Warehouse	City	Shipping cost per lathe (dollars)
W_1	Lafayette	$28
W_1	Baton Rouge	$35
W_2	Lafayette	$32
W_2	Baton Rouge	$40

How should the manufacturer ship the lathes to insure minimum shipping charges and hence maximum profit?

Although the manufacturer has many possible ways of filling the orders, his problem is to ship the lathes so that the shipping cost will be a minimum. In order to compute the shipping cost, we let x represent the number of lathes shipped from W_1 to Lafayette and y represent the number of lathes shipped from W_1 to Baton Rouge. Then $20 - x$ represents the number of lathes shipped from W_2 to Lafayette, and $25 - y$ represents the number of lathes shipped from W_2 to Baton Rouge. Because the domains of the variables x and y are restricted by the number of lathes in W_1 and W_2, we derive the following system of linear inequalities:

$0 \leq x$ (the number of lathes shipped from W_1 to Lafayette cannot be negative),

$0 \leq y$ (the number of lathes shipped from W_1 to Baton Rouge cannot be negative),

$0 \leq 20 - x$ (the number of lathes shipped from W_2 to Lafayette cannot be negative),

$0 \leq 25 - y$ (the number of lathes shipped from W_2 to Baton Rouge cannot be negative),

$x + y \leq 30$ (the number of lathes shipped from W_1 cannot exceed 30),

$(20 - x) + (25 - y) \leq 35$ (the number of lathes shipped from W_2 cannot exceed 35).

The above system reduces to the following:

$$\begin{bmatrix} 0 \leq x \\ x \leq 20 \\ 0 \leq y \\ y \leq 25 \\ x + y \leq 30 \\ 10 \leq x + y \end{bmatrix}.$$

In Example 1 of Section 5.4 we sketched the graph of this system, which is reproduced here for convenience.

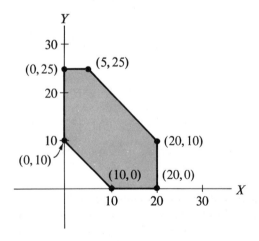

By Theorem 1, the boundary of the region is a convex polygon. The total cost of shipment is given by the expression

$$28x + 35y + 32(20 - x) + 40(25 - y),$$

which is equivalent to $^-4x - 5y + 1640$.

By Theorem 2, the minimum value of the expression $^-4x - 5y + 1640$ occurs at one of the vertices. The following table exhibits the values of $^-4x - 5y + 1640$ at each vertex of the polygon.

Vertex	Value of $^-4x - 5y + 1640$ (Cost of shipment)
(0, 25)	1515
(0, 10)	1590
(10, 0)	1600
(20, 0)	1560
(20, 10)	1510
(5, 25)	1495 (minimum)

From the above table we see that the minimum value of the expression occurs at the vertex (5, 25). That is, the manufacturer minimizes the cost of shipment (and hence maximizes his profit) if he ships 5 lathes from W_1 to Lafayette and 25 lathes from W_1 to Baton Rouge. Of course, he must ship 15 lathes from W_2 to Lafayette.

The only type of linear programming problem which we can solve at this time is the type in the above example which can be formulated by means of a system of weak linear inequalities in two variables. The solution of a system of several weak linear inequalities in more than two variables is not as apparent as the solution of the above example and the solutions of the following problems. In fact, the techniques of this section are too tedious and time-consuming for use in the more complex type of linear programming. The procedures which have been developed since World War II for the solution of the more complex linear programming problems are especially adapted to high-speed electronic computers.

Exercise 5.5

I. In the above example, if the cost of shipment from W_2 to Lafayette is $40 per lathe and the cost of shipment from W_2 to Baton Rouge is $31 per lathe, how should the manufacturer allocate shipment of the lathes?

II. Mr. Bourgeois, who owns a 50-acre farm, wants to plant crop R and crop C. The seed for crop R costs $25 per acre and the seed for crop C costs $40 per acre. Fertility conditions of his farm do not permit him to plant more than 35 acres in crop R but permit him to plant the entire 50 acres in crop C if he desires. Labor and machinery cost for planting, cultivating, and harvesting is $20 per acre for crop R and $15 per acre for crop C. Expected income from crop R is $200 per acre and from crop C is $175 per acre. How many acres of each crop should Mr. Bourgeois plant to insure himself maximum profit?

III. Machine M_1 produces 60 articles per hour and machine M_2 produces 45 articles per hour. The production schedule for the week specifies that a minimum of 1,800 articles be produced. The total running time available for *both* machines is no more than 40 hours, the cost of running machine M_1 is $12 per hour, and the cost of running machine M_2 is $10 per hour. How many hours should each machine operate to minimize the production cost?

IV. If the minimum number of articles in Exercise III is 2,100 and the costs of operating M_1 and M_2 are reversed, compute the number of hours each machine should operate to minimize the production cost.

V. Mr. Brown, who owns a 100-acre farm, wants to plant crop A and crop B. The seed and other costs for crop A amount to $10 per acre and for crop B amount to $40 per acre. Expected income from crop A is $40 per acre and from crop B is $120 per acre. Labor for crop A is one man-day per acre and for crop B is four man-days per acre. If Mr. Brown has a capital of $1100 and 160 man-days of labor to invest in his farm, how many acres of each crop should he plant to insure himself maximum profit?

5.6   Systems of Linear Equations in Three Variables

In Chapter 4 we learned that the graph of a linear function $y = ax + b$, in the two variables x and y, is a straight line. Moreover, in Section 5.1 we learned that the solution of a system of two linear equations in two variables can be represented graphically as the set of all points of intersection of the graphs.

We have already solved physical problems by formulating mathematical models of them as systems of linear equations in two variables. There are other physical problems whose mathematical models require systems of linear equations in three or more variables. In this section we confine our attention to the solution of a system of three linear equations in three variables. The method of solving a system of four linear equations in four variables is analogous to the method of solving a system of three linear equations in three variables.

The equation $ax + by + cz = d$, in which a, b, c, and d are real numbers such that $a \neq 0$ or $b \neq 0$ or $c \neq 0$, is called a *linear equation in the three variables* x, y, and z. The graph of any linear equation in three variables is a plane. If two planes are not parallel, their intersection is a straight line. If this line is not parallel to a third plane and is not a subset of the third plane, then it intersects the third plane in a single point. That is, if the intersection of three (distinct) planes is not the empty set and is not a line, then the intersection set is a single point. Algebraically, the solution set of the system

$$\begin{bmatrix} a_1x + b_1y + c_1z = d_1 \\ a_2x + b_2y + c_2z = d_2 \\ a_3x + b_3y + c_3z = d_3 \end{bmatrix}$$

is the empty set, an infinite set of ordered triplets satisfying a linear equation in two variables, or a single ordered triplet, (x_0, y_0, z_0), of real numbers, provided the three equations in the system represent distinct planes.

To solve a system of three linear equations in three variables, we can combine any pair of the three equations (by addition or substitution) to eliminate one variable (e.g., z) and produce a linear equation in two variables (e.g., x and y). Then we combine any other pair of the three equations in a similar manner to produce a second linear equation in the *same* two variables. We solve the system of the two linear equations in the two variables by the method shown in Sections 5.1 and 5.2. The reader is asked to visualize the two planes p_1 and p_2 intersecting in a line l_2, and then to visualize the two lines l_1 and l_2 intersecting in a point P. For example, if p_1 is the plane of the north wall, p_2 is the plane of the east wall, and p_3 is the plane of the floor, then l_1 (the intersection of p_1 and p_2) is the line of the northeast corner, l_2 (the intersection of p_2 and p_3) is the line of the floor-east corner, and P is the point of the floor-northeast corner, as shown in Figure 5.4.

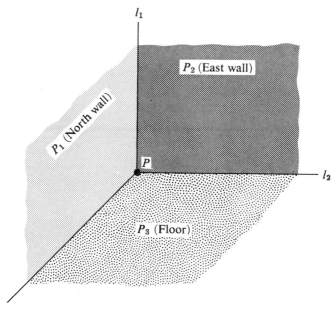

FIGURE 5.4

The following example illustrates the method.

Example. Solve the system

$$\begin{bmatrix} x + y + z = 6 \\ 2x + y - z = 1 \\ 2x - 3y + 2z = 2 \end{bmatrix}.$$

(1) $x + y + z = 6$
(2) $2x + y - z = 1$
(4) $3x + 2y \quad = 7$ $[(1) + (2)]$

(2) $2x + y - z = 1$
(3) $2x - 3y + 2z = 2$
(2') $4x + 2y - 2z = 2$ $[2 \times (2)]$
(3) $2x - 3y + 2z = 2$
(5) $6x - y \quad = 4$ $[(2') + (3)]$

(4) $3x + 2y = 7$
(5') $12x - 2y = 8$ $[2 \times (5)]$
   $15x \quad = 15$ $[(4) + (5')]$
   $x = 1$

(5) $6x - y = 4$
   $6(1) - y = 4$
   $y = 2$
(1) $x + y + z = 6$
   $1 + 2 + z = 6$
   $z = 3$

Thus the solution set of the system consists of the ordered triplet $(1, 2, 3)$. That is, the three planes intersect in the point $(1, 2, 3)$.

Exercise 5.6

I. Solve each of the following systems of linear equations in three variables.

(1) $\begin{bmatrix} x + y + z = 6 \\ 4x + 2y - 2z = 2 \\ 2x - 4y + 3z = 3 \end{bmatrix}$

(2) $\begin{bmatrix} x + 3y - z = {}^-1 \\ 3x + y + 3z = 9 \\ 2x - 2y - z = 0 \end{bmatrix}$

(3) $\begin{bmatrix} 2x + y + 3z = 0 \\ x + 3y - 2z = 5 \\ x - y + 4z = {}^-3 \end{bmatrix}$

(4) $\begin{bmatrix} 2x + 3y + 4z = 2 \\ 4x - y + 2z = {}^-2 \\ 2x - 3y - z = {}^-3 \end{bmatrix}$

(5) $\begin{bmatrix} x + 2y + z = 1 \\ 3x + 2y + 2z = 2 \\ 2x + 4y + 4z = 4 \end{bmatrix}$

(6) $\begin{bmatrix} 3x + y \quad = 1 \\ 2y + 4z = 2 \\ x - y + 2z = {}^-1 \end{bmatrix}$

(7) $\begin{bmatrix} x + 3y - z = 1 \\ x - 2y + 3z = 1 \\ 6y - 3z = 0 \end{bmatrix}$

(9) $\begin{bmatrix} 2x + 3y + z = 0 \\ x - 2y = {}^-3 \\ 4y - z = 5 \end{bmatrix}$

(8) $\begin{bmatrix} x + y + z = 3 \\ 3x - 2y + z = 2 \\ 2x + 4y - 5z = 1 \end{bmatrix}$

(10) $\begin{bmatrix} x - 3y + 2z = 1 \\ 2x + y - 3z = {}^-5 \\ x - 3y + 2z = 3 \end{bmatrix}$

II. Summarize the results of this section as at the end of Section 5.2.

III. Solve the system

$$\begin{bmatrix} w + x + y + z = 2 \\ w + 2x + 3y - z = {}^-4 \\ 2w - x - 2y + 3z = 10 \\ 3w - 2x + y - 2z = {}^-2 \end{bmatrix} .$$

CHAPTER 6

Quadratic Equations and Factoring

6.1 The Quadratic Equation

The quadratic function was defined in Chapter 4 as $y = ax^2 + bx + c$, $a \neq 0$. Recall that the graph of a quadratic function is a parabola which opens upward if a is positive. The six cases which may occur are shown in Figure 6.1.

0 < a

Parabola intersects X-axis in two distinct points

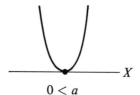

0 < a

Parabola intersects X-axis in a single point

0 < a

Intersection of parabola and X-axis is the null set

a < 0

Parabola intersects X-axis in two distinct points

a < 0

Parabola intersects X-axis in a single point

a < 0

Intersection of parabola and X-axis is the null set

FIGURE 6.1

182

In Chapter 4, we observed that the vertex of a parabola frequently is the solution of the model of an important physical problem. The points of intersection of a parabola and the X-axis also frequently constitute the solution set of a model of an important physical problem. In this chapter we shall learn to compute the vertex and the points of intersection (whenever they exist) of any parabola and the X-axis. Since the X-axis is the graph $\{(x, y): y = 0\}$, we see that the points of intersection are given by $\{(x, y): y = ax^2 + bx + c \wedge a \neq 0\} \cap \{(x, y): y = 0\}$; i.e., the points of intersection constitute the graph of $\{(x, y): y = ax^2 + bx + c \wedge a \neq 0 \wedge y = 0\}$, which is equivalent to $\{(x, y): ax^2 + bx + c = 0 \wedge y = 0 \wedge a \neq 0\}$. Consequently, we compute the points of intersection of the parabola and the X-axis by first computing the solution set of the equation $ax^2 + bx + c = 0$ ($a \neq 0$). Since the equation $ax^2 + bx + c = 0$ ($a \neq 0$) is so important in mathematics, it is given a special name.

DEFINITION 1. The equation $ax^2 + bx + c = 0$, in which $a \neq 0$, is called a *quadratic equation in the variable x* (or simply a *quadratic equation*).

The following examples illustrate the method of computing the intersection of a parabola and the X-axis and, consequently, the method of computing the solution set of a quadratic equation.

Example 1. Compute the intersection of $y = x^2 + 3x + 2$ and the X-axis; i.e., compute $\{(x, y): y = x^2 + 3x + 2\} \cap \{x, y): y = 0\}$.

(1) $y = x^2 + 3x + 2$
(2) $y = 0$

$0 = x^2 + 3x + 2$
$0 = (x + 1)(x + 2)$
  [since $(x + 1)(x + 2) = (x + 1)x + (x + 1)2$
  $\qquad\qquad\qquad\quad = x^2 + x + 2x + 2$
  $\qquad\qquad\qquad\quad = x^2 + 3x + 2$]

$x + 1 = 0$ or $x + 2 = 0$ (by multiplication property
$x = {}^-1$ or $x = {}^-2$ of zero)

(2) $y = 0$

Hence the intersection is the set $\{({}^-1, 0), ({}^-2, 0)\}$.

The accompanying sketch shows that the graph of the given quadratic function intersects the X-axis in the points $({}^-1, 0)$ and $({}^-2, 0)$.

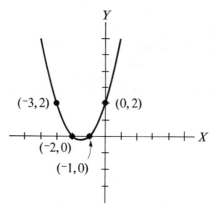

Example 2. Compute the solution set of the quadratic equation
$x^2 - x - 6 = 0$.

$x^2 - x - 6 = 0$
$(x - 3)(x + 2) = 0$
[since $(x - 3)(x + 2) = (x - 3)x + (x - 3)2$
$\qquad\qquad\qquad\quad = x^2 - 3x + 2x - 6$
$\qquad\qquad\qquad\quad = x^2 - x - 6$]
$x - 3 = 0$ or $x + 2 = 0$
$x = 3$ or $x = {}^-2$
Thus the solution set of $x^2 - x - 6 = 0$ is the set $\{{}^-2, 3\}$.

The sketch of the graph of the solution set is shown in the accompanying number line.

The graph of the quadratic function $y = x^2 - x - 6$ intersects the X-axis at the points $({}^-2, 0)$ and $(3, 0)$, as shown in the accompanying sketch.

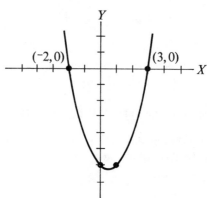

An important step in the computation of the solution set of the quadratic equation $x^2 + 3x + 2 = 0$ (or the intersection of the quadratic function $y = x^2 + 3x + 2$ and the X-axis) is the step in which $x^2 + 3x + 2$ is rewritten $(x + 1)(x + 2)$. In the following section you will have an opportunity to develop the necessary skills to *factor* such quadratic expressions. In the exercises of this section, however, you will have to guess (with the aid of the graph) the factorization of a quadratic expression $ax^2 + bx + c$, and then check the factorization by multiplication and the distributive property.

Exercise 6.1

I. Sketch the graph of each of the following quadratic functions, and label the points of intersection of the graph and the X-axis.

(1) $y = x^2 - 7x + 10$ (6) $y = x^2 - 2x + 15$
(2) $y = x^2 + 7x + 10$ (7) $y = x^2 + 8x + 12$
(3) $y = x^2 + 10x$ (8) $y = x^2 + 8x + 7$
(4) $y = x^2 - 10x$ (9) $y = x^2 - 5x$
(5) $y = x^2 + x - 12$ (10) $y = x^2 - 8x$

II. Compute the points of intersection with the X-axis of each quadratic function in Exercise I. Use the points of intersection with the X-axis to help you *guess* the necessary factorization.

6.2   Factoring

In this section we shall study some of the techniques of factoring; i.e., some methods of writing an expression as a product of two or more expressions. In the next section we shall study some of the applications of factoring. In order to write a given expression as the product of two or more expressions, we first need to consider the inverse problem of multiplying two or more expressions to form their product as a single expression. The following examples illustrate the procedure.

Example 1.   Multiply 5 by $2x + 3$.

$5(2x + 3) = 5(2x) + 5(3)$ (by the distributive property)
              $= 10x + 15$.
Thus $5(2x + 3) = 10x + 15$.
Hence $10x + 15 = 5(2x + 3)$.

Consequently, to factor $10x + 15$, we observe that the greatest common divisor (*gcd*) of 10 and 15 is 5, and $5(2x + 3) = 10x + 15$.

Example 2.   Multiply $5a$ by $4x - 3y + 7$.

$5a(4x - 3y + 7) = 5a(4x) + 5a(^-3y) + 5a(7)$ (by the generalized
distributive property)
$$= 20ax + {}^-15ay + 35a$$
$$= 20ax - 15ay + 35a.$$
Thus $5a(4x - 3y + 7) = 20ax - 15ay + 35a.$
Hence $20ax - 15ay + 35a = 5a(4x - 3y + 7)$.

Consequently, to factor $20ax - 15ay + 35a$, we observe that $5|a|$ is the *gcd* of $20a$, ^-15a, and $35a$, and $5a(4x - 3y + 7) = 20ax - 15ay + 35a$.

Examples 1 and 2 illustrate the simplest type of factoring—that in which all terms of the given expression have a common monomial factor. The following example further illustrates this type of factoring.

Example 3.   Factor the expression $15x^4 + 21x^3 - 9x^2 - 33x$.

We observe that $3x$ is a common factor of all the terms of the given expression.

Thus $15x^4 + 21x^3 - 9x^2 - 33x = 3x(5x^3) + 3x(7x^2) + 3x(^-3x) + 3x(^-11)$.

Hence by the generalized distributive property, $15x^4 + 21x^3 - 9x^2 - 33x = 3x(5x^3 + 7x^2 - 3x - 11)$.

The following examples illustrate the method of factoring the difference of two squares.

Example 4.   Factor $x^2 - y^2$.

First consider the inverse problem of multiplying $x - y$ by $x + y$.

$(x - y)(x + y) = (x - y)x + (x - y)y$ (by the distributive property)
$$= x^2 - yx + xy - y^2$$
$$= x^2 - y^2.$$
Thus $x^2 - y^2 = (x - y)(x + y)$.

Example 5.   Factor $16a^2x^2 - 9y^2$.

$16a^2x^2 - 9y^2 = (4ax)^2 - (3y)^2 = (4ax - 3y)(4ax + 3y)$.

The following examples illustrate the method of factoring a trinomial* which is a perfect square.

———————————

*A *trinomial* is an expression which contains exactly three terms.

Example 6.   Factor $x^2 + 6x + 9$.

First consider the inverse problem of multiplying $(x + 3)$ by $(x + 3)$.

$$(x + 3)(x + 3) = (x + 3)x + (x + 3)3$$
$$= x^2 + 3x + 3x + 3^2$$
$$= x^2 + 6x + 9.$$

Hence $x^2 + 6x + 9 = (x + 3)(x + 3) = (x + 3)^2$.

Example 7.   Factor $x^2 + 2ax + a^2$.

First consider the inverse problem of squaring $x + a$.

$$(x + a)^2 = (x + a)(x + a)$$
$$= (x + a)x + (x + a)a$$
$$= x^2 + ax + ax + a^2$$
$$= x^2 + 2ax + a^2.$$

Hence $x^2 + 2ax + a^2 = (x + a)(x + a) = (x + a)^2$.

Observe the pattern: the square of the binomial $x + a$ is

Example 8.   Factor $x^2 - 2ax + a^2$.

First consider the inverse problem of squaring $x - a$.

$$(x - a)^2 = (x - a)(x - a)$$
$$= (x - a)x + (x - a)(^-a)$$
$$= x^2 - ax - ax + a^2$$
$$= x^2 - 2ax + a^2.$$

Hence $x^2 - 2ax + a^2 = (x - a)(x - a) = (x - a)^2$.

Observe the pattern: the square of the binomial $x - a$ is

Example 9.   Factor $4t^2 - 20t + 25$.

$$4t^2 - 20t + 25 = (2t)^2 - 2(10t) + 5^2$$
$$= (2t - 5)(2t - 5)$$
$$= (2t - 5)^2.$$

The following examples illustrate a general method of factoring an expression of the form $ax^2 + bx + c$, $(a \neq 0)$.

Example 10.   Multiply $(x + d)$ by $(x + e)$.

$$(x + d)(x + e) = (x + d)x + (x + d)e$$
$$= x^2 + dx + ex + de$$
$$= x^2 + (d + e)x + de.$$

Hence $x^2 + (d + e)x + de = (x + d)(x + e)$; i.e., the factors of $x^2 + (d + e)x + de$ are $(x + d)$ and $(x + e)$.

Example 11.   Factor $x^2 + 5x + 6$.

From Example 10, we know that $x^2 + 5x + 6 = (x + d)(x + e)$, in which $d + e = 5$ and $de = 6$. By inspection, we see that $d = 3$ and $e = 2$. Thus $x^2 + 5x + 6 = (x + 3)(x + 2)$.

Example 12.   Factor $x^2 - x - 6$.

$$x^2 - x - 6 = x^2 + (2 + {}^-3)(x) + 2({}^-3)$$
$$= x^2 + 2x + {}^-3x + 2({}^-3)$$
$$= (x + 2)x + (x + 2)({}^-3)$$
$$= (x + 2)[x + {}^-3]$$
$$= (x + 2)(x - 3).$$

Observe that we did not actually apply the *results* of Example 10, but, instead, *the ideas* involved in Example 10.

Example 13.   Multiply $(ax + b)$ by $(cx + d)$.

$$(ax + b)(cx + d) = (ax + b)cx + (ax + b)d$$
$$= (ax)(cx) + b(cx) + (ax)d + bd$$
$$= acx^2 + bcx + adx + bd$$
$$= acx^2 + (ad + bc)x + bd.$$

Hence $acx^2 + (ad + bc)x + bd = (ax + b)(cx + d)$.

Example 14.   Factor $6x^2 + 23x + 20$.

From Example 13 we learned that the factors $(ax + b)$ and $(cx + d)$ of $6x^2 + 23x + 20$ are such that $ac = 6$, $bd = 20$, and $(ad + bc) = 23$.

Consequently we determine factors a and c of 6, b and d of 20, and compute $ad + bc$. If $ad + bc = 23$, we have factored $6x^2 + 23x + 20$ correctly. If $ad + bc \neq 23$, we try other factors of 6 and 20.

We usually factor in this manner by first writing $6x^2 + 23x + 20$ $= (?\ x\ +\ ?)(?\ x\ +\ ?)$ and then filling in the blanks (represented by ?'s) as follows:

$$6x^2 + 23x + 20 = (3x + 5)(2x + 4).$$

Since $3(4) + 5(2) = 22$ rather than 23, we see that this factorization is *incorrect*.

Hence we try other factors of 20 and write

$$6x^2 + 23x + 20 = (3x + 4)(2x + 5).$$

Since $3(5) + 4(2) = 23$, we see that this last factorization is *correct*. Hence $6x^2 + 23x + 20 = (3x + 4)(2x + 5)$.

Example 15.   Factor $10x^2 + 3x - 18$.

First try: $10x^2 + 3x - 18 = (10x + {}^-6)\ (x + 3)$
$\qquad\qquad\qquad\quad = 10x^2 + (30 + {}^-6)x + {}^-18$ *False*
Second try: $10x^2 + 3x - 18 = (5x + 3)\ (2x + {}^-6)$
$\qquad\qquad\qquad\quad = 10x^2 + ({}^-30 + 6)x + {}^-18$ *False*
Third try: $10x^2 + 3x - 18 = (5x + {}^-6)\ (2x + 3)$
$\qquad\qquad\qquad\quad = 10x^2 + (15 + {}^-12)x + {}^-18$ *True*
Hence $10x^2 + 3x - 18 = (5x - 6)\ (2x + 3)$.

We close this section with the following comments.

1. Whenever an expression containing a variable is factored, the quantifier *all* is implied; i.e., the quantifier *all* is understood although not explicitly stated. For example, the *open sentence* "$x^2 - y^2 = (x - y)$ $(x + y)$" is written and spoken but the *sentence* "for all real numbers x and y, $x^2 - y^2 = (x - y)(x + y)$" is intended. Because a sentence, rather than an open sentence, is intended, we may write *false* or *true* as in Example 15.
2. Although many expressions are factorable (can be factored), there are many expressions which are not factorable. For example, $x^2 + y^2$ is not factorable. (Recall that the universe is the set of *real numbers*.)
3. Although you may employ the general procedure for factoring quadratic expressions such as $x^2 - a^2$, it is simpler to factor such expressions by use of the special techniques developed in the examples.
4. Since the inverse of factorization of an expression is multiplication of the factors to produce the expression, proficiency in multiplying expressions yields proficiency in factoring expressions. For example, after you have learned to multiply $(x - 3)$ by $(x + 2)$ rapidly to

obtain the product $x^2 - x - 6$, it will be easier for you to factor $x^2 - x - 6$ into its factors $x - 3$ and $x + 2$.

5. Although you may not be successful in factoring a given expression, you should never guess at a factorization without checking it. After all, checking your proposed factorization is simply a matter of multiplying the proposed factors by application of the distributive property.

Exercise 6.2

I. Express each of the following indicated products as an indicated sum; i.e., multiply the first factor by the second.

(1) $3(2x^2 - 2x + 7)$
(2) $2(3x^2 - 7x + 2)$
(3) $-5x(3ax^3 + 5x^2 - 7x - 4)$
(4) $-3x(5ax^3 - 7x^2 + 4x - 6)$
(5) $-2xy(x + 3y - x^2 - 4xy + 7)$
(6) $-3xy(6 - 5x - 7y + 2x^2 + 4xy)$
(7) $(3x - 1)(3x + 1)$
(8) $(2x - 1)(2x + 1)$
(9) $(3x - 1)(3x - 1)$
(10) $(2x - 1)(2x - 1)$
(11) $(3x + 2)(3x - 2)$
(12) $(5x + 4)(5x - 4)$
(13) $(5x + 4)(5x + 4)$
(14) $(4x + 5)(4x + 5)$
(15) $(1 - 7x)(1 + 7x)$
(16) $(7 - x)(7 + x)$
(17) $(4x + 1)(4x + 1)$
(18) $(2x + 5)(2x + 5)$
(19) $(x + 1)(x + 6)$
(20) $(x + 2)(x + 3)$
(21) $(5x - 3)(x - 2)$
(22) $(3x - 5)(2x - 1)$
(23) $(2x + 7)(3x - 7)$
(24) $(4x - 3)(3x + 4)$
(25) $(8x - 5)(x + 5)$
(26) $(7x - 6)(x + 6)$
(27) $(x + 3)(3x - 4)$
(28) $(2x + 5)(x - 2)$
(29) $(9x - 6)(x + 2y)$
(30) $(2x + y)(x - 9y)$

II. Factor each of the following expressions.

(1) $7x^3 - 21x^2 + 14x + 28$ (16) $x^2 - 14x + 49$
(2) $5x^3 + 20x^2 - 25x - 30$ (17) $x^2 + 4x + 3$
(3) $11x^3 + 33x^2 - 55x$ (18) $x^2 + 5x + 4$
(4) $13x^3 - 26x^2 - 52x$ (19) $2x^2 + 3x - 2$
(5) $x^2 - 25$ (20) $2x^2 - 3x - 2$
(6) $x^2 - 49$ (21) $4x^2 - 12x + 9$
(7) $9x^2 - 16y^2$ (22) $9x^2 - 12x + 4$
(8) $25x^2 - 9y^2$ (23) $4x^2 - 20x + 9$
(9) $32x^2 - 128y^2$ (24) $9x^2 + 15x + 4$
(10) $50x^2 - 32y^2$ (25) $4x^2 + 37x + 9$
(11) $x^2 + 4x + 4$ (26) $9x^2 - 37x + 4$
(12) $x^2 + 10x + 25$ (27) $4x^2 + 13x + 9$
(13) $25x^2 + 10x + 1$ (28) $9x^2 - 13x + 4$
(14) $4x^2 + 4x + 1$ (29) $6x^3 + 8x^2 - 8x$
(15) $x^2 - 12x + 36$ (30) $10x^3 - 29x^2 - 21x$

6.3 Applications of Factoring

Now that we have studied the basic factoring techniques, we are prepared to return to the solution of the quadratic equation, which was introduced in Section 6.1. The following example will review the method.

Example 1. Compute the solution set of the quadratic equation

$$6x^2 - 5x - 21 = 0.$$

$6x^2 - 5x - 21 = 0,$
$(3x - 7)(2x + 3) = 0,$
$3x - 7 = 0$ or $2x + 3 = 0,$
$3x = 7$ or $2x = {}^-3,$
$x = \frac{7}{3}$ or $x = \frac{-3}{2}.$

Thus the solution set of $6x^2 - 5x - 21 = 0$ is the set $\{\frac{7}{3}, \frac{-3}{2}\}$; i.e., replacement of the variable x in the open sentence $6x^2 - 5x - 21 = 0$ by *either* number $\frac{7}{3}$ or $\frac{-3}{2}$ converts that open sentence to a true sentence.

DEFINITION 2. The members of the solution set of a quadratic equation are called the *roots* (or *solutions*) of the quadratic equation.

For example, the roots of $6x^2 - 5x - 21 = 0$ are $\frac{7}{3}$ and $\frac{-3}{2}$. If we let $f(x) = 6x^2 - 5x - 21$, then $f(\frac{7}{3}) = 0$ and $f(\frac{-3}{2}) = 0$; i.e., the graph of the quadratic function $f(x) = 6x^2 - 5x - 21$ intersects the X-axis at

$\left(\frac{7}{3}, 0\right)$ and $\left(\frac{-3}{2}, 0\right)$. For this reason, the *roots* of the quadratic equation $6x^2 - 5x - 21 = 0$ are also called the *zeros* of the quadratic function $\mathbf{f}(x) = 6x^2 - 5x - 21$.

Example 2. Solve the quadratic equation $6x^2 + 5x - 21 = 0$.

$6x^2 + 5x - 21 = 0$,
$(3x + 7)(2x - 3) = 0$,
$3x + 7 = 0$ or $2x - 3 = 0$,
$x = \frac{-7}{3}$ or $x = \frac{3}{2}$.
Thus the roots are $\frac{-7}{3}$ and $\frac{3}{2}$.

Check:

$$6\left(\frac{-7}{3}\right)^2 + 5\left(\frac{-7}{3}\right) - 21 = 6\left(\frac{49}{9}\right) + 5\left(\frac{-7}{3}\right) - 21$$
$$= \frac{98}{3} - \frac{35}{3} - \frac{63}{3}$$
$$= 0.$$

$$6\left(\frac{3}{2}\right)^2 + 5\left(\frac{3}{2}\right) - 21 = 6\left(\frac{9}{4}\right) + \frac{15}{2} - 21$$
$$= \frac{27}{2} + \frac{15}{2} - \frac{42}{2}$$
$$= 0.$$

The following example illustrates that the two roots of a quadratic equation are equal when the corresponding quadratic function intersects the X-axis at one point (i.e., is *tangent* to the X-axis).

Example 3. Compute the zeros of the quadratic function
$$\mathbf{f}(x) = 9x^2 - 6x + 1.$$

$9x^2 - 6x + 1 = 0$
$(3x - 1)(3x - 1) = 0$
$3x - 1 = 0$ or $3x - 1 = 0$
$x = \frac{1}{3}$ or $x = \frac{1}{3}$
$x = \frac{1}{3}$.
Both zeros are equal to $\frac{1}{3}$; that is, $\frac{1}{3}$ is a zero of *multiplicity* 2.

Check:

$\mathbf{f}\left(\frac{1}{3}\right) = 9\left(\frac{1}{3}\right)^2 - 6\left(\frac{1}{3}\right) + 1$
$\quad = 1 - 2 + 1$
$\quad = 0.$

In this case, the graph of the quadratic function is tangent to the X-axis, as shown in the accompanying figure.

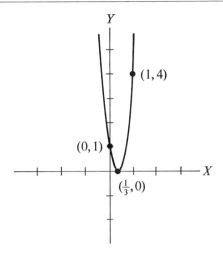

The factoring techniques studied in Section 6.2 are useful in the addition of expressions, as illustrated in the following examples. The techniques for computing the least common denominator of two or more rational numbers are applicable to the sum of two or more rational expressions. The word *compute* in each of the following examples, and in the exercises, indicates that the various rational expressions are to be combined into a single rational expression.

Example 4. Compute the sum of $\frac{x}{x-3}$ and $\frac{2x-5}{x^2-9}$.

$$\frac{x}{x-3} + \frac{2x-5}{x^2-9} = \frac{x}{x-3} + \frac{2x-5}{(x-3)(x+3)}$$
$$= \frac{x(x+3)}{(x-3)(x+3)} + \frac{2x-5}{(x-3)(x+3)}$$
$$= \frac{x^2+3x}{(x-3)(x+3)} + \frac{2x-5}{(x-3)(x+3)}$$
$$= \frac{x^2+3x+2x-5}{(x-3)(x+3)}$$
$$= \frac{x^2+5x-5}{(x-3)(x+3)}.$$

Example 5. Compute the sum $\frac{2x}{x+3} + \frac{5x}{x-2} + \frac{-3}{x^2+x-6}$.

$$\frac{2x}{x+3} + \frac{5x}{x-2} + \frac{-3}{x^2+x-6} = \frac{2x}{x+3} + \frac{5x}{x-2} + \frac{-3}{(x+3)(x-2)}$$
$$= \frac{2x}{x+3} \times \frac{x-2}{x-2} + \frac{5x}{x-2} \times \frac{x+3}{x+3}$$
$$\qquad\qquad + \frac{-3}{(x+3)(x-2)}$$
$$= \frac{2x^2-4x}{(x+3)(x-2)} + \frac{5x^2+15x}{(x+3)(x-2)} + \frac{-3}{(x+3)(x-2)}$$
$$= \frac{2x^2-4x+5x^2+15x+{}^-3}{(x+3)(x-2)}$$
$$= \frac{7x^2+11x-3}{(x+3)(x-2)}.$$

Example 6. Compute $\dfrac{1}{x^2 - y^2} + \dfrac{1}{x^2 + 2xy + y^2}$.

$$\frac{1}{x^2 - y^2} + \frac{1}{x^2 + 2xy + y^2} = \frac{1}{(x - y)(x + y)} + \frac{1}{(x + y)(x + y)}$$

$$= \frac{1}{(x - y)(x + y)} \times \frac{(x + y)}{(x + y)} + \frac{1}{(x + y)(x + y)} \times \frac{(x - y)}{(x - y)}$$

$$= \frac{x + y}{(x - y)(x + y)(x + y)} + \frac{x - y}{(x + y)(x + y)(x - y)}$$

$$= \frac{x + y + x - y}{(x - y)(x + y)(x + y)}$$

$$= \frac{2x}{(x - y)(x + y)(x + y)}$$

$$= \frac{2x}{(x - y)(x + y)^2}.$$

Example 7. Compute the difference $\dfrac{x}{2x^2 + 5x - 12} - \dfrac{2}{x^2 + 2x - 8}$.

$$\frac{x}{2x^2 + 5x - 12} - \frac{2}{x^2 + 2x - 8} = \frac{x}{(2x - 3)(x + 4)} - \frac{2}{(x + 4)(x - 2)}$$

$$= \frac{x}{(2x - 3)(x + 4)} \times \frac{(x - 2)}{(x - 2)} +$$

$$\frac{-2}{(x + 4)(x - 2)} \times \frac{(2x - 3)}{(2x - 3)}$$

$$= \frac{x^2 - 2x}{(2x - 3)(x + 4)(x - 2)} + \frac{-4x^2 + 6}{(x + 4)(x - 2)(2x - 3)}$$

$$= \frac{x^2 - 2x - 4x^2 + 6}{(2x - 3)(x + 4)(x - 2)}$$

$$= \frac{-3x^2 - 2x + 6}{(2x - 3)(x + 4)(x - 2)}.$$

The *numerators* of the answers in Examples 4, 5, and 7 are quadratic expressions which are not factorable (with rational coefficients).* If any of these expressions were factorable (with rational coefficients), we should factor it, and if the numerator and denominator had a common factor, we should reduce the expression by dividing numerator and denominator by the common factor. The following examples illustrate the technique.

Example 8. Simplify the expression $\dfrac{2x^2 + x - 6}{6x^2 - x - 12}$.

$$\frac{2x^2 + x - 6}{6x^2 - x - 12} = \frac{(2x - 3)(x + 2)}{(2x - 3)(3x + 4)}$$

$$= \frac{2x - 3}{2x - 3} \times \frac{x + 2}{3x + 4}$$

$$= 1 \times \frac{x + 2}{3x + 4}$$

$$= \frac{x + 2}{3x + 4}.$$

Example 9. Multiply $\dfrac{2x^2 + 3x - 2}{x^2 - 6x - 7}$ by $\dfrac{x^2 + 8x + 7}{4x^2 + 12x - 7}$.

---

* Henceforth when we say that a quadratic expression with rational coefficients is not factorable, we really mean that it is not factorable with rational coefficients.

$$\frac{2x^2 + 3x - 2}{x^2 - 6x - 7} \times \frac{x^2 + 8x + 7}{4x^2 + 12x - 7} = \frac{(2x - 1)(x + 2)}{(x - 7)(x + 1)} \times \frac{(x + 1)(x + 7)}{(2x - 1)(2x + 7)}$$

$$= \frac{(2x - 1)(x + 2)(x + 1)(x + 7)}{(x - 7)(x + 1)(2x - 1)(2x + 7)}$$

$$= \frac{(2x - 1)(x + 1)}{(2x - 1)(x + 1)} \times \frac{(x + 2)(x + 7)}{(x - 7)(2x + 7)}$$

$$= 1 \times \frac{(x + 2)(x + 7)}{(x - 7)(2x + 7)}$$

$$= \frac{(x + 2)(x + 7)}{(x - 7)(2x + 7)}.$$

Example 10. Divide $\dfrac{x^3 - xy^2}{x^2 + xy - 6y^2}$ by $\dfrac{x^2 - 2xy + y^2}{x^2 - xy - 2y^2}.$

$$\frac{x^3 - xy^2}{x^2 + xy - 6y^2} \div \frac{x^2 - 2xy + y^2}{x^2 - xy - 2y^2} = \frac{x(x - y)(x + y)}{(x - 2y)(x + 3y)} \div \frac{(x - y)(x - y)}{(x - 2y)(x + y)}$$

$$= \frac{x(x - y)(x + y)}{(x - 2y)(x + 3y)} \times \frac{(x - 2y)(x + y)}{(x - y)(x - y)}$$

$$= \frac{(x - y)(x - 2y)x(x + y)^2}{(x - y)(x - 2y)(x - y)(x + 3y)}$$

$$= \frac{x(x + y)^2}{(x - y)(x + 3y)}.$$

We close this section with the following comments.

1. In Examples 4 through 10 and similar examples, the quantifier *all* is implied with the exception that all replacements of the variable which make the denominator 0 are excluded. Thus when we write $\dfrac{(x^2 + 2x + 1)}{(x^2 - 1)}$ $= \dfrac{(x + 1)(x + 1)}{(x - 1)(x + 1)} = \dfrac{(x + 1)}{(x - 1)}$, we mean that $\dfrac{(x^2 + 2x + 1)}{(x^2 - 1)} = \dfrac{(x + 1)}{(x - 1)}$ for *all* real numbers x *except* $x = {}^{-}1$ and $x = 1$. We sometimes indicate this by writing $\dfrac{(x^2 + 2x + 1)}{(x^2 - 1)} = \dfrac{(x + 1)}{(x - 1)}$, $(x \neq {}^{-}1, \; x \neq 1).$

2. Sometimes, factoring an expression does not simplify the computation. For example, factoring $x^2 - 9$ into its factors $x - 3$ and $x + 3$ does not simplify the computation of $\dfrac{1}{(x + 1)} + \dfrac{1}{(x^2 - 9)}.$

Exercise 6.3

I. Compute the solution set (the set of roots) of each of the following quadratic equations.

(1) $x^2 - 25 = 0$ (11) $x^2 - 12x + 36 = 0$

(2) $x^2 - 49 = 0$ (12) $x^2 - 14x + 49 = 0$

(3) $9x^2 - 16 = 0$ (13) $x^2 + 4x + 3 = 0$

(4) $25x^2 - 9 = 0$ (14) $x^2 + 5x + 4 = 0$

(5) $32x^2 - 128 = 0$ (15) $4x^2 - 12x + 9 = 0$

(6) $50x^2 - 32 = 0$ (16) $9x^2 - 12x + 4 = 0$

(7) $x^2 + 4x + 4 = 0$ (17) $4x^2 - 20x + 9 = 0$

(8) $x^2 + 10x + 25 = 0$ (18) $9x^2 + 15x + 4 = 0$

(9) $25x^2 + 10x + 1 = 0$ (19) $9x^2 - 13x + 4 = 0$

(10) $4x^2 + 4x + 1 = 0$ (20) $4x^2 + 13x + 9 = 0$

II. Sketch the graph of each of the following quadratic functions.

(1) $f(x) = x^2 - 25$

(2) $f(x) = x^2 - 49$

(3) $f(x) = 9x^2 - 16$

(4) $f(x) = 25x^2 - 9$

(5) $f(x) = 32x^2 - 128$

(6) $f(x) = 50x^2 - 32$

(7) $f(x) = x^2 + 4x + 4$

(8) $f(x) = x^2 + 10x + 25$

(9) $f(x) = 25x^2 + 10x + 1$

(10) $f(x) = 4x^2 + 4x + 1$

(11) $f(x) = x^2 - 12x + 36$

(12) $f(x) = x^2 - 14x + 49$

(13) $f(x) = x^2 + 4x + 3$

(14) $f(x) = x^2 + 5x + 4$

(15) $f(x) = 4x^2 - 12x + 9$

(16) $f(x) = 9x^2 - 12x + 4$

(17) $f(x) = 4x^2 - 20x + 9$

(18) $f(x) = 9x^2 + 15x + 4$

(19) $f(x) = 9x^2 - 13x + 4$

(20) $f(x) = 4x^2 + 13x + 9$

III. Compute the zeros of each quadratic function in Exercise II.

IV. Compute each of the following sums and differences.

(1) $\dfrac{1}{x + 2} + \dfrac{3}{x^2 + 4x + 4}$

(2) $\dfrac{3}{x - 2} + \dfrac{1}{x^2 - 4x + 4}$

(3) $\dfrac{x}{x - 5} + \dfrac{2x}{x^2 - 25}$

(4) $\dfrac{2}{x + 6} + \dfrac{3x}{x^2 - 36}$

(5) $\dfrac{2x - 3}{2x^2 + 3x - 2} - \dfrac{3}{x^2 + x - 2}$

(6) $\dfrac{2x - 3}{2x^2 + 3x - 2} - \dfrac{3}{x^2 + x - 2}$

(7) $\dfrac{x + 1}{x^2 - 9} - \dfrac{x - 1}{x^2 - 6x + 9}$

(8) $\dfrac{x - 1}{x^2 - 9} + \dfrac{x + 1}{x^2 + 6x + 9}$

(9) $\dfrac{1}{x + 4} + \dfrac{2x}{x - 4} - \dfrac{3x^2}{x^2 - 16}$

(10) $\dfrac{4}{x - 5} + \dfrac{3x}{x + 5} - \dfrac{x^2}{x^2 - 25}$

V. Compute each of the following products and quotients.

(1) $\dfrac{3x + 2}{x^2 - 1} \times \dfrac{2x^2 - x - 3}{9x^2 - 4}$

(2) $\dfrac{2x - 3}{x^2 - 4} \times \dfrac{2x^2 + 7x + 6}{4x^2 - 9}$

(3) $\dfrac{4x^2 - y^2}{4x^2 + 4xy + y^2} \div \dfrac{4x^2 - 4xy + y^2}{2x^2 + 3xy + y^2}$

(4) $\dfrac{9x^2 - 16y^2}{9x^2 - 24xy + 16y^2} \div \dfrac{9x^2 + 24xy + 16y^2}{3x^2 - xy - 4y^2}$

(5) $\dfrac{x^2 - xy - 6y^2}{2x^2 + xy - y^2} \div \dfrac{x^2 + 3xy + 2y^2}{2x^2 - 7xy + 3y^2}$

(6) $\dfrac{2x^2 - 7xy + 3y^2}{x^2 + 3xy + 2y^2} \div \dfrac{2x^2 + 3xy - 2y^2}{x^2 - 2xy - 3y^2}$

(7) $\dfrac{x^2 - xy - 6y^2}{2x^2 + xy - y^2} \times \dfrac{x^2 + 3xy + 2y^2}{2x^2 - 7xy + 3y^2}$

(8) $\dfrac{2x^2 - 7xy + 3y^2}{x^2 + 3xy + 2y^2} \times \dfrac{2x^2 + 3xy - 2y^2}{x^2 - 2xy - 3y^2}$

(9) $\dfrac{x^2 + x - 12}{4x^2 + 4x - 15} \div \dfrac{x^2 - x - 12}{4x^2 - 4x - 15}$

(10) $\dfrac{x^2 - 5x - 14}{6x^2 - x - 2} \div \dfrac{x^2 + 5x + 14}{6x^2 + x - 2}$

6.4 Solution of the Quadratic Equation by Completing the Square

In this section we shall solve the quadratic equation by a technique known as *completing the square*. The procedure is to convert a quadratic expression which is not a perfect square to one which is a perfect square by adding the appropriate expression to both members of the quadratic equation. The following examples illustrate the procedure.

Example 1.   Solve the quadratic equation $x^2 - 2x - 4 = 0$.

Since all attempts to factor $x^2 - 2x - 4$ are unsuccessful, we must solve the given equation by some other method. Hence we convert the left member to a perfect square.

$$x^2 - 2x - 4 = 0$$
$$x^2 - 2x = 4$$
$$x^2 - 2x + 1 = 4 + 1$$
$$(x - 1)^2 = 5$$
$$x - 1 = {}^-\sqrt{5} \text{ or } x - 1 = \sqrt{5}$$
$$x = 1 + {}^-\sqrt{5} \text{ or } x = 1 + \sqrt{5}$$
$$x = 1 - \sqrt{5} \text{ or } x = 1 + \sqrt{5}.$$

Hence the roots of $x^2 - 2x - 4 = 0$ are $1 - \sqrt{5}$ and $1 + \sqrt{5}$.

Let us analyze the above procedure. Since $x^2 - 2x - 4$ is not factorable, we convert it to an expression which is a perfect square, and hence factorable. Recall that $x^2 - 2x + 1 = (x - 1)^2$. If the given expression can be converted to the expression $x^2 - 2x + 1$, then factorization will be possible. To convert $x^2 - 2x - 4$ to $x^2 - 2x + 1$, we must add 5 to it. However, if we add 5 to $x^2 - 2x - 4$ we must add 5 to the right member of the equation. Hence we write

$$x^2 - 2x - 4 = 0,$$
$$x^2 - 2x - 4 + 5 = 0 + 5,$$
$$x^2 - 2x + 1 = 5,$$
$$(x - 1)^2 = 5.$$

The following example suggests a more general method of completing the square.

Example 2.   Solve the quadratic equation $x^2 + 5x + 2 = 0$.

Since $x^2 + 5x + 2$ is not factorable, we complete the square. The first step is to add $^-2$ to both members of $x^2 + 5x + 2 = 0$ to obtain the equivalent equation $x^2 + 5x = {}^-2$. Remember that we are trying to make a perfect square of the left member; i.e., we are trying to convert the left member to $(x + r)^2$. Since $(x + r)^2 = x^2 + 2rx + r^2$, we see that $2r$ must be equal to 5. Consequently $r = \frac{5}{2}$ and we must add $\left(\frac{5}{2}\right)^2$ to both members of $x^2 + 5x = {}^-2$ if we are to complete the square.

$$x^2 + 5x = {}^-2$$
$$x^2 + 5x + \left(\tfrac{5}{2}\right)^2 = {}^-2 + \left(\tfrac{5}{2}\right)^2$$

$$\left(x + \tfrac{5}{2}\right)^2 = \tfrac{17}{4}$$

$$x + \tfrac{5}{2} = -\sqrt{\tfrac{17}{4}} \text{ or } x + \tfrac{5}{2} = \sqrt{\tfrac{17}{4}}$$

$$x = \tfrac{-5}{2} + \tfrac{-\sqrt{17}}{2} \text{ or } x = \tfrac{-5}{2} + \tfrac{\sqrt{17}}{2}$$

$$x = \tfrac{-5}{2} - \tfrac{\sqrt{17}}{2} \text{ or } x = \tfrac{-5}{2} + \tfrac{\sqrt{17}}{2}.$$

It is customary to indicate the two roots as follows:

$$x = \frac{-5 \pm \sqrt{17}}{2}.$$

Example 3. Solve the quadratic equation $5x^2 + 20x - 8 = 0$.

We know from Example 2 that we could complete the square if the coefficient of x^2 were equal to 1 rather than 5. Consequently by multiplying both members by $\tfrac{1}{5}$, we convert the given equation to an equivalent equation in which the coefficient of x^2 is 1.

$$5x^2 + 20x - 8 = 0$$
$$5x^2 + 20x = 8$$
$$\left(\tfrac{1}{5}\right)(5x^2 + 20x) = \left(\tfrac{1}{5}\right)8$$
$$x^2 + 4x = \tfrac{8}{5}$$
$$x^2 + 4x + \left(\tfrac{4}{2}\right)^2 = \tfrac{8}{5} + \left(\tfrac{4}{2}\right)^2$$
$$x^2 + 4x + (2)^2 = \tfrac{8}{5} + (2)^2$$
$$(x + 2)^2 = \tfrac{28}{5}$$
$$x + 2 = -\sqrt{\tfrac{28}{5}} \text{ or } x + 2 = \sqrt{\tfrac{28}{5}}$$
$$x = {}^-2 - \sqrt{\tfrac{28}{5}} \text{ or } x = {}^-2 + \sqrt{\tfrac{28}{5}}$$
$$x = {}^-2 \pm \sqrt{\tfrac{28}{5}}.$$

Example 4. Solve the quadratic equation $2x^2 - 3x + 4 = 0$.

$$2x^2 - 3x + 4 = 0$$
$$2x^2 - 3x = {}^-4$$
$$x^2 - \left(\tfrac{3}{2}\right)x = {}^-2$$
$$x^2 - \left(\tfrac{3}{2}\right)x + \left(\tfrac{1}{2} \times \tfrac{3}{2}\right)^2 = {}^-2 + \left(\tfrac{1}{2} \times \tfrac{3}{2}\right)^2$$
$$x^2 - \left(\tfrac{3}{2}\right)x + \left(\tfrac{3}{4}\right)^2 = {}^-2 + \tfrac{9}{16}$$
$$\left(x - \tfrac{3}{4}\right)^2 = \tfrac{-23}{16}.$$

The solution set is empty, since the square of every real number is nonnegative and hence cannot be equal to $\tfrac{-23}{16}$.

Hence the open sentence $2x^2 - 3x + 4 = 0$ cannot be converted to a true sentence by replacement of the variable x by a real number.

Example 5. Compute the intersection of the quadratic function $y = 3x^2 + 3x + 4$ and the X-axis.

Since the equation of the X-axis is $y = 0$, the intersection is the set $\{(x, y): y = 3x^2 + 3x + 4 \text{ and } y = 0\}$.

$$0 = 3x^2 + 3x + 4$$

$$3x^2 + 3x = {}^-4$$

$$x^2 + x = \frac{-4}{3}$$

$$x^2 + x + \left(\tfrac{1}{2}\right)^2 = \frac{-4}{3} + \left(\tfrac{1}{2}\right)^2$$

$$\left(x + \tfrac{1}{2}\right)^2 = \frac{-13}{12}.$$

The solution set is empty, since $\left(x + \tfrac{1}{2}\right)^2$ is nonnegative for every real number x and hence cannot be equal to $\frac{-13}{12}$.

Hence the graph of the quadratic function does not intersect the X-axis. The sketch is shown in the accompanying figure.

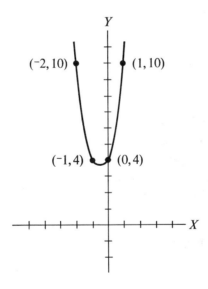

Examples 4 and 5 illustrate a serious defect of the real number system. *There exist quadratic equations which cannot be converted to true sentences by replacement of the variables by real numbers.* We say that such a quadratic equation does not have *real roots.* Since the universe is the *real number system*, at this point in the development such an equation has no roots. If we desire that every quadratic equation shall have roots, we must extend the real number system. In the next chapter we shall extend the real number system to the *complex number system*. In the new system, every quadratic equation will have roots. In the following section we shall develop a formula for computing the real roots of a quadratic equation and in the last sections we shall consider some applications of quadratic equations to physical problems.

Exercise 6.4

I. By completing the square, compute the solution set of each of the following quadratic equations.

(1) $x^2 - 5 = 0$	(6) $2x^2 - x - 2 = 0$
(2) $x^2 - 4x + 3 = 0$	(7) $2x^2 - 2x - 1 = 0$
(3) $x^2 - 4x - 2 = 0$	(8) $3x^2 + 5x - 2 = 0$
(4) $x^2 - x - 2 = 0$	(9) $x^2 + x + 1 = 0$
(5) $x^2 + 2x - 5 = 0$	(10) $2x^2 + x + 1 = 0$

II. Sketch the graph of each of the following quadratic functions, and compute the points of intersection of the graph and the X-axis.

(1) $y = x^2 - 9$	(5) $y = -2x^2 + x + 1$
(2) $y = x^2 - x$	(6) $y = -3x^2 + x + 2$
(3) $y = 4x^2 - 4x + 1$	(7) $y = x^2 + x + 1$
(4) $y = 4x^2 + 4x + 1$	(8) $y = x^2 - x + 1$

6.5 The Quadratic Formula

So far we have developed two methods of solving the quadratic equation—the method of factoring and the method of completing the square. As we have seen, some quadratic expressions are not factorable; hence there exist quadratic equations which cannot be solved by the factoring method. However, every quadratic equation with real roots can be solved by the method of completing the square. In this section we shall develop a formula (called the *quadratic formula*) for solving the general quadratic equation $ax^2 + bx + c = 0$, $(a \neq 0)$. We develop the formula by completing the square on $ax^2 + bx + c = 0$:

$$ax^2 + bx + c = 0 \qquad (a \neq 0)$$
$$ax^2 + bx = {}^-c$$
$$\left(\tfrac{1}{a}\right)(ax^2 + bx) = \tfrac{-c}{a} \qquad (\text{since } a \neq 0)$$
$$x^2 + \left(\tfrac{b}{a}\right)x = \tfrac{-c}{a}$$
$$x^2 + \left(\tfrac{b}{a}\right)x + \left(\tfrac{1}{2} \times \tfrac{b}{a}\right)^2 = \tfrac{-c}{a} + \left(\tfrac{1}{2} \times \tfrac{b}{a}\right)^2$$

$$\left(x + \tfrac{1}{2} \times \tfrac{b}{a}\right)^2 = \tfrac{-c}{a} + \tfrac{b^2}{4a^2}$$

$$\left(x + \tfrac{b}{2a}\right)^2 = \tfrac{(b^2 - 4ac)}{4a^2}$$

$$x + \tfrac{b}{2a} = \sqrt{\tfrac{(b^2 - 4ac)}{4a^2}} \quad \text{or} \quad x + \tfrac{b}{2a} = -\sqrt{\tfrac{(b^2 - 4ac)}{4a^2}}$$

$$(\text{provided } 0 \le b^2 - 4ac)$$

$$x = \tfrac{-b}{2a} + \sqrt{\tfrac{(b^2 - 4ac)}{4a^2}} \quad \text{or} \quad x = \tfrac{-b}{2a} - \sqrt{\tfrac{(b^2 - 4ac)}{4a^2}}$$

$$x = \tfrac{-b}{2a} + \tfrac{\sqrt{(b^2 - 4ac)}}{2a} \quad \text{or} \quad x = \tfrac{-b}{2a} - \tfrac{\sqrt{(b^2 - 4ac)}}{2a}$$

Hence $x = \left(\tfrac{-b \pm \sqrt{b^2 - 4ac}}{2a}\right)$.

Thus the roots of $ax^2 + bx + c = 0$, $(a \neq 0)$, are $\left(\tfrac{-b + \sqrt{b^2 - 4ac}}{2a}\right)$ and $\left(\tfrac{-b - \sqrt{b^2 - 4ac}}{2a}\right)$ (provided $b^2 - 4ac$ is *not* negative). If $b^2 - 4ac < 0$, then $\tfrac{(b^2 - 4ac)}{4a^2} < 0$ (since $4a^2$ is positive). But $\left(x + \tfrac{b}{2a}\right)^2$ cannot be negative. Thus if $b^2 - 4ac < 0$, the open sentence $\left(x + \tfrac{b}{2a}\right)^2 = \tfrac{(b^2 - 4ac)}{4a^2}$ cannot be converted to a true sentence by replacement of the variable x by a real number. In this case, the quadratic equation $ax^2 + bx + c = 0$ has no real roots.

We summarize the above results by cases.

Case 1. If $0 < b^2 - 4ac$, then the quadratic equation $ax^2 + bx + c = 0$ has the *two distinct roots* $\left(\tfrac{-b + \sqrt{b^2 - 4ac}}{2a}\right)$ and $\left(\tfrac{-b - \sqrt{b^2 - 4ac}}{2a}\right)$. In this case the graph of the quadratic function $y = ax^2 + bx + c$ intersects the X-axis in the distinct points $\left(\tfrac{-b + \sqrt{b^2 - 4ac}}{2a}, 0\right)$ and $\left(\tfrac{-b - \sqrt{b^2 - 4ac}}{2a}, 0\right)$.

Case 2. If $b^2 - 4ac = 0$, then the quadratic equation $ax^2 + bx + c = 0$ has exactly one real root $\tfrac{-b}{2a}$. In this case the graph of the quadratic function $y = ax^2 + bx + c$ is tangent to the X-axis at the point $\left(\tfrac{-b}{2a}, 0\right)$. We sometimes say that the quadratic equation has *two* real and *equal* roots.

Case 3. If $b^2 - 4ac < 0$, then the quadratic equation $ax^2 + bx + c = 0$ has *no* real roots. In this case the graph of the quadratic function $y = ax^2 + bx + c$ does not intersect the X-axis.

The following examples illustrate the application of the quadratic formula to computing the roots of a quadratic equation.

Example 1. Solve the quadratic equation $3x^2 + 4x - 5 = 0$.

$a = 3$, $b = 4$, $c = {}^-5$.
Hence $b^2 - 4ac = 4^2 - 4(3)({}^-5) = 16 + 60 = 76$.

Since $0 < b^2 - 4ac$, this example belongs to Case 1.

$$x = \left(\frac{-b \pm \sqrt{b^2 - 4ac}}{2a} \right)$$

$$= \left(\frac{-4 \pm \sqrt{76}}{2(3)} \right)$$

$$= \left(\frac{-4 \pm \sqrt{4(19)}}{2(3)} \right)$$

$$= \left(\frac{-4 \pm 2\sqrt{19}}{2(3)} \right)$$

$$= 2\left(\frac{-2 \pm \sqrt{19}}{2(3)} \right)$$

$$= \left(\frac{-2 \pm \sqrt{19}}{3} \right).$$

Example 2. Solve the quadratic equation $9x^2 - 12x + 4 = 0$.

$a = 9$, $b = {}^-12$, $c = 4$.
Hence $b^2 - 4ac = ({}^-12)^2 - 4(9)(4) = 144 - 144 = 0$.
Since $b^2 - 4ac = 0$, this example belongs to Case 2.

$$x = \left(\frac{-b \pm \sqrt{b^2 - 4ac}}{2a} \right)$$

$$= \left[\frac{-(-12) \pm \sqrt{0}}{2(9)} \right]$$

$$= \frac{(12 \pm 0)}{18}$$

$$= \frac{2}{3}.$$

Example 3. Solve the quadratic equation $9x^2 - 11x + 4 = 0$.

$a = 9$, $b = {}^-11$, $c = 4$.
Hence $b^2 - 4ac = ({}^-11)^2 - 4(9)(4) = 121 - 144 = {}^-23$.
Since $b^2 - 4ac < 0$, this example belongs to Case 3.
Hence $9x^2 - 11x + 4 = 0$ has no real roots.

Example 4. Compute the points of intersection of the X-axis and the graph of the quadratic function $\mathbf{f}(x) = {}^-x^2 + x + 2$.

The points of intersection are given by $\{(x, y): y = {}^-x^2 + x + 2 \wedge y = 0\}$.
Thus we solve the quadratic equation ${}^-x^2 + x + 2 = 0$.
$a = {}^-1$, $b = 1$, $c = 2$.
$b^2 - 4ac = (1)^2 - 4({}^-1)(2) = 1 + 8 = 9$.
Since $0 < b^2 - 4ac$, this example belongs to Case 1.

$$x = \left(\frac{-b \pm \sqrt{b^2 - 4ac}}{2a} \right)$$

$$= \left(\frac{-1 \pm \sqrt{9}}{2(-1)} \right)$$

$$= \frac{(-1 \pm 3)}{-2}$$

$$x = \frac{(-1 + 3)}{-2} \text{ or } x = \frac{(-1 - 3)}{-2}$$

$$x = \frac{2}{-2} \text{ or } x = \frac{-4}{-2}$$

$$x = {}^-1 \text{ or } x = 2.$$

Thus $\{(x, y): y = {}^-1x^2 + x + 2 \wedge y = 0\} = \{({}^-1, 0), (2, 0)\}$.
Hence the graph intersects the X-axis at $({}^-1, 0)$ and $(2, 0)$.

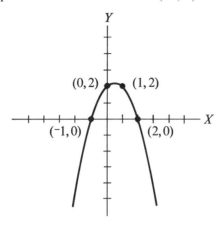

Exercise 6.5

I. Use the quadratic formula to compute the solution set of each of the following quadratic equations.

(1) $x^2 - 4x + 3 = 0$

(2) $x^2 + 4x + 3 = 0$

(3) $x^2 - x - 2 = 0$

(4) $x^2 - 4x - 2 = 0$

(5) $2x^2 - x - 2 = 0$

(6) $x^2 + 2x - 5 = 0$

(7) $3x^2 + 5x - 2 = 0$

(8) $2x^2 - 2x - 1 = 0$

(9) $2x^2 + x + 1 = 0$

(10) $x^2 + x + 1 = 0$

(11) $5x^2 - 3x - 9 = 0$

(12) $x^2 - 4x + 13 = 0$

(13) $6x^2 + 5x - 6 = 0$

(14) $7x^2 + 6x + 18 = 0$

(15) $2x^2 - 2x + 1 = 0$

(16) $7x^2 + 8x - 4 = 0$

(17) $x^2 + 6x + 13 = 0$

(18) $x^2 + ax + 2a^2 = 0$

(19) $9x^2 - 30x + 23 = 0$

(20) $x^2 + 2x + 10 = 0$

II. Sketch the graph of the quadratic function corresponding to each of the quadratic equations in Exercise I. How do the x-coordinates of the points of intersection of the graph with the X-axis compare with the roots of the corresponding quadratic equation in Exercise I?

6.6 Applications of Quadratic Equations

In this section we shall consider some of the applications of quadratic equations to certain physical problems. The mathematical model of a given problem will be formulated by means of a quadratic equation. The following examples illustrate the application.

Example 1. The area of a rectangular plot of land is 1,575 square yards. The depth of the plot exceeds the width by 10 yards. What are the dimensions of the plot?

Let x represent the width of the plot.
Then $x + 10$ represents the depth of the plot.
Thus $x(x + 10)$ represents the area of the plot.

$$x(x + 10) = 1575 \qquad (x \in I^+)$$
$$x^2 + 10x = 1575$$
$$x^2 + 10x - 1575 = 0.$$
$$b^2 - 4ac = 10^2 - 4(1)(^-1575)$$
$$= 100 + 6300$$
$$= 6400.$$

Since $b^2 - 4ac$ is positive, there are two real roots.

$$x = \left(\frac{-b \pm \sqrt{b^2 - 4ac}}{2a} \right)$$
$$= \left(\frac{-10 \pm \sqrt{6400}}{2(1)} \right)$$
$$= \frac{(-10 \pm 80)}{2}$$
$$= \frac{(-10 + 80)}{2} \text{ or } \frac{(-10 - 80)}{2}$$
$$= \frac{70}{2} \text{ or } \frac{-90}{2}$$
$$= 35 \text{ or } ^-45.$$

Since $x \in I^+$, x cannot be equal to $^-45$. Hence $x = 35$ and $x + 10 = 45$.

Thus the width is 35 yards and the depth is 45 yards. We check the problem by computing the area of the plot from the computed width and depth. Since $35(45) = 1575$, we see that the solution is correct. Although the root $^-45$ is a valid root of the quadratic equation, it is not used in the physical problem because the width of a plot cannot be negative.

Example 2. Amy has 20 more quarters than nickels. The product of the number of quarters and the number of nickels is 800. How many of each coin does she have?

Let x represent the number of nickels. Then $x + 20$ represents the number of quarters.

Thus $x(x + 20) = 800 \qquad (x \in I^+)$
$$x^2 + 20x = 800$$
$$x^2 + 20x - 800 = 0 \qquad (x \in I^+)$$
$$(x + 40)(x - 20) = 0$$
$$x + 40 = 0 \text{ or } x - 20 = 0$$
$$x = ^-40 \text{ or } x = 20.$$

Since $x \in I^+$, it follows that $x = 20$. Hence Amy has 20 nickels and 40 quarters. As a check, we observe that $(20)(40) = 800$.

Example 3. From a motionless helicopter 150 feet high, Joel throws a ball upward with an initial speed of 20 feet/sec. The equation describing the motion of the ball is $s = ^-16t^2 + 20t + 150$, in which s represents the distance above ground and t represents the time in seconds. When does the ball strike the ground?

The ball strikes the ground when $s = 0$. This occurs *after* the ball has been thrown; i.e., for a positive value of t. Thus the positive root of the quadratic equation $^-16t^2 + 20t + 150 = 0$ represents the time in seconds required for the ball to strike the ground.

$$^-16t^2 + 20t + 150 = 0 \qquad (0 < t)$$

$$8t^2 - 10t - 75 = 0$$

$$b^2 - 4ac = (^-10)^2 - 4(8)(^-75)$$

$$= 100 + 2400$$

$$= 2500$$

$$t = \left[\frac{-(-10) \pm \sqrt{2500}}{2(8)} \right]$$

$$t = \frac{(10 \pm 50)}{16}$$

$$t = \frac{60}{16} \text{ or } t = \frac{-40}{16}$$

$$t = \frac{15}{4} = 3.75, \text{ or } t = \frac{-5}{2} = {}^-2.5.$$

But $0 < t$. Hence the ball strikes the ground 3.75 seconds after it is thrown.

Example 4. From experience a manufacturer knows that the unit cost is a function of the number of machines operating. The unit cost is given by the formula $y = x^2 - 20x + 105$, in which y represents the unit cost and x represents the number of machines in operation. Compute the number of machines he should operate in order to minimize the unit cost.

The sketch of the graph of the quadratic function for $x \in R$ is shown in the accompanying figure.

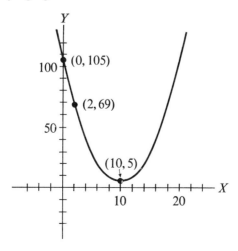

To compute the minimum cost, we first compute the vertex of the parabola.

In order to compute the vertex, we complete the square.

$$y = x^2 - 20x + 105$$
$$y - 105 = x^2 - 20x$$
$$y - 105 + 10^2 = x^2 - 20x + 10^2$$
$$y - 5 = (x - 10)^2$$
$$y = (x - 10)^2 + 5$$

Since $(x - 10)^2$ cannot be negative, we see that y is minimum when $(x - 10)^2 = 0$; i.e., when $x = 10$. Thus the vertex is the point $(10, 5)$. Hence he should operate 10 machines to minimize the unit cost.

If the x-coordinate of the vertex had not been an integer, the manufacturer would minimize unit cost by choosing the nearest integer to the x-coordinate of the vertex.

Example 5.   Paul is standing on the top of a building 100 feet high and throws a ball straight up with a speed of 32 feet per second. The equation describing the motion of the ball is $s = 100 + 32t + {}^-16t^2$, in which t represents the time measured in seconds and s represents the height of the ball measured in feet. Compute the maximum height reached by the ball.

The sketch of the graph of the quadratic function is shown in the accompanying figure.

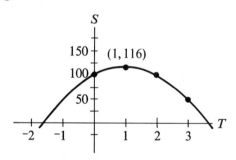

To compute the maximum height, we compute the vertex of the parabola.

In order to compute the vertex, we complete the square.

$$s = {}^-16t^2 + 32t + 100$$
$$s - 100 = {}^-16(t^2 - 2t)$$
$$s - 100 - 16 = {}^-16(t^2 - 2t + 1)$$
$$s - 116 = {}^-16(t - 1)^2$$
$$s = {}^-16(t - 1)^2 + 116.$$

Since $^-16(t - 1)^2$ cannot be positive, we see that s is maximum when $(t - 1)^2 = 0$; i.e., when $t = 1$. Thus the vertex is the point $(1, 116)$. Hence the maximum height reached by the ball is 116 feet.

The following example illustrates how certain inequalities may be solved by use of quadratic expressions.

Example 6. Solve the inequality $\frac{4x + 3}{x + 5} < 2$.

To simplify the inequality, we might be tempted to multiply both members by $x + 5$. However, since $x + 5$ is negative if $x < ^-5$, we multiply by $(x + 5)^2$, which is positive for all x in R.

$$\frac{4x + 3}{x + 5} < 2,$$
$$\frac{4x + 3}{x + 5} (x + 5)^2 < 2(x + 5)^2,$$
$$(4x + 3)(x + 5) < 2(x^2 + 10x + 25),$$
$$4x^2 + 23x + 15 < 2x^2 + 20x + 50,$$
$$2x^2 + 3x - 35 < 0,$$
$$(2x - 7)(x + 5) < 0.$$

Recalling that $ab < 0$ if and only if $a < 0$ and $0 < b$ *or* $0 < a$ and $b < 0$, we see that $(2x - 7)(x + 5) < 0$ if and only if $2x - 7 < 0$ and $0 < x + 5$ *or* $0 < 2x - 7$ and $x + 5 < 0$.

Consequently $\{x: \frac{4x + 3}{x + 5} < 2\}$
$= \{x: (2x - 7 < 0) \wedge (0 < x + 5)\} \cup \{x: (0 < 2x - 7) \wedge (x + 5 < 0)\}$
$= \{x: (2x < 7) \wedge (^-5 < x)\} \cup \{x: (7 < 2x) \wedge (x < ^-5)\}$
$= \{x: (x < \frac{7}{2}) \wedge (^-5 < x)\} \cup \{x: (\frac{7}{2} < x) \wedge (x < ^-5)\}$
$= \{x: ^-5 < x < \frac{7}{2}\} \cup \varnothing$
$= \{x: ^-5 < x < \frac{7}{2}\}.$

An alternate method, which does not employ quadratic expressions, is illustrated in the following example.

Example 7. Solve the inequality $\frac{4x + 3}{x + 5} < 2$.

$$\frac{4x + 3}{x + 5} < 2,$$
$$\frac{4x + 3}{x + 5} - 2 < 0,$$
$$\frac{4x + 3 - 2(x + 5)}{x + 5} < 0,$$
$$\frac{4x + 3 - 2x - 10}{x + 5} < 0,$$
$$\frac{2x - 7}{x + 5} < 0.$$

Recalling that $\frac{a}{b} < 0$ if and only if $a < 0$ and $0 < b$ *or* $0 < a$ and $b < 0$, we see that $\frac{2x - 7}{x + 5} < 0$ if and only if $2x - 7 < 0$ and $0 < x + 5$ *or* $0 < 2x - 7$ and $x + 5 < 0$.

Consequently $\{x: \frac{2x - 7}{x + 5} < 0\}$

$= \{x: (2x - 7 < 0) \wedge (0 < x + 5)\} \cup \{x: (0 < 2x - 7) \wedge (x + 5 < 0)\}$

$= \{x: {}^-5 < x < \frac{7}{2}\}$.

Exercise 6.6

I. Formulate a mathematical model of each of the following and compute the solution set of the model. From the solution set of the model select the solution set of the given problem.

(1) The square of Theresa's age exceeds 8 times her age by 9. How old is Theresa?

(2) The square of Elizabeth's age exceeds 17 times her age by 60. How old is Elizabeth?

(3) Bud has 25 pencils more than Donald has. However, the square of the number of Donald's pencils is 5 more than the number of Bud's pencils. How many pencils does each have?

(4) Sarah can type 60 words per minute. Sixty-one times Ursula's typing speed exceeds Sarah's typing speed by the square of Ursula's typing speed. Compute Ursula's typing speed.

(5) Homer is driving 5 mph slower than William. The square of Homer's speed exceeds William's speed by 1 mph. How fast is each driving?

(6) Catherine has a rectangular field whose area is 180,000 square feet. The perimeter of the field is 1720 feet. Compute the dimensions of the field.

(7) On Tuesday Joseph worked 20 more problems than on Monday. The product of the number of problems he worked on Monday and the number he worked on Tuesday is 800. How many problems did he work on Tuesday?

(8) J.T. has 10 more nickels than pennies. The square of the number of his pennies exceeds the square of the number of his nickels by 20. How many nickels does J.T. have? How many pennies does J.T. have?

(9) On a hike Melvin traveled 23 miles more the first day than the second day. The square of the number of miles he traveled the second day exceeds by 7 the number of miles he traveled the first day. How many miles did he travel the first day? How many miles did he travel altogether?

(10) Milton observes that the tens digit of a number exceeds the units digit by 5 and that the square of the units digit exceeds the tens digit by 7. What is the number?

(11) Velma and Laureen are working problems. Laureen notices that Velma worked 6 more problems than she did. She notices also that the square of the number of problems she worked is 6 more than the number of problems Velma worked. How many problems did Laureen work?

(12) Lester notices that the units digit of a two digit number is 3 times the tens digit. Lloyd notices that the number exceeds the square of the tens digit by 30. What is the number?

(13) Edwin asked Carol to think of a number, square it, add the number, increase the result by 10, and add twice the number. When Carol said that the result was 64, Edwin said that the number was 6. Was he correct? Is there more than one answer to the problem?

(14) Lacy notices that the square of a number is 5 times the number. Larry notices that this is true of another number. What numbers are Lacy and Larry considering?

(15) Nathan notices that the square of a number is 6 times the number. Roy notices that this is true of another number. What numbers are Nathan and Roy considering?

(16) From the top of a building 100 feet high Phil throws a baseball upward with an initial speed of 10 feet per second. The equation describing the motion of the ball is $s = {}^-16t^2 + 10t + 100$. When does the ball strike the ground? What is the significance of the negative root? (See Example 3.)

(17) From the graph of the quadratic function in (16), estimate the maximum height reached by the ball. Check your estimate by computing the vertex of the parabola. (See Example 5.)

(18) If the unit cost is given by the formula $y = x^2 + {}^-21x + 117$, compute the number of machines the manufacturer in Example 4 should operate in order to minimize the unit cost.

(19) If the unit cost is given by the formula $y = x^2 - 19x + 91$, compute the number of machines the manufacturer in Example 4 should operate in order to minimize the unit cost.

(20) If the unit cost is given by the formula $y = 4x^2 - 120x + 900$, compute the number of machines the manufacturer in Example 4 should operate in order to minimize the unit cost.

(21) Henry stapled 10 more sets of papers on Thursday than on Friday. The square of the number he stapled on Thursday exceeds 217 times the number he stapled on Friday by 700. How many sets did he staple on Thursday?

(22) James took a taxi to school. On the return trip he noticed that the driver drove 10 more blocks than on the trip to school. He observed that the square of the number of blocks on the return trip was equal to the sum of 700 and 217 times the number of blocks on the trip to school. How many blocks did James ride on the way to school? How many blocks did James ride on the return trip?

II. Compute the solution set of each of the following *quadratic inequalities*. [*Hint:* Recall that the product of two real numbers is positive if and only if they are both positive or both negative; the product of two real numbers is negative if and only if one is positive and the other is negative; the product of two real numbers is zero if and only if one of them is zero (or both are zero).]

(1) $x^2 - 2x - 3 < 0$ (6) $x^2 - x - 20 \leq 0$
(2) $x^2 - 2x < 0$ (7) $0 < x^2 - 4x - 21$
(3) $x^2 - 5x < 0$ (8) $0 < x^2 + 4x - 21$
(4) $x^2 - x - 2 < 0$ (9) $0 \leq x^2 - 3x$
(5) $x^2 + x - 20 \leq 0$ (10) $0 \leq 3x^2 - x$

III. By sketching the graph of the corresponding function, compute the solution set of each of the quadratic inequalities in Exercise II.

IV. Employ the method of Example 6 to solve each of the following inequalities.

(1) $\frac{x+5}{4x+3} < 2$ (6) $2 < \frac{x-1}{x+1}$
(2) $\frac{x-1}{x+1} < 1$ (7) $^-2 < \frac{x+1}{x-2}$
(3) $\frac{x+1}{x-1} < 1$ (8) $^-1 < \frac{x+2}{2x-1}$
(4) $\frac{2x-3}{3x+2} < 3$ (9) $4 < \frac{2x-3}{2x-3}$
(5) $\frac{2x+5}{3x-1} < {}^-4$ (10) $\frac{3x-2}{3x-2} < 4$

V. Employ the method of Example 7 to solve each of the inequalities in Exercise IV.

6.7 Applications of Quadratic Equations (Continued)

Sometimes an equation which is not a quadratic equation in x can be converted to a quadratic equation by certain operations on the members of the given equation. Under certain conditions, as shown in Chapter 3, the resulting quadratic equation is equivalent to the given equation. However, certain operations on the given equation yield a resulting quadratic equation which is *not* equivalent to the given equation. Since all roots of the original equation are roots of the derived equation, it is sufficient to substitute the roots of the resulting equation into the original equation. The following examples illustrate the method of solution.

Example 1. Solve the equation $x + \sqrt{x} = 2$.

Although $x + \sqrt{x} = 2$ is not quadratic in x, it is quadratic in $\sqrt{x}$. We may solve the equation by converting it to a quadratic equation in x.

$$x + \sqrt{x} = 2$$
$$x - 2 = {}^{-}\sqrt{x}$$
$$(x - 2)^2 = ({}^{-}\sqrt{x})^2$$
$$x^2 - 4x + 4 = x$$
$$x^2 - 5x + 4 = 0$$
$$(x - 1)(x - 4) = 0$$

$$x - 1 = 0 \qquad \text{or} \qquad x - 4 = 0$$
$$x = 1 \qquad \text{or} \qquad x = 4$$

Check: $x = 1$	Check: $x = 4$
$x + \sqrt{x} = 2$	$x + \sqrt{x} = 2$
$1 + \sqrt{1} = 2$	$4 + \sqrt{4} = 2$
$1 + 1 = 2$	$4 + 2 = 2$
$2 = 2 \qquad$ T	$6 = 2 \qquad\qquad$ F

Since $2 = 2$ is a true sentence but $6 = 2$ is a false sentence, the only root of $x + \sqrt{x} = 2$ is 1. That is, $\{x: x + \sqrt{x} = 2\} = \{1\}$. Although 4 is a root of $x^2 - 5x + 4 = 0$, 4 is *not* a root of $x + \sqrt{x} = 2$.

The reader may wonder why 4 is *not* a root of $x + \sqrt{x} = 2$. If so, he should recall that the above sequence of steps is an abbreviation for the following sequence:

If $x + \sqrt{x} = 2$, then $x - 2 = {}^{-}\sqrt{x}$.
If $x - 2 = {}^{-}\sqrt{x}$, then $(x - 2)^2 = ({}^{-}\sqrt{x})^2$.
If $(x - 2)^2 = ({}^{-}\sqrt{x})^2$, then $x^2 - 4x + 4 = x$.
If $x^2 - 4x + 4 = x$, then $x^2 - 5x + 4 = 0$.
If $x^2 - 5x + 4 = 0$, then $(x - 1)(x - 4) = 0$.
If $(x - 1)(x - 4) = 0$, then $x - 1 = 0$ or $x - 4 = 0$.
If $x - 1 = 0$ or $x - 4 = 0$, then $x = 1$ or $x = 4$.

Therefore, if $x + \sqrt{x} = 2$, then $x = 1$ or $x = 4$. To be certain that both 1 and 4 are roots of $x + \sqrt{x} = 2$, we would need to know that the converse, "If $x = 1$ or $x = 4$, then $x + \sqrt{x} = 2$," is true. However, the converse is a *false* sentence because $4 + \sqrt{4} \neq 2$. The converse of each sentence in the above sequence is true except the converse of the sentence, "If $x - 2 = {}^{-}\sqrt{x}$, then $(x - 2)^2 = ({}^{-}\sqrt{x})^2$." That is, the sentence, "If $(x - 2)^2 = ({}^{-}\sqrt{x})^2$, then $x - 2 = {}^{-}\sqrt{x}$" is *false* because $(4 - 2)^2 = ({}^{-}\sqrt{4})^2$ but $4 - 2 \neq {}^{-}\sqrt{4}$. The method of solution guarantees that the solution set of the original equation is a subset of the solution set of the derived equation. The solution set of the original equation is the same as the solution set of the derived equation if and only if each step in the solution procedure is reversible. The reader should reread Theorem 1 of Chapter 3.

Example 2. Solve the equation $x - 4 = \sqrt{2x}$.

$x - 4 = \sqrt{2x}$
$(x - 4)^2 = (\sqrt{2x})^2$
$x^2 - 8x + 16 = 2x$
$x^2 - 10x + 16 = 0.$
$(x - 2)(x - 8) = 0$

$x - 2 = 0$	or	$x - 8 = 0$
$x = 2$	or	$x = 8$

Check: $x = 2$ Check: $x = 8$
$x - 4 = \sqrt{2x}$ $x - 4 = \sqrt{2x}$
$2 - 4 = \sqrt{2 \times 2}$ $8 - 4 = \sqrt{2 \times 8}$
$^-2 = \sqrt{4}$ $4 = \sqrt{16}$
$^-2 = 2$ F $4 = 4$ T

The only root of $x - 4 = \sqrt{2x}$ is 8; i.e., $\{x: x - 4 = \sqrt{2x}\} = \{8\}$.

Example 3. Solve the equation $\sqrt{x + 4} - 4 = x$.

$\sqrt{x + 4} - 4 = x$
$\sqrt{x + 4} = x + 4$
$(\sqrt{x + 4})^2 = (x + 4)^2$
$x + 4 = x^2 + 8x + 16$
$x^2 + 7x + 12 = 0$
$(x + 3)(x + 4) = 0$

$x + 3 = 0$	or	$x + 4 = 0$
$x = ^-3$	or	$x = ^-4$

Check: $x = ^-3$ Check: $x = ^-4$
$\sqrt{^-3 + 4} - 4 = ^-3$ $\sqrt{^- 4 + 4} - 4 = ^-4$
$\sqrt{1} - 4 = ^-3$ $0 - 4 = ^-4$
$1 - 4 = ^-3$ $- 4 = - 4$ T
$^-3 = ^-3$ T

The roots of $\sqrt{x + 4} - 4 = x$ are $^-3$ and $^-4$; i.e., $\{x: \sqrt{x + 4} - 4 = x\} = \{^-3, ^-4\}$.

Example 4. Solve the equation $\frac{(x^2 - 4)}{(5x - 15)} = \frac{1}{(x - 3)}.$

$$\frac{(x^2 - 4)}{(5x - 15)} = \frac{1}{(x - 3)}$$

$$\frac{(x^2 - 4)}{5(x - 3)} = \frac{1}{(x - 3)}$$

$$5(x - 3) \times \left[\frac{(x^2 - 4)}{5(x - 3)}\right] = 5(x - 3) \times \left[\frac{1}{(x - 3)}\right]$$

$$x^2 - 4 = 5$$

$$x^2 - 9 = 0$$

$$(x - 3)(x + 3) = 0$$

$$x = 3 \qquad \text{or} \qquad x = {}^-3$$

Check: $x = 3$ Check: $x = {}^-3$

$$\frac{(x^2 - 4)}{(5x - 15)} = \frac{1}{(x - 3)} \qquad\qquad \frac{(x^2 - 4)}{(5x - 15)} = \frac{1}{(x - 3)}$$

$$\frac{(3^2 - 4)}{[5(3) - 15]} = \frac{1}{(3 - 3)} \qquad\qquad \frac{(-3)^2 - 4}{[5(-3) - 15]} = \frac{-1}{-3 - 3}$$

$$\frac{5}{0} = \frac{1}{0} \quad \text{(undefined)} \qquad\qquad \frac{(9 - 4)}{-30} = \frac{1}{-6}$$

$$\frac{1}{-6} = \frac{1}{-6} \qquad \text{T}$$

The only root of $\frac{(x^2 - 4)}{(5x - 15)} = \frac{1}{(x - 3)}$ is $^-3$; i.e., $\left\{x: \frac{(x^2 - 4)}{(5x - 15)} = \frac{1}{(x - 3)}\right\} = \{^-3\}$.

Whenever an equation which is *not* quadratic in x is converted to a quadratic equation in x, one of the roots of the resulting quadratic equation may fail to be a root of the original equation. In each case one must be careful to check each root of the resulting quadratic equation in the *original* equation rather than in the *resulting* quadratic equation. The following exercises will provide the reader an opportunity to compute solution sets of nonquadratic equations which can be converted to quadratic equations.

Exercise 6.7

I. Solve each of the following equations.

(1) $x - \sqrt{4x - 3} = 0$ (6) $\sqrt{2x + 2} = 2x$

(2) $\sqrt{x + 3} = x + 3$ (7) $x - 3 = 2\sqrt{x}$

(3) $\sqrt{x} = x$ (8) $x - 5 = 4\sqrt{x}$

(4) $\sqrt{x^2 + 7x + 12} = 3$ (9) $\sqrt{x + 4} = x + 2$

(5) $\sqrt{x + 2} = x$ (10) $\sqrt{x + 10} = x - 2$

II. Solve each of the following equations.

(*Hint.* Whenever an equation involves two radicals, we express it with one radical on each side of the equal sign before squaring both members. Then we simplify and solve as in Exercise I.)

(1) $\sqrt{2x - 1} = 2 + \sqrt{x - 4}$

(2) $\sqrt{5x - 1} = 2 + \sqrt{x - 1}$

(3) $\sqrt{x + 3} + \sqrt{3x + 7} = 8$

(4) $\sqrt{2x + 1} - \sqrt{x - 3} = 2$
(5) $\sqrt{11 - x} - \sqrt{x + 6} - 3 = 0$

III. Explain why the sentence, "For all a, if $a = b$, then $a^2 = b^2$," is *true*, whereas the sentence, "For all a, if $a^2 = b^2$, then $a = b$," is *false*.

6.8   Intersection of a Parabola and a Line

In the preceding sections we learned that the intersection of the parabola which is the graph of $y = ax^2 + bx + c$, $a \neq 0$, and the X-axis is $\{(x, y): y = ax^2 + bx + c\} \cap \{(x, y): y = 0\}$, which is $\left\{ \left(\frac{-b + \sqrt{b^2 - 4ac}}{2a}, 0 \right), \left(\frac{-b - \sqrt{b^2 - 4ac}}{2a}, 0 \right) \right\}$. For example, the intersection of the graph of $y = x^2 - x - 6$ and the X-axis is $\{(^-2, 0), (3, 0)\}$. To compute the intersection of a parabola and *any* line whose equation is $y = mx + k$, we *substitute* $mx + k$ for y in the equation of the parabola as follows:

$y = ax^2 + bx + c$
$y = mx + k$
$ax^2 + bx + c = mx + k$
$ax^2 + bx - mx + c - k = 0$
$ax^2 + (b - m)x + (c - k) = 0.$

Then we solve the resulting quadratic equation, $ax^2 + (b - m)x + (c - k) = 0$, by factoring or by the quadratic formula. The following examples illustrate the procedure.

Example 1.   Compute the intersection of the parabola $y = x^2 - x - 6$ and the line $y = 2x + 4$. That is, solve the system $\begin{bmatrix} y = x^2 - x - 6 \\ y = 2x + 4 \end{bmatrix}$.

$y = x^2 - x - 6$
$y = 2x + 4$
$x^2 - x - 6 = 2x + 4$
$x^2 - 3x - 10 = 0$
$(x - 5)(x + 2) = 0$
$x = 5$ or $x = {}^-2$
$y = 2x + 4$
$y = 2 \times 5 + 4$ or $y = 2 \times {}^-2 + 4$
$y = 14$ or $y = 0$

Thus the parabola and the line intersect in the two points $(5, 14)$ and $(^-2, 0)$. In other words, $\{(x, y): y = x^2 - x - 6\} \cap \{(x, y): y = 2x + 4\} = \{(5, 14), (^-2, 0)\}$. We may check the two solutions by substituting 5 and 14 for x and y, respectively, in both equations and then substituting $^-2$ and 0. The graph is shown in the accompanying figure.

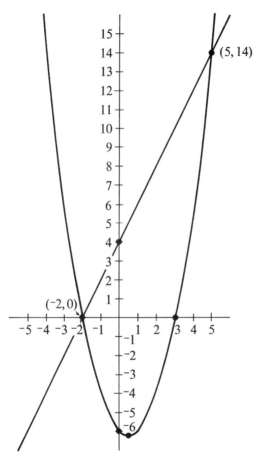

Example 2. Compute the intersection of the parabola $y = {}^-1x^2 + x + 2$ and the line $x + y = 4$. That is, solve the system $\begin{bmatrix} y = {}^-1x^2 + x + 2 \\ y = 4 - x \end{bmatrix}$.

$y = {}^-1x^2 + x + 2$
$y = 4 - x$
${}^-1x^2 + x + 2 = 4 - x$
${}^-1x^2 + 2x - 2 = 0$
Now $b^2 - 4ac = 2^2 - 4({}^-1)({}^-2)$
$\qquad\qquad\quad = 4 - 8$
$\qquad\qquad\quad = {}^-4 < 0.$

Hence the equation $^-1x^2 + 2x - 2 = 0$ has no real roots. That is, the intersection of the parabola and the line is the empty set. In other words, the parabola and the line do not intersect. The graph is shown in the accompanying figure.

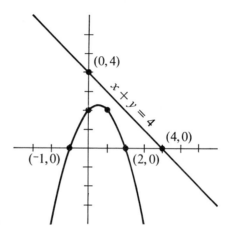

The reader should observe that a parabola and a line may intersect in (1) exactly two points, (2) exactly one point, or (3) no points. In the first case, the line and parabola enclose a region; in the second case, the line is tangent to the parabola at the point of intersection; and in the third case, the line does not intersect the parabola.

Exercise 6.8

I. Compute the intersection set of the parabola and the line in each of the following.

(1) $\begin{bmatrix} y = x^2 - 9 \\ y = x - 3 \end{bmatrix}$

(2) $\begin{bmatrix} y = x^2 - x \\ y = -2x + 2 \end{bmatrix}$

(3) $\begin{bmatrix} y = 4x^2 - 4x + 1 \\ 16x + y - 1 = 0 \end{bmatrix}$

(4) $\begin{bmatrix} y = x^2 + x + 1 \\ y = 3 \end{bmatrix}$

(5) $\begin{bmatrix} y = -2x^2 + x + 1 \\ 3x - 5y + 24 = 0 \end{bmatrix}$

(6) $\begin{bmatrix} y = -3x^2 + x + 2 \\ 7x - y - 22 = 0 \end{bmatrix}$

(7) $\begin{bmatrix} y = x^2 + x + 1 \\ 7x - y - 4 = 0 \end{bmatrix}$

(8) $\begin{bmatrix} y = x^2 - x + 1 \\ x - y - 3 = 0 \end{bmatrix}$

(9) $\begin{bmatrix} y = 3x^2 + 5x - 2 \\ x + y - 7 = 0 \end{bmatrix}$

(10) $\begin{bmatrix} y = 2x^2 - 2x - 1 \\ y = \frac{-3}{2} \end{bmatrix}$

II. Sketch the graph of the parabola and the line in each part of Exercise

I Label all points of intersection.

6.9   Factoring (Continued)

In Section 6.2 we studied factorization techniques useful in factoring certain expressions, mainly quadratic expressions. In this section we shall study the factorization of other expressions, many of which are encountered in a standard calculus course. The following examples illustrate procedures for discovering the factorizations of certain types of algebraic expressions.

Example 1.   Compute the product of $x - y$ and $x^2 + xy + y^2$.

$$(x - y)(x^2 + xy + y^2) = x(x^2 + xy + y^2) - y(x^2 + xy + y^2)$$
$$= x^3 + x^2y + xy^2 - x^2y - xy^2 - y^3$$
$$= x^3 - y^3.$$

Since the *product* of the given expressions is $x^3 - y^3$, it follows that the *factors* of $x^3 - y^3$ are $x - y$ and $x^2 + xy + y^2$. That is, $x^3 - y^3 = (x - y)(x^2 + xy + y^2)$.

Example 2.   Compute the product of $x + y$ and $x^2 - xy + y^2$.

$$(x + y)(x^2 - xy + y^2) = x(x^2 - xy + y^2) + y(x^2 - xy + y^2)$$
$$= x^3 - x^2y + xy^2 + x^2y - xy^2 + y^3$$
$$= x^3 + y^3.$$

Since the *product* of the given expressions is $x^3 + y^3$, it follows that the *factors* of $x^3 + y^3$ are $x + y$ and $x^2 - xy + y^2$. That is, $x^3 + y^3 = (x + y)(x^2 - xy + y^2)$.

Since expressions of the form $x^3 - y^3$ and $x^3 + y^3$ occur frequently in mathematics it is advisable to *remember* the factorizations of $x^3 - y^3$ and $x^3 + y^3$ and to realize that x and y represent *any* real numbers.

The following examples illustrate the factorizations of other expressions which are of this form.

Example 3.   Factor $8a^3 - 27b^3$.

We recognize this expression as $x^3 - y^3$, in which $x = 2a$ and $y = 3b$. Since $x^3 - y^3 = (x - y)(x^2 + xy + y^2)$, it follows that $8a^3 - 27b^3 = (2a - 3b)(4a^2 + 6ab + 9b^2)$.

Example 4.   Factor $64a^3 + 125b^3$.

We recognize this expression as $x^3 + y^3$, in which $x = 4a$ and $y = 5b$. Hence $64a^3 + 125b^3 = (4a + 5b)(16a^2 - 20ab + 25b^2)$.

Example 5. Factor $16a^6 + 54b^3$.

$$16a^6 + 54b^3 = 2(8a^6 + 27b^3)$$
$$= 2(2a^2 + 3b)(4a^4 - 6a^2b + 9b^2).$$

Example 6. Factor $a^6 - 64b^6$.

$$a^6 - 64b^6 = (a^2 - 4b^2)(a^4 + 4a^2b^2 + 16b^4)$$
$$= (a - 2b)(a + 2b)(a^4 + 4a^2b^2 + 16b^4).$$

Example 7. Factor $(x + 1)^3 - 8y^3$.

$$(x + 1)^3 - 8y^3 = [(x + 1) - 2y][(x + 1)^2 + 2(x + 1)y + 4y^2].$$

Sometimes an expression which contains four terms can be factored as illustrated in the following examples.

Example 8. Factor $2x + 6 + ax + 3a$.

$$2x + 6 + ax + 3a = (2x + 6) + (ax + 3a)$$
$$= 2(x + 3) + a(x + 3)$$
$$= (2 + a)(x + 3).$$

Example 9. Factor $x^3 - xy^2 + 2x^2 - 2y^2$.

$$x^3 - xy^2 + 2x^2 - 2y^2 = (x^3 - xy^2) + (2x^2 - 2y^2)$$
$$= x(x^2 - y^2) + 2(x^2 - y^2)$$
$$= (x + 2)(x^2 - y^2)$$
$$= (x + 2)(x - y)(x + y).$$

Example 10. Factor $x^2 + 4x - y^2 - 4y$.

$$x^2 + 4x - y^2 - 4y = x^2 - y^2 + 4x - 4y$$
$$= (x - y)(x + y) + 4(x - y)$$
$$= (x - y)[(x + y) + 4]$$
$$= (x - y)(x + y + 4).$$

Exercise 6.9

I. Factor each of the following expressions.

    (1) $y^3 + a^3$
    (2) $a^3 - y^3$
    (3) $27a^3 - 8b^3$

(4) $125a^3 + 64b^3$

(5) $16a^3 + 54b^6$

(6) $54a^3 + 16b^6$

(7) $a^6 + 64b^6$

(8) $2a^6 - 128b^6$

(9) $(x - 1)^3 + 8y^3$

(10) $8(x - 1)^3 - 27y^3$

(11) $a^4 - 16b^4$

(12) $16a^4 - 81b^4$

(13) $a^4 - 4b^4$

(14) $16a^4 - 9b^4$

(15) $(x^2 + 1)^2 - y^2$

(16) $(x^2 + 1)^2 - 4y^2$

(17) $(x^2 + 1)^3 - y^3$

(18) $(x^2 + 1)^3 - 8y^3$

(19) $(x + a - 2)^2 - 9b^2y^2$

(20) $16a^2x^2 - (y - b + 3)^2$

(21) $2x + 4y + ax + 2ay$

(22) $4x + 8y + ax + 2ay$

(23) $x^2 - y^2 + 5x - 5y$

(24) $4x^2 - y^2 + 10x - 5y$

(25) $x^2 + 8x - y^2 - 8y$

(26) $4x^2 + 8x - y^2 - 4y$

(27) $x^3 - y^3 + 3x - 3y$

(28) $x^3 + y^3 + 7x + 7y$

(29) $27x^3 + y^3 + 6x + 2y$

(30) $x^3 - 27y^3 + 6x - 18y$

II. Compute each of the following.

(1) $\dfrac{x}{x^3 + 8} + \dfrac{3}{x + 2}$

(2) $\dfrac{3}{x^3 - 8} + \dfrac{x}{x - 2}$

(3) $\dfrac{x}{27x^3 - 8} - \dfrac{5}{3x - 2}$

(4) $\dfrac{5}{8x^3 + 27} - \dfrac{x}{2x + 3}$

(5) $\dfrac{2x}{x^2 - 1} - \dfrac{3}{x - 1}$

(6) $\dfrac{2x}{x^2 - 1} - \dfrac{3}{x^3 - 1}$

(7) $\dfrac{x + 2}{x^2 - 1} - \dfrac{x - 1}{x + 1}$

(8) $\dfrac{x - 2}{x^2 - 1} - \dfrac{1 - x}{x^3 + 1}$

III. Simplify each of the following.

(1) $\dfrac{1 - \frac{y^2}{x^2}}{1 - \frac{y}{x}}$

(2) $\dfrac{\frac{y^2}{x^2} - 4}{\frac{y}{x} - 2}$

(3) $\dfrac{\frac{1}{a+3} + \frac{1}{a^3 + 27}}{\frac{2}{a+3} - \frac{1}{a^2 - 3a + 9}}$

(4) $\dfrac{\frac{1}{a-3} - \frac{1}{a^3 - 27}}{\frac{2}{a-3} - \frac{1}{a^2 + 3a + 9}}$

(5) $\dfrac{\frac{4}{x-y} - \frac{2}{x^2 - y^2}}{\frac{1}{x-y} - \frac{1}{x+y}}$

(6) $\dfrac{\frac{4}{y-x} - \frac{2}{x^2 - y^2}}{\frac{1}{y-x} - \frac{1}{x+y}}$

(7) $\dfrac{1}{a+1} + \dfrac{1}{a - \frac{1}{a}}$

(8) $\dfrac{1}{a-1} - \dfrac{1}{a^2 - \frac{1}{a}}$

(9) $1 + \dfrac{x}{x+1} - \dfrac{1}{x + \frac{1}{x-1}}$

(10) $1 - \dfrac{x}{x+1} + \dfrac{1}{x + \frac{1}{x-1}}$

CHAPTER 7

The Complex Number System

7.1 Equality, Addition, and Multiplication of Complex Numbers

Recall that not every quadratic equation has a real root; i.e., there are quadratic equations which do not have real roots. For example, the quadratic equation $x^2 + 1 = 0$ has no real root. The purpose of this chapter is to extend the real number system to a more inclusive number system so that *every* quadratic equation shall have roots. First we consider the quadratic equation $x^2 = {}^-1$. Since the square of every real number is nonnegative, we must invent a new kind of number if the quadratic equation $x^2 = {}^-1$ shall have one or more roots. Consequently, we invent a new number, denote it by i, and extend the binary operator $\times$ so that $i \times i = {}^-1$; i.e., $i^2 = {}^-1$. In order to extend the real number system to include the new number i, we need to define the binary operators $+$ and $\times$ so that all of the field properties which are true in the real number system shall still be true in the extended system. How should we define the product of a real number b and the number i? Obviously, if we wish to retain the multiplication property of 0, we must define $\times$ so that $0 \times i = i \times 0 = 0$. If $b \neq 0$, we might be tempted to define $\times$ so that $b \times i = r$, a real number. However, if the field properties are retained, then the following sequence of steps must be valid.

$$bi = r$$
$$\tfrac{1}{b}(bi) = \tfrac{1}{b}(r)$$
$$i = \tfrac{r}{b}.$$

221

But i is *not* a real number and $\frac{r}{b}$ is a real number. Consequently, if we wish to retain the field properties, we cannot define the product of i and a nonzero real number b to be a real number. Obviously, if we wish to retain the identity property for multiplication, we must define $\times$ so that $1 \times i = i$ and $i \times 1 = i$; moreover, if $b \neq 1$, then we must define $\times$ so that $bi \neq i$. Since we wish to retain the closure property for multiplication, we must invent a new number for the product of b and i. It is natural to denote the new number for the product of b and i by the symbol bi and say that the product of b and i is the number bi. Now the real number system has been extended to include other numbers which are not real numbers. For example, the numbers i, ^-1i, ^-7i, $\frac{4}{3}i$, $\frac{-2}{5}i$, $\sqrt{3}i$, i, and $0.4\overline{58}i$ are included in the new number system.

If we wish to retain the field properties, how should we define the binary operator $+$ between any two numbers of the new system? Obviously, if we wish to retain the identity property for addition, we must define $+$ so that $0 + bi = bi + 0 = bi$ for any real number b. If $a \neq 0$, $b \neq 0$, and we wish to retain the field properties, then we must invent a new number for the sum of a and bi. It is natural to denote the new number for the sum of a and bi by the symbol $a + bi$ and say that the sum of a and bi is the number $a + bi$. For example, the numbers $1 + i$, $^-1 + i$, $1 + 3i$, $^-1 + {}^-2i$, $3 + 2i$, $\frac{-4}{5} + \frac{7}{3}i$, $0 + 0i$, $\frac{4}{5} + 0i$, and $0 + {}^-7i$ are included in the new number system.

Now that we have invented a new system of numbers and have defined addition and multiplication so that the sum and the product of any real number a and any number bi are in the system, we need to extend the definition of $+$ and $\times$ so that $(a + bi) + (c + di)$ and $(a + bi)(c + di)$ are also in the system (and the field properties are retained). The following examples illustrate the method by which the definitions of $+$ and $\times$ will be made.

Example 1. How should we define $(a + bi) + (c + di)$ if we wish to retain the field properties?

If we retain the field properties, then we retain the generalized commutative and associative property for addition and the distributive property. Consequently we may write

$$(a + bi) + (c + di) = (a + c) + (bi + di) \qquad \text{(by GCAAPFA)}$$
$$= (a + c) + (b + d)i \qquad \text{(by DP).}$$

Thus we should define $+$ so that $(a + bi) + (c + di) = (a + c) + (b + d)i$ (if the field properties are to be retained).

Example 2. How should we define $(a + bi) \times (c + di)$ if we wish to retain the field properties?

If we retain the field properties, then we retain the generalized commutative and associative property for multiplication, and the distributive property. Consequently we may write

$$
\begin{aligned}
(a + bi)(c + di) &= (a + bi)c + (a + bi)di \\
&= ac + (bi)c + (a)(di) + (bi)(di) \\
&= ac + bci + adi + bdi^2 \\
&= ac + bci + adi + bd(^-1) \\
&= ac + {}^-bd + bci + adi \\
&= (ac - bd) + (bc + ad)i.
\end{aligned}
$$

Thus we should define $\times$ or $\cdot$ so that $(a + bi) \times (c + di) = (ac - bd) + (bc + ad)i$ (if the field properties are to be retained).

Because of the above considerations we make the following definition of the *complex number system.*

DEFINITION 1. *The complex number system* is the system $(C, +, \times)$, in which

(a) $C = \{a + bi: a \in R \land b \in R \land i^2 = {}^-1\}$,
(b) $a + bi = c + di$ if and only if $a = c$ and $b = d$,
(c) $0 \times i = 0$,
(d) $1 \times i = i$,
(e) $(a + bi) + (c + di) = (a + c) + (b + d)i$,
(f) $(a + bi) \times (c + di) = (ac - bd) + (bc + ad)i$.

Since $a = a + 0i$, we see that every real number is a complex number; i.e., $R \subset C$. Moreover, the definitions of addition and multiplication of any two complex numbers are consistent with the corresponding definitions for any two real numbers.

The following examples illustrate computations with complex numbers.

Example 3. If $(a + 3) + 5i = {}^-7 + 3di$, compute a and d.

By Definition 1, $(a + 3) + 5i = {}^-7 + 3di$ if and only if $a + 3 = {}^-7$ and $5 = 3d$.

Hence $a = {}^-10$ and $d = \frac{5}{3}$.

Example 4. Compute the sum of $^-3 + 7i$ and $^-1 + {}^-2i$.

$$
\begin{aligned}
(^-3 + 7i) + (^-1 + {}^-2i) &= (^-3 + {}^-1) + (7 + {}^-2)i \\
&= {}^-4 + 5i.
\end{aligned}
$$

Example 5. Compute the product of $(3 + {}^-2i)$ and $(^-4 + 5i)$.

$$
\begin{aligned}
(3 + {}^-2i)(^-4 + 5i) &= [3(^-4) - (^-2)(5)] + [(^-2)(^-4) + (3)(5)]i \\
&= [^-12 + 10] + [8 + 15]i \\
&= {}^-2 + 23i.
\end{aligned}
$$

In the next section we shall prove that the complex number system is a field.

Exercise 7.1

I. Convert each of the following open sentences to a true sentence by replacement of each variable by a real number or prove that no replacement will convert the open sentence to a true sentence.

(1) $a + 5i = {}^-7 + di$
(2) $3 + bi = c + {}^-5i$
(3) $6 + {}^-3i = {}^-c + di$
(4) $a + {}^-bi = 5 + {}^-7i$
(5) $6 + {}^-7i = 7 + di$
(6) $a + {}^-3i = 6 + 5i$
(7) $(a + {}^-4) + bi = 6 + 5i$
(8) $a + (b + {}^-3)i = {}^-5 + 7i$
(9) $(2a + 5) + ({}^-3b + {}^-7)i = \frac{{}^-5}{3} + \left(\frac{{}^-3}{2}\right)i$
(10) $({}^-2a + 7) + (4b + {}^-3)i = \frac{6}{5} + \left(\frac{{}^-4}{3}\right)i$

II. Compute the sum of each of the following pairs of complex numbers.

(1) $2 + {}^-13i,\quad {}^-4 + 7i$ (6) ${}^-3 + {}^-4i,\quad {}^-3 + 4i$
(2) ${}^-1 + 5i,\quad 2 + {}^-3i$ (7) $1 + 3i,\quad {}^-1 + 3i$
(3) $\frac{{}^-5}{4} + 0i,\quad 0 + {}^-7i$ (8) $1 + {}^-3i,\quad 1 + 3i$
(4) $0 + \left(\frac{{}^-3}{4}\right)i,\quad 6 + 0i$ (9) $2 + {}^-3i,\quad {}^-2 + 3i$
(5) $7 + 3i,\quad 7 + {}^-3i$ (10) ${}^-6 + 3i,\quad 6 + {}^-3i$

III. Compute the product of each pair of complex numbers in Exercise II.

IV. Assume that the complex number system obeys the field properties. State the field properties for the system $(C, +, \times)$.

7.2 Field Properties of the Complex Number System

We have already observed that the set of real numbers is a proper subset of the set of complex numbers. In Definition 1 we set the stage so that the complex number system $(C, +, \times)$ would be a field and that $(R, +, \times)$ would be a subfield of $(C, +, \times)$. In this section we shall prove that $(C, +, \times)$ is actually a field; i.e., $(C, +, \times)$ obeys the following properties:

F1. If $a + bi$ and $c + di$ are any elements of C, then $(a + bi) + (c + di)$ is a unique element of C (*closure property for addition*).

F2. If $a + bi$, $c + di$, and $e + fi$ are any elements of C, then $[(a + bi) + (c + di)] + (e + fi) = (a + bi) + [(c + di) + (e + fi)]$ *(associative property for addition)*.

F3. There exists a unique element 0 of C such that $(a + bi) + 0 = (a + bi)$ for any element $a + bi$ of C *(identity property for addition)*.

F4. If $a + bi$ is any element of C, then there exists a unique element $^-a + {^-bi}$ of C such that $(a + bi) + (^-a + {^-bi}) = 0$ *(inverse property for addition)*.

F5. If $a + bi$ and $c + di$ are any elements of C, then $(a + bi) + (c + di) = (c + di) + (a + bi)$ *(commutative property for addition)*.

F6. If $a + bi$ and $c + di$ are any element of C, then $(a + bi)(c + di)$ is a unique element of C *(closure property for multiplication)*.

F7. If $(a + bi)$, $(c + di)$, and $(e + fi)$ are any elements of C, then $[(a + bi)(c + di)] (e + fi) = (a + bi)[(c + di)(e + fi)]$ *(associative property for multiplication)*.

F8. There exists a unique element 1 of C such that $(a + bi) \times 1 = a + bi$ for any element $a + bi$ of C *(identity property for multiplication)*.

F9. If $a + bi$ is any nonzero element of C, then there exists a unique element $\left[\left(\frac{a}{a^2 + b^2}\right) + \left(\frac{-b}{a^2 + b^2}\right)i\right]$ of C such that $(a + bi)\left[\frac{a}{a^2 + b^2} + \left(\frac{-b}{a^2 + b^2}\right)i\right] = 1$ *(inverse property for multiplication)*.

F10. If $a + bi$ and $c + di$ are any elements of C, then $(a + bi)(c + di) = (c + di)(a + bi)$ *(commutative property for multiplication)*.

F11. If $(a + bi)$, $(c + di)$, and $(e + fi)$ are any elements of C, then $(a + bi)[(c + di) + (e + fi)] = (a + bi)(c + di) + (a + bi)(e + fi)$ *(distributive property)*.

To prove $F1$ we observe from Definition 1(e) that $(a + bi) + (c + di) = (a + c) + (b + d)i$. Since $a + c$ is a unique real number and $b + d$ is a unique real number, we see that $(a + c) + (b + d)i$ is a unique complex number.

We prove $F2$ as follows:

$$[(a + bi) + (c + di)] + (e + fi) = [(a + c) + (b + d)i] + (e + fi)$$
$$\text{(by Definition 1(e))}$$
$$= [(a + c) + e] + [(b + d) + f]i$$
$$\text{(by Definition 1(e))}$$
$$= [a + (c + e)] + [b + (d + f)]i$$
$$= (a + bi) + [(c + e) + (d + f)i]$$
$$\text{(by Definition 1(e))}$$
$$= (a + bi) + [(c + di) + (e + fi)]$$
$$\text{(by Definition 1(e))}.$$

We prove $F3$ as follows:

$$(a + bi) + 0 = (a + bi) + (0 + 0)$$
$$= (a + bi) + (0 + 0i) \qquad \text{(by Definition 1(c))}$$
$$= (a + 0) + (b + 0)i \qquad \text{(by Definition 1(e))}$$
$$= a + bi.$$

The uniqueness follows from the uniqueness of the additive identity for real numbers.

We prove $F4$ as follows:

$$(a + bi) + (^-a + {}^-bi) = (a + {}^-a) + (b + {}^-b)i$$
$$\qquad \text{(by Definition 1(e))}$$
$$= 0 + 0i$$
$$= 0 + 0 \qquad \text{(by Definition 1(c))}$$
$$= 0.$$

Since the inverse property for addition of real numbers guarantees that ^-a is the only real number such that $a + {}^-a = 0$ and ^-b is the only real number such that $b + {}^-b = 0$, we are assured that $^-a + {}^-bi$ is the only complex number such that $(a + bi) + (^-a + {}^-bi) = 0$. That is, the additive inverse of any given complex number is *unique*.

We prove $F5$ as follows:

$$(a + bi) + (c + di) = (a + c) + (b + d)i$$
$$\qquad \text{(by Definition 1(e))}$$
$$= (c + a) + (d + b)i$$
$$= (c + di) + (a + bi)$$
$$\qquad \text{(by Definition 1(e))}.$$

To prove $F6$ we observe from definition 1(f) that $(a + bi)(c + di) = (ac - bd) + (bc + ad)i$. Since $(ac - bd)$ is a unique real number and $(bc + ad)$ is a unique real number, we see that $(ac - bd) + (bc + ad)i$ is a unique complex number.

We prove $F7$ as follows:

$$[(a + bi)(c + di)](e + fi) = [(ac - bd) + (bc + ad)i](e + fi)$$
$$\qquad \text{(by Definition 1(f))}$$
$$= [(ac - bd)e - (bc + ad)f]$$
$$\quad + [(bc + ad)e + (ac - bd)f]i$$
$$\qquad \text{(by Definition 1(f))}$$
$$= [ace - bde - bcf - adf]$$
$$\quad + [bce + ade + acf - bdf]i$$
$$\qquad \text{(by Definition 1(f))}$$

$$= [ace - adf - bde - bcf]$$
$$+ [bce - bdf + ade + acf]i$$
$$= [a(ce - df) - b(de + cf)]$$
$$+ [b(ce - df) + a(de + cf)]i$$
$$= (a + bi)[(ce - df) + (de + cf)i]$$

(by Definition 1(f))

$$= (a + bi)[(c + di)(e + fi)]$$

(by Definition 1(f)).

We prove *F*8 as follows:

$$(a + bi)1 = (a + bi)(1 + 0)$$
$$= (a + bi)(1 + 0i) \qquad \text{(by Definition 1(c))}$$
$$= (a \times 1 - b \times 0) + (b \times 1 + a \times 0)i \qquad \text{(by Definition 1(f))}$$
$$= (a - 0) + (b + 0)i$$
$$= a + bi.$$

The uniqueness follows from the uniqueness of the multiplicative identity for real numbers.

To prove *F*9, we consider the complex number $a + bi$, where $ab \neq 0$, and let $(a + bi)(c + di) = 1$ and prove that $c = \frac{a}{(a^2 + b^2)}$ and $d = \frac{-b}{(a^2 + b^2)}$. Observe that if $ab \neq 0$, then $a^2 + b^2 \neq 0$.

$$(a + bi)(c + di) = 1$$
$$(ac - bd) + (bc + ad)i = 1 + 0i \qquad \text{(by Definition 1(c) and 1(f))}$$
$$ac - bd = 1 \text{ and } bc + ad = 0 \qquad \text{(by Definition 1(b))}$$
$$a(ac - bd) = a \times 1 \text{ and } b(bc + ad) = b \times 0$$
$$a^2c - abd = a \text{ and } b^2c + abd = 0$$
$$(a^2c - abd) + (b^2c + abd) = a + 0 \text{ and } b^2c + abd = 0$$
$$(a^2 + b^2)c = a \text{ and } b^2c + abd = 0$$
$$c = \frac{a}{(a^2 + b^2)} \text{ and } b^2 \times \frac{a}{(a^2 + b^2)} + abd = 0 \qquad (ab \neq 0)$$
$$c = \frac{a}{(a^2 + b^2)} \text{ and } abd = \frac{-b^2a}{(a^2 + b^2)}$$
$$c = \frac{a}{(a^2 + b^2)} \text{ and } d = \frac{-b}{(a^2 + b^2)}, \ (ab \neq 0).$$

Although this *proof* is valid *only if* $ab \neq 0$, the *result* is valid even if $a = 0$ or $b = 0$ (but not both).

As a check, we compute the product of $(a + bi)$ and

$$\left(\frac{a}{a^2 + b^2}\right) + \left(\frac{-b}{a^2 + b^2}\right)i$$
$$(a + bi)\left[\left(\frac{a}{a^2 + b^2}\right) + \left(\frac{-b}{a^2 + b^2}\right)i\right] = \left[a\left(\frac{a}{a^2 + b^2}\right) - b\left(\frac{-b}{a^2 + b^2}\right)\right] + \left[b\left(\frac{a}{a^2 + b^2}\right)\right.$$
$$\left. + a\left(\frac{-b}{a^2 + b^2}\right)\right]i$$

(by Definition 1(f))

$$= \left[\frac{a^2}{a^2 + b^2} + \frac{b^2}{a^2 + b^2} \right] + \left[\frac{ab}{a^2 + b^2} + \frac{-ab}{a^2 + b^2} \right] i$$
$$= \frac{a^2 + b^2}{a^2 + b^2} + 0i$$
$$= 1 + 0i$$
$$= 1.$$

We prove $F10$ as follows:

$$
\begin{aligned}
(a + bi)(c + di) &= (ac - bd) + (bc + ad)i && \text{(by Definition 1(f))} \\
&= (ca - db) + (da + cb)i \\
&= (c + di)(a + bi) && \text{(by Definition 1(f)).}
\end{aligned}
$$

We prove $F11$ as follows:

$$
\begin{aligned}
(a + bi)[(c + di) + (e + fi)] &= (a + bi)[(c + e) + (d + f)i] \\
&\qquad\qquad \text{(by Definition 1(e))} \\
&= [a(c + e) - b(d + f)] + [b(c + e) + a(d + f)]i \\
&\qquad\qquad \text{(by Definition 1(f))} \\
&= [ac + ae - bd - bf] + [bc + be + ad + af]i \\
&= [(ac - bd) + (ae - bf)] + [(bc + ad) + (be + af)]i \\
&= [(ac - bd) + (bc + ad)i] + [(ae - bf) + (be + af)i] \\
&= [(a + bi)(c + di)] + [(a + bi)(e + fi)] \\
&\qquad\qquad \text{(by Definition 1(f)).}
\end{aligned}
$$

Observe that the manner in which we defined $(C, +, \times)$ in Definition 1 enabled us to prove the field properties for $(C, +, \times)$ from Definition 1 and the field properties for $(R, +, \times)$. That is, from Definition 1 and the knowledge that the real number system is a field, we have proved that the complex number system is also a field. Recalling that the real number system is an ordered field, you may wonder whether the complex number system is an ordered field also. In Section 7.5 we shall consider this question. In the next section we shall discuss subtraction and division of complex numbers.

Exercise 7.2

I. Compute the additive inverse of each of the following complex numbers.

(1) 5

(2) $^-8$

(3) $\left(\frac{6}{7}\right)i$

(4) i

(5) $1 + 3i$

(6) $7 + 8i$

(7) $^-5 + 3i$

(8) $3 + {}^-5i$

(9) $\left(\frac{-6}{5}\right) + \left(\frac{-2}{3}\right)i$

(10) $\frac{-7}{8} + \frac{-3}{5} i$

(11) $0 + 0i$

(12) 0

II. Compute the multiplicative inverse of each of the following complex numbers.

(1) $\frac{2}{3}$ (5) $3 + {}^-4i$

(2) $\frac{{}^-3}{5}$ (6) ${}^-4 + 3i$

(3) $0 + 3i$ (7) ${}^-7 + 24i$

(4) ${}^-7i$ (8) $24 + {}^-7i$

III. Denote the multiplicative inverse of each of the following complex numbers by $c + di$ and compute the inverse by the *method* of proof of *F9* in the text.

(1) $3 + {}^-4i$ (3) ${}^-7 + 24i$

(2) ${}^-4 + 3i$ (4) $24 + {}^-7i$

IV. Illustrate the commutative property for addition of each of the following pairs of complex numbers.

(1) $2 + {}^-3i$, ${}^-5 + 7i$ (6) ${}^-2 + {}^-1i$, $3 + i$

(2) ${}^-6 + 7i$, $4 + {}^-3i$ (7) ${}^-7 + 8i$, $7 + 8i$

(3) $0 + {}^-6i$, $3 + 0i$ (8) $6 + 5i$, ${}^-6 + {}^-2i$

(4) ${}^-5 + 0i$, $0 + 3i$ (9) ${}^-3 + 2i$, $3 + {}^-2i$

(5) $1 + i$, $2 + {}^-1i$ (10) $7 + {}^-5i$, ${}^-7 + 5i$

V. Illustrate the commutative property for multiplication of each of the pairs of complex numbers in Exercise IV.

VI. Illustrate the associative property for addition for each of the following triplets of complex numbers.

(1) $1 + 0i$, $2 + 5i$, ${}^-3 + i$ (4) $6 + 3i$, ${}^-7 + 4i$, $7 + {}^-4i$

(2) $1 + i$, $3 + {}^-2i$, $2 + 3i$ (5) $0 + 3i$, $4 + {}^-1i$, ${}^-3 + 7i$

(3) ${}^-4 + 3i$, $4 + {}^-3i$, $5 + 7i$ (6) $1 + {}^-4i$, $3 + 2i$, $0 + i$

VII. Illustrate the associative property for multiplication for each triplet of complex numbers in Exercise VI.

VIII. Illustrate the distributive property for each triplet of complex numbers in Exercise VI.

7.3   Subtraction and Division of Complex Numbers

We have proved that the complex number system $(C, +, \cdot)$, or $(C, +, \times)$, is a field, in which addition and multiplication are as defined in Definition 1. In this section we shall define subtraction and division. For convenience we shall denote ${}^-1i$ *by* ${}^-i$; i.e., ${}^-i = {}^-1i$. This is consistent with the fact that $1i = i$. The binary operator $-$, the operation *subtraction*, and the *difference* of two complex numbers is given in Definition 2.

DEFINITION 2. The *difference* in the subtraction of the complex number $c + di$ from the complex number $a + bi$ [written $(a + bi)$ $- (c + di)$] is the complex number $e + fi$ if and only if $a + bi$ $= (c + di) + (e + fi)$. [That is, $(a + bi) - (c + di) = e + fi$ if and only if $a + bi = (c + di) + (e + fi)$.]

It follows immediately from $F4$ that $(a + bi) - (c + di) = (a + bi)$ $+ (^-c + {}^-di)$. The following examples illustrate the method of subtraction.

Example 1. Compute $(3 + {}^-7i) - ({}^-6 + 5i)$.

$$
\begin{aligned}
(3 + {}^-7i) - ({}^-6 + 5i) &= (3 + {}^-7i) + (6 + {}^-5i) \\
&= (3 + 6) + ({}^-7 + {}^-5)i \\
&= 9 + {}^-12i \\
&= (9 + 0i) + (0 + {}^-12i) \\
&= (9 + 0i) - ({}^-0 + 12i) \\
&= 9 - 12i.
\end{aligned}
$$

Example 2. Compute $({}^-4 + 3i) - (1 + {}^-2i)$.

$$
\begin{aligned}
({}^-4 + 3i) - (1 + {}^-2i) &= ({}^-4 + 3i) + ({}^-1 + 2i) \\
&= ({}^-4 + {}^-1) + (3 + 2)i \\
&= {}^-5 + 5i.
\end{aligned}
$$

We observe from Definition 2 and the above examples that $(a + bi)$ $- (c + di) = (a - c) + (b - d)i$. The following example illustrates this fact.

Example 3. Compute $(5 + 3i) - (2 + 7i)$.

$$
\begin{aligned}
(5 + 3i) - (2 + 7i) &= (5 - 2) + (3 - 7)i \\
&= 3 + {}^-4i.
\end{aligned}
$$

The binary operator $\div$, the operation *division*, and the *quotient* of two complex numbers is given in Definition 3.

DEFINITION 3. The *quotient* in the division of the complex number $a + bi$ by the nonzero complex number $c + di$ [written $(a + bi)$ $\div (c + di)$ or $\frac{(a + bi)}{(c + di)}$] is the complex number $e + fi$ if and only if $a + bi = (c + di)(e + fi)$. [That is, $\frac{(a + bi)}{(c + di)} = e + fi$ if and only if $a + bi = (c + di)(e + fi)$.]

To actually compute the quotient $\frac{(a + bi)}{(c + di)}$, we may proceed as follows:

$a + bi = (a + bi) \times 1$ (by $F8$)

$ = (a + bi)\left[(c + di)(\frac{c}{c^2 + d^2} + \frac{-d}{c^2 + d^2}i)\right]$ (by $F9$)

$ = (c + di)\left[(a + bi)(\frac{c}{c^2 + d^2} + \frac{-d}{c^2 + d^2}i)\right]$ (by $F7$ and $F10$).

But $\left[(a + bi)(\frac{c}{c^2 + d^2} + \frac{-d}{c^2 + d^2}i)\right]$ is a complex number $e + fi$ (by $F6$).

Thus $a + bi = (c + di)(e + fi)$.

Hence $\frac{(a + bi)}{(c + di)} = e + fi$ (by Definition 3).

Consequently $\frac{(a + bi)}{(c + di)} = (a + bi)(\frac{c}{c^2 + d^2} + \frac{-d}{c^2 + d^2}i)$.

In particular, $\frac{1}{(c + di)} = \frac{(1 + 0i)}{(c + di)} = (\frac{c}{c^2 + d^2} + \frac{-d}{c^2 + d^2}i)$.

The following examples illustrate the computation of the quotient of two complex numbers.

Example 4.   Compute $\frac{(-6 + 5i)}{(3 + -4i)}$.

$\frac{(-6 + 5i)}{(3 + -4i)} = (-6 + 5i)(\frac{3}{3^2 + (-4)^2} + \frac{-(-4)}{3^2 + (-4)^2}i)$

$\phantom{\frac{(-6 + 5i)}{(3 + -4i)}} = (-6 + 5i)[\frac{3}{25} + (\frac{4}{25})i]$

$\phantom{\frac{(-6 + 5i)}{(3 + -4i)}} = (\frac{1}{25})\left[\left(-6(3) - 5(4)\right) + \left(5(3) + (-6)(4)\right)i\right]$

$\phantom{\frac{(-6 + 5i)}{(3 + -4i)}} = (\frac{1}{25})[(-18 - 20) + (15 - 24)i]$

$\phantom{\frac{(-6 + 5i)}{(3 + -4i)}} = (\frac{1}{25})[-38 + -9i]$

$\phantom{\frac{(-6 + 5i)}{(3 + -4i)}} = \frac{-38}{25} + (\frac{-9}{25})i.$

Example 5.   Compute $\frac{2i}{(1 + 3i)}$.

$\frac{2i}{(1 + 3i)} = (2i)(\frac{1}{1^2 + 3^2} + \frac{-3}{1^2 + 3^2}i)$

$\phantom{\frac{2i}{(1 + 3i)}} = 2i[\frac{1}{10} + (\frac{-3}{10})i]$

$\phantom{\frac{2i}{(1 + 3i)}} = 2i(\frac{1}{10}) + 2i(\frac{-3}{10})i$

$\phantom{\frac{2i}{(1 + 3i)}} = (\frac{1}{5})i + (\frac{-3}{5})i^2$

$\phantom{\frac{2i}{(1 + 3i)}} = (\frac{1}{5})i + (\frac{-3}{5})(-1)$

$\phantom{\frac{2i}{(1 + 3i)}} = (\frac{3}{5}) + (\frac{1}{5})i.$

Traditionally quotients are computed in another way, which eliminates the necessity of memorizing that $\frac{a}{a^2 + b^2} + \frac{-b}{a^2 + b^2}i$ is the multiplicative inverse of $a + bi$, ($a \neq 0$ or $b \neq 0$). Before we introduce this method, we define the *conjugate* of a complex number.

DEFINITION 4.   The *conjugate* of the complex number $a + bi$ is the complex number $a + -bi$.

For example, the conjugate of $2 + {}^-7i$ is $2 + 7i$, and the conjugate of $2 + 7i$ is $2 + {}^-7i$. The product of the complex number $a + bi$ and its conjugate $a + {}^-bi$ is the real number $a^2 + b^2$. Thus any division problem is reducible to a multiplication problem. The following examples illustrate the traditional method of computing a quotient by use of the conjugate.

Example 6.   Compute $\frac{(-4 + 3i)}{(5 + 2i)}$.

$$\frac{-4 + 3i}{5 + 2i} = \frac{-4 + 3i}{5 + 2i} \times \frac{5 + -2i}{5 + -2i}$$

$$= \frac{[(-4)(5) - (3)(-2)] + [3(5) + (-4)(-2)]i}{[5(5) - 2(-2)] + [2(5) + 5(-2)]i}$$

$$= \frac{(-20 + 6) + (15 + 8)i}{(5^2 + 2^2) + (10 - 10)i}$$

$$= \frac{(-14 + 23i)}{29}$$

$$= \frac{-14}{29} + \frac{23}{29}i.$$

Example 7.   Compute $\frac{(1 + 3i)}{(-2 - 7i)}$.

$$\frac{(1 + 3i)}{(-2 - 7i)} = \frac{(1 + 3i)}{(-2 + -7i)}$$

$$= \frac{1 + 3i}{-2 + -7i} \times \frac{-2 + 7i}{-2 + 7i}$$

$$= \frac{[1(-2) - (3)(7)] + [3(-2) + 1(7)]i}{[(-2)(-2) - (-7)(7)] + [(-7)(-2) + (-2)(7)]i}$$

$$= \frac{(-23 + i)}{53}$$

$$= -\left(\frac{23}{53}\right) + \left(\frac{1}{53}\right)i.$$

For each real number property which follows from the field properties $F1$ through $F11$, there is a corresponding complex number property. For example, the generalized commutative and associative property for addition and for multiplication and the generalized distributive property are true for complex numbers as well as for real numbers. We close this section by listing three of the more important of these properties.

CANCELLATION PROPERTY FOR ADDITION OF COMPLEX NUMBERS (CPFAOCN)

If $(a + bi) + (c + di) = (a + bi) + (e + fi)$, then $(c + di) = (e + fi)$.

CANCELLATION PROPERTY FOR MULTIPLICATION OF COMPLEX NUMBERS (CPFMOCN).

If $(a + bi)(c + di) = (a + bi)(e + fi)$, and $a + bi \neq 0$, then $c + di = e + fi$.

MULTIPLICATION PROPERTY OF ZERO (MPOZ)

$(a + bi)(c + di) = 0$ if and only if $a + bi = 0$ or $c + di = 0$.

Exercise 7.3

I. Compute each of the following differences.

(1) $(2 + 7i) - (3 + 2i)$
(2) $(5 + 3i) - (4 + 5i)$
(3) $(^-4 + 7i) - (2 + ^-3i)$
(4) $(4 + ^-7i) - (^-2 + 3i)$
(5) $2i - (5 + i)$
(6) $4 - (5 + i)$
(7) $i - 5i$
(8) $^-i - ^-5i$
(9) $[(k + 2) + 3i] - [(k - 1) + ^-3i]$
(10) $[(m - 3) + ^-2i] - [(m + 1) + 2.1]$

II. Compute each of the following quotients.

(1) $\frac{(2 + 7i)}{(3 + 2i)}$ (6) $\frac{-2}{(4 + ^-i)}$

(2) $\frac{(5 + 3i)}{(4 + 5i)}$ (7) $\frac{2i}{(3 + 2i)}$

(3) $\frac{(5 + ^-3i)}{(-4 + 5i)}$ (8) $\frac{-3i}{(2 + ^-3i)}$

(4) $\frac{(5 + ^-3i)}{(-4 + ^-5i)}$ (9) $\frac{(3 + ^-2i)}{-2i}$

(5) $\frac{4}{(5 + i)}$ (10) $\frac{(1 + 5i)}{5i}$

III. (1) Prove that $(a + bi) - (c + di) = (a + bi) + (^-c + ^-di)$.
(2) Prove that $(a + bi) - (c + di) = (a - c) + (b - d)i$.

7.4 The Quadratic Formula

Since $i^2 = ^-1$ and $(^-i)^2 = (^-i)(^-i) = (^-1i)(^-1i) = (^-1)(^-1)(i \times i)$ $= 1 \times i^2 = i^2 = ^-1$, we see that the quadratic equation $x^2 = ^-1$ has the *two* roots i and ^-i. Before we extended the real number system to the complex number system, the quadratic equation $x^2 = ^-1$ had *no* roots. The reason we extended the real number system to the complex number system was that we desired every quadratic equation to have at least one root. Now we shall prove (*in the field of complex numbers*) that every quadratic equation has two roots, provided that we count the real root a in the equation $(x - a)^2 = 0$ as *two real and equal* roots. In Chapter 6 we proved that the quadratic equation $ax^2 + bx + c = 0$ has two real roots if and only if $0 \leq b^2 - 4ac$. Now we prove that the quadratic equation $ax^2 + bx + c = 0$ has two complex roots which are *not* real if and only if $b^2 - 4ac < 0$.

Let $ax^2 + bx + c = 0$, $a \neq 0$, and $b^2 - 4ac < 0$.

$$ax^2 + bx = {}^-c$$

$$x^2 + \left(\tfrac{b}{a}\right)x = \tfrac{-c}{a}$$

$$x^2 + \left(\tfrac{b}{a}\right)x + \left(\tfrac{b}{2a}\right)^2 = \tfrac{-c}{a} + \left(\tfrac{b}{2a}\right)^2$$

$$\left(x + \tfrac{b}{2a}\right)^2 = \tfrac{(-4ac + b^2)}{4a^2}$$

$$\left(x + \tfrac{b}{2a}\right)^2 + \tfrac{(4ac - b^2)}{4a^2} = 0$$

$$\left[\left(x + \tfrac{b}{2a}\right) + \sqrt{\tfrac{4ac - b^2}{4a^2}}\,i\right]\left[\left(x + \tfrac{b}{2a}\right) - \sqrt{\tfrac{4ac - b^2}{4a^2}}\,i\right] = 0 \qquad \text{(by Definition 1(f))}$$

$$x + \tfrac{b}{2a} + \sqrt{\tfrac{4ac - b^2}{4a^2}}\,i = 0 \text{ or } x + \tfrac{b}{2a} - \sqrt{\tfrac{4ac - b^2}{4a^2}}\,i = 0 \quad \text{(by multiplication property of 0)}$$

$$x = \tfrac{-b}{2a} - \left(\tfrac{\sqrt{4ac - b^2}}{2a}\right) \times i, \text{ or } x = \tfrac{-b}{2a} + \left(\tfrac{\sqrt{4ac - b^2}}{2a}\right) \times i.$$

Thus there are two complex roots of the quadratic equation $ax^2 + bx + c = 0$ if $b^2 - 4ac < 0$. Observe that the two roots $\tfrac{-b}{2a} - \left(\tfrac{\sqrt{4ac - b^2}}{2a}\right)i$ and $\tfrac{-b}{2a} + \left(\tfrac{\sqrt{4ac - b^2}}{2a}\right)i$ are conjugates.

In order to consolidate *all cases* ($b^2 - 4ac < 0$, $b^2 - 4ac = 0$, and $0 < b^2 - 4ac$) into *one case*, we introduce the notation $\sqrt{-a}$ for $\sqrt{a} \times i$ if a is a positive real; i.e., $\sqrt{a} \times i = \sqrt{-a}$. It follows immediately that $\sqrt{1} \times i = \sqrt{-1}$; i.e., $i = \sqrt{-1}$. If $b^2 - 4ac < 0$, then $\left(\tfrac{\sqrt{4ac - b^2}}{2a}\right) \times i = \tfrac{\sqrt{-(4ac - b^2)}}{2a} = \tfrac{\sqrt{b^2 - 4ac}}{2a}$, and the quadratic equation $ax^2 + bx + c = 0$ has the complex roots $\left(\tfrac{-b \pm \sqrt{b^2 - 4ac}}{2a}\right)$. Thus, *in all cases*, the roots of the quadratic equation $ax^2 + bx + c = 0$ are $\left(\tfrac{-b \pm \sqrt{b^2 - 4ac}}{2a}\right)$. Consequently we have extended the quadratic formula of Section 6.5 so that the roots of *any* quadratic equation may be computed from it; i.e., $ax^2 + bx + c = 0$, $a \neq 0$, if and only if $x = \left(\tfrac{-b \pm \sqrt{b^2 - 4ac}}{2a}\right)$. Henceforth, the *new* formula, $x = \left(\tfrac{-b \pm \sqrt{b^2 - 4ac}}{2a}\right)$, will be called the *quadratic formula*.

The following examples illustrate the application of the quadratic formula to the solution of quadratic equations.

Example 1. Solve the quadratic equation $2x^2 + 5x - 12 = 0$

$$a = 2, \ b = 5, \ c = {}^-12$$

$$x = \left(\tfrac{-b \pm \sqrt{b^2 - 4ac}}{2a}\right)$$

$$x = \left(\tfrac{-5 \pm \sqrt{5^2 - 4(2)(-12)}}{2(2)}\right)$$

$$x = \left(\tfrac{-5 \pm \sqrt{121}}{4}\right)$$

$x = \frac{(-5 \pm 11)}{4}$

$x = \frac{(-5 + 11)}{4}$ or $x = \frac{(-5 - 11)}{4}$

$x = \frac{3}{2}$ or $x = {}^-4$.

The roots are *real and unequal.*

Example 2. Solve the quadratic equation $x^2 - x + 1 = 0$.

$a = 1, \; b = {}^-1, \; c = 1$

$x = \left(\frac{-b \pm \sqrt{b^2 - 4ac}}{2a} \right)$

$x = \left(\frac{1 \pm \sqrt{(-1)^2 - 4(1)(1)}}{2(1)} \right)$

$x = \left(\frac{1 \pm \sqrt{-3}}{2} \right)$

$x = \left(\frac{1 \pm \sqrt{3}\,i}{2} \right)$

$x = \frac{1}{2} + \left(\frac{\sqrt{3}}{2} \right)i$ or $x = \frac{1}{2} - \left(\frac{\sqrt{3}}{2} \right)i$.

The roots are *complex conjugates.*

Example 3. Solve the quadratic equation $9x^2 - 12x + 4 = 0$.

$a = 9, \; b = {}^-12, \; c = 4$

$x = \left(\frac{-b \pm \sqrt{b^2 - 4ac}}{2a} \right)$

$x = \left(\frac{12 \pm \sqrt{(-12)^2 - 4(9)(4)}}{2(9)} \right)$

$x = \left(\frac{12 \pm \sqrt{144 - 144}}{18} \right)$

$x = \frac{(12 \pm 0)}{18}$

$x = \frac{2}{3}$.

The roots are *real and equal.* Observe that the given quadratic equation can be written $(3x - 2)^2 = 0$, from which it follows readily that both roots are $\frac{2}{3}$.

Example 4. Solve the quadratic equation $9x^2 - 11x + 4 = 0$.

$a = 9, \; b = {}^-11, \; c = 4$

$x = \left(\frac{-b \pm \sqrt{b^2 - 4ac}}{2a} \right)$

$x = \left(\frac{11 \pm \sqrt{(-11)^2 - 4(9)(4)}}{2(9)} \right)$

$x = \left(\frac{11 \pm \sqrt{-23}}{18} \right)$

$x = \left(\frac{11 \pm \sqrt{23}\,i}{18} \right)$

$x = \frac{11}{18} + \left(\frac{\sqrt{23}}{18} \right)i$ or $x = \frac{11}{18} - \left(\frac{\sqrt{23}}{18} \right)i$.

The roots are *complex conjugates.*

Exercise 7.4

I. Solve each of the following quadratic equations by use of the quadratic formula.

(1) $2x^2 - 3x + 2 = 0$ (11) $2x^2 + 3x + 1 = x^2$
(2) $3x^2 + x - 1 = 0$ (12) $4x^2 + 3x + 2 = 1$
(3) $x^2 - x + 6 = 0$ (13) $2x^2 = {}^-4$
(4) $5x^2 - 11x - 12 = 0$ (14) $3x^2 = {}^-5x$
(5) $x^2 + 7x + 9 = 0$ (15) $3x^2 = 7x$
(6) $2x^2 + 2x + 5 = 0$ (16) $5 = {}^-3x^2$
(7) $3x^2 + 1 + 5x = 0$ (17) $x^2 + 9 = 0$
(8) $6x + 1 - 2x^2 = 0$ (18) $x^2 + 16 = 0$
(9) $x^2 - 5 + 4x = 0$ (19) $x^2 = 2 + 6x$
(10) $1 + 2x - 3x^2 = 0$ (20) $x^2 = 5 - 4x$

II. If the roots of any quadratic equation of Exercise I are rational numbers, check your results by factoring the quadratic function and solving the quadratic equation by the method of factoring.

7.5 Geometric Representation of Complex Numbers, Imaginary Numbers

You have already learned that the set of real numbers may be represented geometrically on the number line. Since $a + bi = c + di$ if and only if $a = c$ and $b = d$, we see that any complex number determines exactly one ordered pair of real numbers and, conversely, any ordered pair of real numbers determines exactly one complex number. That is, the set of complex numbers is in one-to-one correspondence with the set of ordered pairs of real numbers. The correspondence is illustrated in Figure 7.1.

$$3 + 2i \leftrightarrow (3, 2)$$
$${}^-3 + 2i \leftrightarrow ({}^-3, 2)$$
$$3 + {}^-2i \leftrightarrow (3, {}^-2)$$
$${}^-3 + {}^-2i \leftrightarrow ({}^-3, {}^-2)$$
$$a + bi \leftrightarrow (a, b)$$

FIGURE 7.1

Thus we see that each complex number can be represented geometrically by a point in the Cartesian plane, as illustrated in Figure 7.2. *To graph the complex number $a + bi$, we graph the ordered pair (a, b).* The Cartesian plane of Figure 7.2 is sometimes called the *complex plane.*

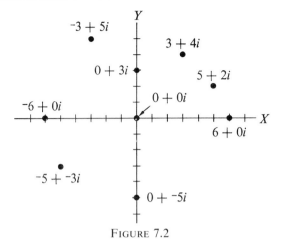

FIGURE 7.2

The length of the line segment from the origin to the point which represents a given complex number can be computed by the Pythagorean Theorem. For example, we compute the length of the line segment from $(0, 0)$ to $(^-3, 4)$ by observing that the base of the triangle in Figure 7.3 is $|^-3|$ units long and the altitude is $|4|$ units long. By the *Pythagorean Theorem*, the hypotenuse is $\sqrt{|^-3|^2 + |4|^2}$ units long; i.e., the length of the hypotenuse is 5 units. In general, the length of the line segment from the origin to the point (a, b) is $\sqrt{|a|^2 + |b|^2}$ units. Since $|a|^2 = a^2$ and $|b|^2 = b^2$ for any real numbers a and b, we can write this length as $\sqrt{a^2 + b^2}$. Whenever the point which represents a complex number lies on one of the axes, there is no triangle. Nevertheless, the length of the line segment from $(0, 0)$ to that point can still be computed from $\sqrt{a^2 + b^2}$. In this case, however, $a = 0$ or $b = 0$. For example, if the point representing the complex number lies on the X-axis, then $b = 0$, and the length of the segment from $(0, 0)$ to the point $(a, 0)$ is $\sqrt{a^2}$, which is equal to $|a|$. To illustrate, we consider the point $(^-5, 0)$ corresponding to the complex number $^-5 + 0i$. The length of the line segment from $(0, 0)$ to $(^-5, 0)$ is $\sqrt{(^-5)^2 + 0^2} = \sqrt{25} = 5 = |^-5|$.

The above discussion enables us to extend the concept of absolute value of a real number.

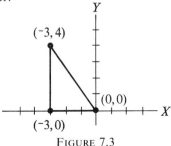

FIGURE 7.3

DEFINITION 4. The *absolute value* of the complex number $a + bi$ (denoted by $|a + bi|$) is the real number $\sqrt{a^2 + b^2}$; i.e., $|a + bi| = \sqrt{a^2 + b^2}$.

For example, the absolute value of $^-3 + 4i$ is $\sqrt{(^-3)^2 + (4)^2}$; i.e., $|^-3 + 4i| = \sqrt{9 + 16} = 5$. Similarly, $|0 + ^-5i| = 5$ and $|^-7 + 0i| = 7$. Observe that the latter example illustrates that the definition of *absolute value of a complex number* is truly an extension of the definition of *absolute value of a real number*. We see that $|a + bi| = \sqrt{(a + bi)(a - bi)}$; i.e., the absolute value of a complex number is the square root of the product of that complex number and its conjugate.

We are now prepared to discuss the possibility of ordering the complex numbers. The following possibilities of an order relation seem plausible:

(1) $a + bi < c + di$ if and only if $a < c$,
(2) $a + bi < c + di$ if and only if $a < c$ and $b \leq d$,
(3) $a + bi < c + di$ if and only if $|a + bi| < |c + di|$.

If we accept (1) as a definition of order, then $2 + 100i \not< 2 + 3i$, $2 + 3i \not< 2 + 100i$, and $2 + 100i \neq 2 + 3i$. Thus there would be no trichotomy.

If we accept (2) as a definition of order, then $2 + 5i \not< 3 + 4i$, $3 + 4i \not< 2 + 5i$, and $2 + 5i \neq 3 + 4i$. Thus there would be no trichotomy.

If we accept (3) as a definition of order, then $3 + 4i \not< 4 + 3i$, $4 + 3i \not< 3 + 4i$, and $3 + 4i \neq 4 + 3i$. Thus there would be no trichotomy.

From the above discussion we conjecture that there is no extension of the order relation from the real numbers to the complex numbers such that $(C, +, \times)$ is an ordered field. In fact, this conjecture can be proved but the proof is not included in this text.

In classical terminology any complex number of the form $0 + bi$, in which $b \neq 0$, is called a *pure imaginary number*, and any complex number of the form $a + bi$, in which $b \neq 0$, is called an *imaginary number*. Thus any nonzero complex number which is represented by a point on the Y-axis (in the complex plane) is a pure imaginary number, any complex number represented by a point not on the X-axis is an imaginary number, and any complex number represented by a point on the X-axis is a real number.

We summarize the complex number system with the following comments and figures. In Figure 7.4 we list some of the reasons for the invention of the various number systems. In Figure 7.5 we illustrate the set of complex numbers and its subsets.

Most mathematical models of physical problems have $(R_a, +, \times, <)$, $(R, +, \times, <)$, or $(C, +, \times)$ as their universe.

The universe of the mathematical model of a problem involving electric circuits of the RLC variety is $(C, +, \times)$. Hence there are extensive applications of imaginary numbers to physical problems.

$$C_0 \subset I \subset R_a \subset R \subset C$$

Number System	One Reason for Its Invention
C_0 (Counting numbers)	To count the elements of a set.
I (Integers)	To convert any open sentence of the type $x + 5 = 0$ to a true sentence by replacement of the variable.
R_a (Rationals)	To convert any open sentence of the type $2x + 3 = 0$ to a true sentence by replacement of the variable.
R (Reals)	To convert any open sentence of the type $x^2 - 2 = 0$ to a true sentence by replacement of the variable.
C (Complex numbers)	To convert any open sentence of the type $x^2 + 1 = 0$ to a true sentence by replacement of the variable.

FIGURE 7.4

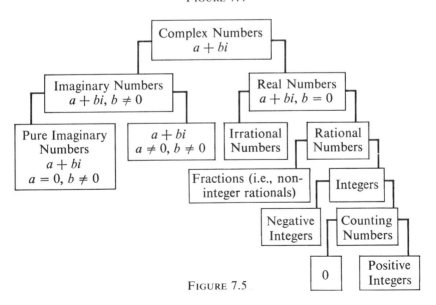

FIGURE 7.5

Exercise 7.5

I. Represent geometrically each of the following complex numbers.

(1) $2 + 3i$

(2) $3 + 2i$

(3) $^-4 + 3i$

(4) $4 + ^-3i$

(5) $^-4 + ^-3i$

(6) $^-3 + ^-4i$

(7) $^-3 + 0i$

(8) $^-3$

(9) 5

(10) $5 + 0i$

(11) $0 + ^-3i$

(12) ^-4i

(13) $6i$

(14) $0 + 5i$

(15) $1 + i$

(16) $1 + ^-1i$

(17) $^-1 + ^-1i$

(18) $^-1 + i$

(19) i

(20) 0

II. Compute the absolute value of each complex number in Exercise I.

III. Write a short paper on the development of the complex numbers from the counting numbers.

CHAPTER 8

Exponents, Radicals, and the Binomial Theorem

8.1 Exponents and Radicals

Recall that $a^m = \underbrace{a \times a \times \ldots \times a}_{m\text{-factors}}$ for any real number a and any

positive integer m. For example, $5^3 = 5 \times 5 \times 5$, $3^5 = 3 \times 3 \times 3 \times 3 \times 3$, and $\left(\frac{5}{7}\right)^2 = \left(\frac{5}{7}\right) \times \left(\frac{5}{7}\right) = \frac{(5 \times 5)}{(7 \times 7)} = \frac{(5)^2}{(7)^2}$. Moreover, recall that we extended the definition of the exponential a^m so that $a^0 = 1$ for any nonzero real number a, and $a^{-k} = 1/a^k$ for any nonzero real number a and any integer k. For example, $5^0 = 1$, $(-7)^0 = 1$, $-7^0 = -1$, $5^{-3} = \frac{1}{5^3}$, $4^{-1} = \frac{1}{4^1} = \frac{1}{4}$, and $10^{-3} = \frac{1}{10^3}$.

For any *positive* real number a and any *positive* integer m, we have defined the principal mth root of a and denoted it by $a^{1/m}$ or $\sqrt[m]{a}$. For example, $8^{1/3} = \sqrt[3]{8} = 2$ and $81^{1/4} = \sqrt[4]{81} = 3$. Similarly, for any *negative* real number a and any *positive odd* integer m, we have denoted the principal mth root of a by $a^{1/m}$ or $\sqrt[m]{a}$. For example, $(-8)^{1/3} = \sqrt[3]{-8} = -2$ and $(-64)^{1/3} = \sqrt[3]{-64} = -4$. However, if m is an even *positive* integer and a is a *negative* real number, then $a^{1/m}$ is *not* a real number but an imaginary number. For example, $(-1)^{1/2} = \sqrt{-1} = i$ and $(-81)^{1/2} = \sqrt{-81} = \sqrt{81 \times -1} = \sqrt{81} \times \sqrt{-1} = 9i$. Similarly, $\sqrt{\frac{-4}{9}} = \sqrt{\frac{4}{9} \times -1} = \sqrt{\left(\frac{4}{9}\right)} \times \sqrt{-1} = \left(\frac{\sqrt{4}}{\sqrt{9}}\right)i = \left(\frac{2}{3}\right)i$.

In Chapter 2 we observed that every real number has two square roots, three cube roots, four fourth roots, etc. In order to have a notation consistent with the notation for the principal mth root of the real number a, we extend the definition of exponential so that the symbol "$a^{k/m}$" will

241

denote the *principal mth root of a^k*. We generalize the definition in the following three stages:

1. a is any positive real number and r is any rational number.
2. $a = 0$ and r is any positive rational number.
3. a is any negative real number and r is any rational number which may be expressed in lowest terms as $\frac{k}{m}$ whose denominator m is odd.

DEFINITION 1.   For any positive real number a and any rational number r which may be expressed in lowest terms as $\frac{k}{m}$,

$$a^r = (a^k)^{1/m}.$$

For example, $8^{0.666\cdots} = 8^{2/3} = (8^2)^{1/3} = 64^{1/3} = 4$.

Observe also that $(8^{1/3})^2 = 2^2 = 4$ and hence that $(8^2)^{1/3} = (8^{1/3})^2$. Thus $8^{2/3} = (8^2)^{1/3} = (8^{1/3})^2$. Although this example does not guarantee that $a^{k/m} = (a^{1/m})^k$, the following theorem asserts this equality and provides an alternate method of computing $a^{k/m}$.

THEOREM 1.   *If a is any positive real number and $\frac{k}{m}$ is any rational number in lowest terms, then $a^{k/m} = (a^{1/m})^k$.*

Proof: Now $a^{k/m} = (a^k)^{1/m}$ (by Definition 1).

Hence $[a^{k/m}]^m = a^k$.
Moreover, $[(a^{1/m})^k]^m = (a^{1/m})^{km}$
$$= [(a^{1/m})^m]^k$$
$$= a^k.$$
Thus $[a^{k/m}]^m = [(a^{1/m})^k]^m$.
Hence $a^{k/m} = (a^{1/m})^k$ (since a is positive). $\diamondsuit$

It follows from Definition 1 and Theorem 1 that $a^{k/m} = (a^k)^{1/m} = (a^{1/m})^k$ for any positive real number a and any rational number $\frac{k}{m}$ expressed in lowest terms.

The following examples illustrate Definition 1 and Theorem 1.

Example 1. $8^{5/3} = (8^5)^{1/3} = (32,788)^{1/3} = 32$.

Example 2. $8^{5/3} = (8^{1/3})^5 = 2^5 = 32$.

Example 3. $81^{0.75} = 81^{3/4} = (81^{1/4})^3 = 3^3 = 27$.

Example 4. $4^{1.5} = 4^{3/2} = (4^{1/2})^3 = 2^3 = 8$.

The following theorems, some of which are generalizations of theorems in Chapter 2, are stated without proof.

THEOREM 2. *If a is any positive real number and r is any rational number, then* $a^{-r} = 1/a^r$.

For example, $8^{-1/3} = 1/(8)^{1/3} = \frac{1}{2}$, and $\pi^{-2/5} = 1/(\pi)^{2/5}$.

THEOREM 3. *If a is any positive real number and r and s are any rational numbers, then* $a^r \times a^s = a^{r+s}$.

It follows immediately from Theorems 2 and 3 that $a^r \div a^s = a^{r-s}$ for any positive real number a and any rational numbers r and s.

THEOREM 4. *If a is any positive real number and r and s are any rational numbers, then* $(a^r)^s = a^{rs}$.

For example, $(5^{2/3})^{7/8} = 5^{(2/3) \times (7/8)} = 5^{7/12}$.

THEOREM 5. *If a and b are any positive real numbers and r is any rational number, then* $(ab)^r = a^r b^r$.

It follows immediately from Theorems 4 and 5 that $(a/b)^r = a^r/b^r$ for any positive real numbers a and b and any rational number r.

The following examples illustrate some applications of Theorems 1 through 5.

Example 5. $\left(\frac{4}{9}\right)^{1/2} = (4)^{1/2}/(9)^{1/2} = \frac{2}{3}$.

Example 6. $\left(\frac{4}{9}\right)^{-1/2} = 1/\left(\frac{4}{9}\right)^{1/2} = 1/\left(\frac{2}{3}\right) = \frac{3}{2}$.

Example 7. $\pi^{-1} + 2^{-1} = \left(\frac{1}{\pi}\right) + \left(\frac{1}{2}\right) = \frac{(2+\pi)}{2\pi}$.

Example 8. $(81 \times 16)^{3/4} = 81^{3/4} \times 16^{3/4}$
$= (81^{1/4})^3 \times (16^{1/4})^3$
$= 3^3 \times 2^3$
$= 27 \times 8$
$= 216$.

Example 9. $[(9 + 16) \times (36)]^{1/2}$
$= [25 \times 36]^{1/2} = 25^{1/2} \times 36^{1/2}$
$= 5 \times 6$
$= 30$.

Example 10. If a is any positive real number, then
$\sqrt[3]{a} \times \sqrt{a} = a^{1/3} \times a^{1/2} = a^{1/3 + 1/2} = a^{5/6}$.

Example 11. $\sqrt{\sqrt[3]{64}} = (64^{1/3})^{1/2}$
$= 4^{1/2} = 2.$

Example 12. $\sqrt{\sqrt[3]{64}} = (64^{1/3})^{1/2} = 64^{1/6} = 2.$

Example 13. If a and b are any positive real numbers, then

$5a^{-1/2} + (9b)^{-1/2}$
$= 5/a^{1/2} + 1/(9b)^{1/2} = 5/a^{1/2} + 1/3b^{1/2}$
$= (15b^{1/2} + a^{1/2})/3a^{1/2}b^{1/2} = (a^{1/2} + 15b^{1/2})/3(ab)^{1/2}.$

Example 14. $\sqrt[5]{\sqrt[3]{32}} = (32^{1/3})^{1/5}$
$= (32^{1/5})^{1/3} = 2^{1/3}.$

Example 15. $\sqrt{2916} = (2916)^{1/2}$
$= (81 \times 36)^{1/2} = 81^{1/2} \times 36^{1/2}$
$= 9 \times 6 = 54.$

Example 16. $\sqrt[3]{12.5} \times \sqrt[3]{10} = (12.5)^{1/3} \times (10)^{1/3}$
$= (12.5 \times 10)^{1/3}$
$= (125)^{1/3} = 5.$

The reader will observe that computation with radicals is frequently simplified if the radical forms are converted to exponential forms.

Exercise 8.1

I. Express each of the following as an exponential of the form $a^{k/m}$.

(1) $\sqrt[3]{a^5}$

(2) $\sqrt[5]{a^7}$

(3) $\sqrt[7]{(2a)^3}$

(4) $\sqrt[3]{(5a)^5}$

(5) $\sqrt[3]{243a^5}$

(6) $\sqrt[4]{8^3}$

(7) $\sqrt[6]{5^7}$

(8) $\sqrt{8^5}$

(9) $\sqrt[6]{2^5}$

(10) $\sqrt[4]{4^3}$

II. Express each of the following exponentials as an integer.

(1) $27^{4/3}$

(2) $\left(\frac{1}{27}\right)^{-4/3}$

(3) $125^{4/3}$

(4) $25^{3/2}$

(5) $49^{3/2}$

(6) $64^{-5/2}$

(7) $4^{3/2}$

(8) $64^{1/2}$

(9) $64^{1/3}$

(10) $64^{2/3}$

(11) $128^{3/7}$

(12) $125^{2/3}$

(13) $\left(\frac{1}{125}\right)^{-2/3}$

(14) $\left(\frac{1}{8}\right)^{-2/3}$

(15) $\left(\frac{1}{64}\right)^{-1/6}$

III. Express each of the following in another way. (For example, $\sqrt{98}$ $= \sqrt{49 \times 2} = \sqrt{49} \times \sqrt{2} = 7\sqrt{2}$.) In all cases a and b are positive reals.

(1) $\sqrt{8}$

(2) $\sqrt{50}$

(3) $\sqrt{75}$

(4) $\sqrt{108}$

(5) $\sqrt[3]{16a^6}$

(6) $\sqrt[3]{128b^{12}}$

(7) $\sqrt{128b}$

(8) $\sqrt{\frac{8a}{25b^2}}$

(9) $\sqrt[3]{\frac{8}{27}}$

(10) $\sqrt[3]{\frac{8a}{125}}$

(11) $\sqrt[5]{\frac{32a^5}{243b^6}}$

(12) $\sqrt{\sqrt[5]{1024}}$

(13) $\sqrt[3]{\sqrt[5]{125}}$

(14) $\sqrt[5]{\sqrt[7]{32}}$

(15) $\sqrt{\sqrt[4]{16}}$

(16) $\sqrt{64a^2}$

(17) $\sqrt{128a^3}$

(18) $\sqrt[3]{125a^3b^6}$

(19) $\sqrt{25(a+b)^2}$

(20) $\sqrt{25(a^2+b^2)}$

IV. Employ Theorem 3 to express each of the following in another way.

(1) $2^{1/2} \times 2^{1/3}$

(2) $\sqrt{2} \times \sqrt[3]{2}$

(3) $\sqrt[3]{0.15} \times \sqrt[4]{0.15}$

(4) $\sqrt[3]{1.25} \times \sqrt{1.25}$

(5) $(\pi + 2)^{2/5} \times (2 + \pi)^{1/7}$

(6) $(a^{1/2} \times a^7)^2$

(7) $a^{1/2}(a^{3/2} + a^{7/2})$

(8) $a^{2/3}(a^{5/3} - a^{4/3})$

(9) $a^{-1/2}b^{1/2}(a + b^{1/2})$

(10) $a^{-1/2}a^2(a + b)^{1/2}$

8.2   Exponents and Radicals (Continued)

We have learned that $0^k = 0$ for every positive integer k and that 0^m is not defined if m is 0 or a negative integer. We now extend the definition of *exponential* so that $0^r = 0$ for every *positive* rational number r. With this definition of 0^r, we can extend Theorems 3, 4, and 5 to include the case in which $a = 0$. However, in this case we must restrict r and s to be positive rationals. For example, $0^r \times 0^s = 0^{r+s} = 0$, provided r and s are positive rationals.

In Definition 1, a^r is defined only for any *positive* real number a. We now define a^r for any *negative* real number a. However, in this case we must restrict the rational number r.

DEFINITION 2. For any negative real number a and any rational number r which can be expressed in lowest terms as $\frac{k}{m}$, in which m is odd,
$$a^r = (a^k)^{1/m}.$$

For example, $(-8)^{0.666\cdots} = (-8)^{2/3} = [(-8)^2]^{1/3} = 64^{1/3} = 4$. Moreover, $(-32)^{0.6} = (-32)^{3/5} = [(-32)^3]^{1/5} = [-32,788]^{1/5} = -8$. Since $[(-32)^{1/5}]^3 = [-2]^3 = -8$, we see that $(-32)^{3/5} = [(-32)^3]^{1/5} = [(-32)^{1/5}]^3$. The following theorem, which is analogous to Theorem 1, is stated without proof.

THEOREM 6. *If a is any negative real number and k/m is any rational number in lowest terms, whose denominator m is odd, then $a^{k/m} = (a^{1/m})^k$.*

It follows from Definition 2 and Theorem 6 that $a^{k/m} = (a^k)^{1/m} = (a^{1/m})^k$ for any negative real number a and any rational number k/m in lowest terms whose denominator m is odd.

The following examples illustrate Definition 2 and Theorem 6.

Example 1. $(-8)^{5/3} = [(-8)^5]^{1/3} = [(-8)^{1/3}]^5 = [-2]^5 = -32$.

Example 2. $(-27)^{4/3} = [(-27)^4]^{1/3} = [(-27)^{1/3}]^4 = [-3]^4 = 81$.

Example 3. $\sqrt[5]{-32} = (-32)^{1/5} = -2$.

Example 4. $(-0.125)^{2/3} = [(-0.125)^{1/3}]^2 = [-0.5]^2 = 0.25$.

The following theorems are analogous to those in Section 8.1.

THEOREM 7. *If a is any negative real number and r is any rational number which can be expressed in lowest terms as k/m, in which m is odd, then $a^{-r} = 1/a^r$.*

For example, $(-8)^{-1/3} = 1/(-8)^{1/3} = 1/-2 = -1/2$.

THEOREM 8. *If a is any negative number and r and s are any rational numbers which can be expressed in lowest terms as k_1/m_1 and k_2/m_2, respectively, in which m_1 and m_2 are odd, then $a^r \times a^s = a^{r+s}$.*

For example, $(-2\pi)^{3/5} \times (-2\pi)^{2/7} = (-2\pi)^{3/5 + 2/7} = (-2\pi)^{31/35}$.

It follows immediately from Theorems 7 and 8 that $a^r \div a^s = a^{r-s}$ under the hypotheses of Theorem 8.

THEOREM 9. *If a is any negative real number and r and s are any ra-*

tional numbers which can be expressed in lowest terms as k_1/m_1 and k_2/m_2, in which m_1 and m_2 are odd, then $(a^r)^s = a^{rs}$.

THEOREM 10.   *If a and b are any nonzero real numbers and r is any rational number which can be expressed in lowest terms as k/m, in which m is odd, then $(ab)^r = a^r b^r$.*

It follows immediately from Theorems 9 and 10 that $(a/b)^r = a^r/b^r$ under the hypotheses of Theorem 10.

The reader should exercise extreme care that the hypotheses of each theorem are satisfied before he employs the conclusion of that theorem. For example, one may *carelessly* conclude from Theorem 10 that $\sqrt{ab} = \sqrt{a}\sqrt{b}$ for all real numbers a and b. However, $\sqrt{-4 \times -9} = \sqrt{36} = 6$, whereas $\sqrt{-4} \times \sqrt{-9} = 2i \times 3i = 6i^2 = -6$. Hence $\sqrt{-4 \times -9} \neq \sqrt{-4} \times \sqrt{-9}$. The reason that Theorem 10 does not apply in this case is that $\sqrt{-4 \times -9} = (-4 \times -9)^{1/2}$ and 2 is *even* rather than *odd*.

However, $\sqrt{4 \times 9} = (4 \times 9)^{1/2} = 4^{1/2} \times 9^{1/2} = 2 \times 3$. Although 2 is even in this case, we can conclude that $\sqrt{ab} = \sqrt{a}\sqrt{b}$. The reason for this conclusion is that both real numbers, 4 and 9, are *positive*. Thus the conclusion follows from Theorem 5 rather than Theorem 10.

The following examples illustrate Theorems 1 through 10.

Example 5. $\sqrt[3]{16} + \sqrt[3]{54}$

$$= 16^{1/3} + 54^{1/3}$$
$$= (8 \times 2)^{1/3} + (27 \times 2)^{1/3}$$
$$= 8^{1/3} \times 2^{1/3} + 27^{1/3} \times 2^{1/3}$$
$$= 2 \times 2^{1/3} + 3 \times 2^{1/3}$$
$$= (2 + 3) \times 2^{1/3}$$
$$= 5 \times 2^{1/3}$$
$$= 5\sqrt[3]{2}.$$

Example 6. $\sqrt[3]{-54} + \sqrt[3]{128}$

$$= (-54)^{1/3} + 128^{1/3}$$
$$= (-27 \times 2)^{1/3} + (64 \times 2)^{1/3}$$
$$= (-27)^{1/3} \times 2^{1/3} + 64^{1/3} \times 2^{1/3}$$
$$= -3 \times 2^{1/3} + 4 \times 2^{1/3}$$
$$= (-3 + 4) \times 2^{1/3}$$
$$= 2^{1/3}$$
$$= \sqrt[3]{2}.$$

Example 7. $\sqrt{\tfrac{1}{2}} + \sqrt{2}$

$$= \sqrt{\tfrac{1}{2} \times \tfrac{2}{2}} + \sqrt{2}$$
$$= \sqrt{\tfrac{2}{4}} + \sqrt{2}$$

$$= \sqrt{2}/\sqrt{4} + \sqrt{2}$$
$$= \sqrt{2}/2 + \sqrt{2}$$
$$= (3/2)\sqrt{2}.$$

Example 8. $\sqrt[3]{2a^4/3} + \sqrt[3]{-9a^4/4}$
$$= \sqrt[3]{2a^4/3 \times 9/9} + \sqrt[3]{-9a^4/4 \times 2/2}$$
$$= \sqrt[3]{18a^4/27} + \sqrt[3]{-18a^4/8}$$
$$= \sqrt[3]{18a^4}/\sqrt[3]{27} + \sqrt[3]{-18a^4}/\sqrt[3]{8}$$
$$= a\sqrt[3]{18a}/3 + {}^-a\sqrt[3]{18a}/2$$
$$= ({}^-a/6)\sqrt[3]{18a}, \text{ for any real number } a.$$

Example 9. $\sqrt{\frac{1}{3}} + \sqrt{\frac{2}{3}}$

$$= \sqrt{\frac{1}{3} \times \frac{3}{3}} + \sqrt{\frac{2}{3} \times \frac{3}{3}}$$

$$= \sqrt{\frac{3}{9}} + \sqrt{\frac{6}{9}}$$

$$= \sqrt{3}/\sqrt{9} + \sqrt{6}/\sqrt{9}$$

$$= (\sqrt{3} + \sqrt{6})/3.$$

Example 10. $\dfrac{1}{\sqrt{2} + \sqrt{3}} = \dfrac{1}{\sqrt{2} + \sqrt{3}} \times \dfrac{\sqrt{2} - \sqrt{3}}{\sqrt{2} - \sqrt{3}}$

$$= \frac{\sqrt{2} - \sqrt{3}}{(\sqrt{2})^2 - (\sqrt{3})^2}$$

$$= \frac{\sqrt{2} - \sqrt{3}}{2 - 3}$$

$$= \frac{\sqrt{2} - \sqrt{3}}{-1}$$

$$= \sqrt{3} - \sqrt{2}.$$

Examples 7 through 10 illustrate the familiar procedure known as *rationalizing the denominator*. The advantage of expressing $\sqrt{2/3}$ as $\sqrt{6}/3$ is that the arithmetic involved in approximating $\sqrt{6}/3$ is simpler than in approximating $\sqrt{2/3}$. Since $\sqrt{6}$ is approximately equal to 2.4495, we divide 2.4495 by 3 to conclude that $\sqrt{6}/3$ is approximately equal to 0.8165.

The reader should be careful not to conclude that $\sqrt{4x^2} = 2x$ for every real number x. Since $\sqrt{x^2} = |x|$, it follows that $\sqrt{4x^2} = 2|x|$, which is equal to $2x$ if x is nonnegative and $-2x$ if x is negative.

Exercise 8.2

I. Express each of the following indicated sums as an indicated product.

(1) $\sqrt{8} + \sqrt{50}$ (3) $\sqrt{75} + \sqrt{108} + \sqrt{27}$

(2) $\sqrt[3]{54} + \sqrt[3]{-128}$ (4) $\sqrt[3]{-24} + \sqrt[3]{81} + \sqrt[3]{-375}$

(5) $\sqrt[3]{\frac{3}{8}} + \sqrt[3]{\frac{-24}{27}}$

(6) $\sqrt[3]{\frac{2}{27}} + \sqrt[3]{\frac{-16}{27}} + \sqrt[3]{\frac{54}{125}}$

(7) $\sqrt[3]{\sqrt{2}} + \sqrt{\sqrt[3]{16}}$

(8) $\sqrt[3]{2a^3} + \sqrt[3]{16}$

(9) $\sqrt[4]{48} + \sqrt{\sqrt{3a^4}}$

(10) $\sqrt[3]{250b} + \sqrt[3]{250(a^2 - b^2)}$

II. Express each of the following indicated sums as an indicated product. In each case, a is a positive real number.

(1) $\sqrt{\frac{1}{3}} + \sqrt{12}$

(2) $\sqrt{\frac{2a^3}{5}} + \sqrt{40a}$

(3) $\sqrt{\frac{1}{2}} + \sqrt{\frac{3}{2}}$

(4) $\sqrt{\frac{3}{5a}} + \sqrt{\frac{2}{5a^3}}$

(5) $\sqrt[3]{\frac{3}{4}} + \sqrt[3]{\frac{2}{9}}$

(6) $\sqrt[3]{\frac{4}{5}} + \sqrt[3]{\frac{25}{2}}$

(7) $\sqrt[3]{\frac{x}{4}} + \sqrt[3]{\frac{y}{9}}$

(8) $\sqrt[3]{\frac{x}{2}} + \sqrt[3]{\frac{y}{5}}$

III. Recall that $\sqrt{x^2} = |x|$ for every real number x.
   (1) Give an example in which $\sqrt{x^2} = x$, and give an example in which $\sqrt{x^2} = {}^-x$.
   (2) Give an example in which $\sqrt{25y^2}$ is *not* equal to $5y$.

IV. Employ the appropriate theorems to simplify each of the following.

(1) $\sqrt[3]{x^4 y^7}$

(2) $\sqrt[5]{x^{11} y^{17}}$

(3) $\sqrt[5]{x^{20} y^{30}}$

(4) $\sqrt[3]{\sqrt[5]{x^{16} y^{33}}}$

(5) $\sqrt[5]{\sqrt[3]{x^{33} y^{16}}}$

(6) $\sqrt[3]{1250a}/\sqrt[3]{10a}$ (a is a nonzero real number)

(7) $\sqrt[3]{12.5a}/\sqrt[3]{100a}$ (a is a nonzero real number)

(8) $1/(\sqrt{3} - \sqrt{2})$

(9) $\sqrt{3}/(\sqrt{3} - \sqrt{2})$

(10) $3/(\sqrt{2} - \sqrt{3})$

(11) $(1 + \sqrt{5})/(\sqrt{7} + \sqrt{5})$

(12) $a/(\sqrt{3a} + \sqrt{5b})$ (a and b are positive real numbers)

V. Employ the definitions and theorems of this section and the previous section to simplify and express each of the following without negative exponents.

(1) $(a^4b^2c^3)(a^5bc^2)$

(2) $\dfrac{(a^3b^2c)^4}{(ab^2c^5)}$

(3) $\dfrac{(a + ab)}{abc}$

(4) $\dfrac{(a^2 - b^2)}{(a - b)^2}$

(5) $(a^{-3}b^2c^{-1})(a^4b^{-2}c^3)$

(6) $\dfrac{(ab^2c^3)^{-2}}{(a^2b^{-5})}$

(7) $(x^{-1} + y^{-1})(x + y)^2$

(8) $\dfrac{(x^{-1} + y^{-1})}{(x + y)^2}$

(9) $(8xy^3)^{2/3}(27^{2/3}\,x^{1/3}\,y^{2/5})$

(10) $\dfrac{(8^{-1/3}\,x^{-2/3}\,y^{-2})^6}{(2^{-2}\,x^{1/5}\,y^4)^{1/2}}$

8.3   The Binomial Theorem

In Chapter 3 we learned that a *binomial* is an expression consisting of exactly two terms. For example, the expression $x + 2$ is a binomial. However, the multinomial $x^2 + 2x + 1$, punctuated in this manner, is *not* a binomial but the *square* of the binomial $x + 1$. Similarly, the multinomial $x^3 + 3x^2 + 3x + 1$ is the *cube* of the binomial $x + 1$. The reader may verify that, for any variable x for which $x + 1 \neq 0$,

$(x + 1)^0 = 1$
$(x + 1)^1 = x + 1$
$(x + 1)^2 = x^2 + 2x + 1$
$(x + 1)^3 = x^3 + 3x^2 + 3x + 1$
$(x + 1)^4 = x^4 + 4x^3 + 6x^2 + 4x + 1$
$(x + 1)^5 = x^5 + 5x^4 + 10x^3 + 10x^2 + 5x + 1$, etc.

Expressions of the above type are called *polynomials in the variable x*. In particular, $x^3 + 3x^2 + 3x + 1$ is a *third degree* or *cubic* polynomial in x.

DEFINITION 3.   Any expression of the form $a_0 + a_1x + a_2x^2 + \ldots + a_mx^m$, in which the a_i are real numbers, x is a variable, and m is a non-negative integer, is called an *mth degree polynomial in the variable x* (or briefly a *polynomial of degree m*) over the field of real numbers.

In the third degree polynomial $x^3 + 3x^2 + 3x + 1$, which may be expressed $1 + 3x + 3x^2 + x^3$, we observe that $a_0 = 1$, $a_1 = 3$,

$a_2 = 3$, and $a_3 = 1$ and hence $m = 3$. Of course, the binomial $1 + x$ is a first degree polynomial, and the monomial x^5 is a fifth degree polynomial. The monomial a_0, which may be expressed $a_0 x^0$, is a polynomial of degree 0, if $a_0 \neq 0$. However, there is no degree associated with the monomial 0. The polynomial $3x^4 + x^2 - 2$ is of the fourth degree; $a_0 = {}^-2$, $a_1 = 0$, $a_2 = 1$, $a_3 = 0$, $a_4 = 3$, and $m = 4$.

Application of the definition and properties of exponentials, of the distributive, commutative, and associative properties yield the following results:

$(x + y)^0 = 1$
$(x + y)^1 = x + y$
$(x + y)^2 = x^2 + 2xy + y^2$
$(x + y)^3 = x^3 + 3x^2y + 3xy^2 + y^3$
$(x + y)^4 = x^4 + 4x^3y + 6x^2y^2 + 4xy^3 + y^4$
$(x + y)^5 = x^5 + 5x^4y + 10x^3y^2 + 10x^2y^3 + 5xy^4 + y^5$

$\cdot \quad \cdot \quad \cdot$

From the above list of *expansions* of $(x + y)^m$ we observe the following:

1. The expansion of $(x + y)^m$ contains $(m + 1)$ terms.
2. The first term of $(x + y)^m$ is x^m and the last term of $(x + y)^m$ is y^m.
3. The sum of the exponents of x and y in any term of $(x + y)^m$ is m.
4. As the exponent of x decreases by 1, the exponent of y increases by 1.
5. The numerical coefficients of the terms in $(x + y)^m$, for each non-negative integer m, are the numbers indicated in the array in Figure 8.1, known as *Pascal's Triangle*.

$(x + y)^0$	1
$(x + y)^1$	1 1
$(x + y)^2$	1 2 1
$(x + y)^3$	1 3 3 1
$(x + y)^4$	1 4 6 4 1
$(x + y)^5$	1 5 10 10 5 1
$(x + y)^6$	1 6 15 20 15 6 1
$(x + y)^7$	1 7 21 35 35 21 7 1
$\vdots$	$\vdots$

Pascal's Triangle for Coefficients

FIGURE 8.1

The reader should analyze Pascal's triangle and complete a sufficient part of it so that he can determine the coefficients in the expansion of

$(x + y)^{10}$. To determine the coefficients in the expansion of $(x + y)^{20}$, for example, requires a much larger part of Pascal's triangle than that shown in Figure 8.1. Although it is simple, the arithmetic is tedious. Moreover, the partial form of Pascal's triangle does not immediately provide a general set of coefficients in the expansion of $(x + y)^m$ for every positive integer m. For this reason we state below a general theorem known as the *binomial theorem* which does provide a general formula for the coefficients in the expansion of $(x + y)^m$. Since the proof of the binomial theorem depends on the *postulate of finite induction*, which we have not included in this text, we omit the proof. In the binomial theorem the *factorial notation, k!*, is used as a simplified expression of the product of the first k positive integers. For example, $1! = 1,\ 2! = 1 \times 2,\ 3! = 1 \times 2 \times 3,\ldots,\ k! = 1 \times 2 \times 3 \times \ldots \times k$.

THEOREM 3.   *(Binomial Theorem) If x and y are any real numbers and m is any positive integer, then* $(x + y)^m = x^m + mx^{m-1}y + \left[\frac{m(m-1)}{2!}\right]x^{m-2}y^2 + \left[\frac{m(m-1)(m-2)}{3!}\right]x^{m-3}y^3 + \cdots + y^m.$

Exercise 8.3

I. Expand each of the following by use of *Pascal's Triangle*.

(1) $(x + y)^7$

(2) $(x + y)^9$

(3) $(x + y)^{10}$

(4) $(x - y)^9$

(5) $(x - y)^7$

(6) $(x + 2y)^4$

(7) $(2x - y)^4$

(8) $(2x + 3y)^5$

(9) $(3x^2 + 1)^4$

(10) $(2x^2 + 3)^5$

(11) $\left(\frac{a}{2} + 1\right)^5$

(12) $\left(\frac{3}{4} + y\right)^5$

(13) $\left(\frac{3a}{2} - 1\right)^4$

(14) $(a^2 + x^2)^4$

(15) $(a^2 + x)^4$

(16) $(a + x^2)^4$

(17) $(2a^2 + x)^3$

(18) $(2a^2 - x)^3$

(19) $(x^3 + 1)^5$

(20) $(x^3 + a)^5$

II. Expand each of the above by use of the binomial theorem.

III. Employ the binomial theorem to approximate each of the following to six decimal places.

(1) $(1.01)^4$

(2) $(1.01)^5$

(3) $(1.01)^6$

(4) $(1.1)^6$

IV. (1) Prove that $\dfrac{[7(7-1)(7-2)]}{3!} = \dfrac{7!}{[3!\,4!]}$.

(2) Prove that $\dfrac{[m(m-1)(m-2)\ldots(m-k)]}{(k+1)!} = \dfrac{m!}{[(k+1)!(m-k-1)!]}$.

(3) Use the above results to restate the binomial theorem.

CHAPTER 9

Theory of Polynomial Equations

9.1 Division of Polynomials

We have learned that the linear equation in one variable is frequently the mathematical model of some physical problem. Later we learned that the quadratic equation in one variable is frequently the mathematical model of some physical problem. Frequently the cubic equation (e.g., $x^3 + 3x^2 + 3x + 1 = 0$) and other higher degree equations serve as the mathematical models of physical problems. We *could* investigate the cubic equation and other higher degree equations separately, as we investigated the linear equation and the quadratic equation; however, it is more economical to investigate the general polynomial equation of degree m, which is defined in Definition 1.

DEFINITION 1.   Any equation of the form $a_m x^m + a_{m-1} x^{m-1} + \cdots + a_1 x + a_0 = 0$, in which $a_m x^m + a_{m-1} x^{m-1} + \cdots + a_1 x + a_0$ is a polynomial of degree m, is called an mth *degree polynomial equation in the variable x.*[*]

For example, $x^5 - x^4 + 5x^2 - 3 = 0$ is a 5th degree polynomial equation in x, in which $a_3 = 0$ and $a_1 = 0$.

Before we develop the general theory of polynomial equations, we first consider the problem of dividing a polynomial by a polynomial. The following examples illustrate the procedure.

---

[*] The reader will recall that the coefficients, $a_0, a_1, \ldots, a_m$, are real numbers.

Example 1. Divide the polynomial $x^4 + 5x^3 - 2x^2 + x - 50$ by the polynomial $x - 2$.

$$
\begin{array}{r}
x^3 + 7x^2 + 12x + 25 \\
x - 2\,\overline{\big|\,x^4 + 5x^3 - 2x^2 + x - 50} \\
\underline{x^4 - 2x^3} \\
7x^3 - 2x^2 + x - 50 \\
\underline{7x^3 - 14x^2} \\
12x^2 + x - 50 \\
\underline{12x^2 - 24x} \\
25x - 50 \\
25x - 50
\end{array}
$$

To check the division, we observe that

$$x^4 + 5x^3 - 2x^2 + x - 50 = (x - 2)(x^3 + 7x^2 + 12x + 25).$$

Example 2. Divide the polynomial $x^5 - 3x^4 + 5x^3 - x^2 + x + 3$ by $x^2 - x + 1$.

$$
\begin{array}{r}
x^3 - 2x^2 + 2x + 3 \\
x^2 - x + 1\,\overline{\big|\,x^5 - 3x^4 + 5x^3 - x^2 + x + 3} \\
\underline{x^5 - x^4 + x^3} \\
-2x^4 + 4x^3 - x^2 + x + 3 \\
\underline{-2x^4 + 2x^3 - 2x^2} \\
2x^3 + x^2 + x + 3 \\
\underline{2x^3 - 2x^2 + 2x} \\
3x^2 - x + 3 \\
\underline{3x^2 - 3x + 3} \\
2x
\end{array}
$$

To check the division, we observe that $x^5 - 3x^4 + 5x^3 - x^2 + x + 3$
$= (x^2 - x + 1)(x^3 - 2x^2 + 2x + 3) + 2x$.

Example 3. Divide $x^3 - 3x^2 + 5x + 7$ by $x + 3$.

$$
\begin{array}{r}
x^2 - 6x + 23 \\
x + 3\,\overline{\big|\,x^3 - 3x^2 + 5x + 7} \\
\underline{x^3 + 3x^2} \\
-6x^2 + 5x + 7 \\
\underline{-6x^2 - 18x} \\
23x + 7 \\
\underline{23x + 69} \\
-62
\end{array}
$$

To check the division, we observe that $x^3 - 3x^2 + 5x + 7 = (x + 3)(x^2 - 6x + 23) - 62$.

In the above examples, the details of the procedure were recorded. We may simplify the recording (bookkeeping) procedure by recording only the coefficients of the variable and "bringing down" the terms one at a time.

Example 4.   Divide $x^4 + 5x^3 - 2x^2 + x - 50$ by $x - 2$.

$$
\begin{array}{r}
①+⑦+⑫+㉕ \\
1 - 2 | 1 + 5 - 2 + 1 - 50 \\
1 \ (-2) \\
\hline
7 - 2 \\
7 \ \boxed{-14} \\
\hline
12 + 1 \\
12 \ -24 \\
\hline
25 - 50 \\
25 - 50 \\
\end{array}
$$

The quotient is $1x^3 + 7x^2 + 12x + 25$.

In Example 4, we observe the following:

1. The repetitions of coefficients indicated by the arrows,
2. The relationship between the coefficients enclosed in the circles, the coefficients enclosed in the squares, the coefficients enclosed in the triangles, and the coefficients enclosed in the parallelograms (e.g., $\boxed{7} \times {}^-2 = \boxed{-14}$).

Because of the above observations we can abbreviate the form of Example 4 as follows:

$$
\begin{array}{r}
^-2 | 1 + 5 - 2 + 1 - 50 \\
(-2) \ \boxed{-14} \ -24 \ -50 \\
\hline
①+⑦+⑫+㉕ \\
\end{array}
$$

We can avoid the subtraction in each step in the above form of the division by replacing $^-2$ by its additive inverse, $^-({}^-2)$, which is equal to 2, as follows:

$$
\begin{array}{r}
1 + 5 - 2 + 1 - 50 \ \underline{|2} \\
2 + 14 + 24 + 50 \\
\hline
1 + 7 + 12 + 25 + 0 \\
\end{array}
$$

The last form of the division procedure is usually called *synthetic division*. Observe that synthetic division is applicable only to division of a polynomial by a polynomial of the form $x - a$.

The following examples further illustrate synthetic division.

Example 5.   Divide $x^3 - 3x^2 + 5x + 7$ by $x + 3$.

$$\begin{array}{r} 1 - 3 + 5 + 7 \ \underline{|^-3} \\ \underline{-3 + 18 - 69} \\ 1 - 6 + 23 - 62 \end{array}$$

Hence the quotient is $x^2 - 6x + 23$, and the remainder is $^-62$. The reason for writing "$^-3$" is that $x + 3 = x - {}^-3$.

Example 6.   Divide $3y^4 - y^3 + 30y$ by $y + 2$.

$$\begin{array}{r} 3 - 1 + 0 + 30 + 0 \ \underline{|^-2} \\ \underline{-6 + 14 - 28 - 4} \\ 3 - 7 + 14 + 2 - 4 \end{array}$$

Hence the quotient is $3y^3 - 7y^2 + 14y + 2$, and the remainder is $^-4$.

Exercise 9.1

I. (1) Divide $x^5 - x^4 + x^3 + 3x^2 + x - 1$ by $x^2 - x - 1$.
   (2) Divide $x^5 + x^4 - x^3 - 3x^2 - x + 1$ by $x^2 + x + 1$.
   (3) Divide $6x^5 - x^4 + 2x^3 - 2x + 7$ by $2x - 7$.
   (4) Divide $9x^5 - 3x^4 - x^2 + x$ by $3x + 2$.
   (5) Divide $10x^6 - x^4 + 3x^2 + 5$ by $5x^2 + 2$.
   (6) Divide $10x^6 - x^4 + 3x^3 - x$ by $2x - 5$.
   (7) Divide $8x^7 - x^5 + x^3 - x$ by $x^2 - 3$.
   (8) Divide $10x^7 + x^6 - 2x^3 + x^2 - 2$ by $2x + 3$.

II. Employ synthetic division in each of the following.
   (1) Divide $x^3 + x^2 - x - 1$ by $x - 1$.
   (2) Divide $5x^3 + x^2 + 7x + 1$ by $x - 2$.
   (3) Divide $x^4 + 3x^3 - 2x^2 - x + 4$ by $x + 3$.
   (4) Divide $x^4 - 7x^2 + 2x - 1$ by $x + 1$.
   (5) Divide $x^5 - 3x^3 - x - 6$ by $x - 2$.
   (6) Divide $x^4 - 3x^2 + 2x$ by $x + 5$.
   (7) Divide $y^7 - 3y^4 + y^2$ by $y + 1$.
   (8) Divide $y^3 + 3y^2 - 3y + 1$ by $y + \frac{1}{2}$.
   (9) Divide $y^4 + y^2 - 2$ by $y - \frac{3}{2}$.
   (10) Divide $x^4 + 3x^2 - 5$ by $x - \frac{1}{2}$.

9.2   Remainder Theorem and Factor Theorem

Recall the *division algorithm*: If a and b are any positive integers, then there exists a unique positive integer q and *a* unique integer r such that $a = bq + r$ and $0 \leq r < b$. Usually we compute q and r by long division. For example, because of the long division

$$
\begin{array}{r}
12 \\
53\overline{)659} \\
53 \\
\hline
129 \\
106 \\
\hline
23
\end{array}
$$

we conclude that $659 = 53 \times 12 + 23$. There is a similar general division algorithm for polynomials. In this text we state and use the following special case of it.

If $\mathbf{p}(x)$ is any polynomial of degree m (greater than 1) and if x_1 is any real number, then there exists a unique polynomial $\mathbf{q}(x)$ and a unique real number r such that $\mathbf{p}(x) = (x - x_1)\mathbf{q}(x) + r$ and $\mathbf{q}(x)$ is of degree $m - 1$. Usually we compute $\mathbf{q}(x)$ and r by synthetic division. For example, $x^3 - 3x^2 + 5x + 7 = (x + 3)(x^2 - 6x + 23) + {}^-62$.

This special form of the division algorithm for polynomials is useful in the proof of the following theorem, known as the *remainder theorem*.

THEOREM 1. (*Remainder Theorem*) *If the polynomial* $\mathbf{p}(x)$ *is divided by* $(x - x_1)$, *then the remainder* r *is equal to* $\mathbf{p}(x_1)$.

Proof. $\mathbf{p}(x) = (x - x_1)\mathbf{q}(x) + r$.
  Hence $\mathbf{p}(x_1) = (x_1 - x_1)\mathbf{q}(x_1) + r$.
  Thus $\mathbf{p}(x_1) = r.\diamond$

The following examples illustrate the remainder theorem.

Example 1. If $\mathbf{p}(x) = x^3 - 2x^2 + 5x - 6$ and $x_1 = 1$, then $\mathbf{p}(x_1) = \mathbf{p}(1)$
$= 1^3 - 2(1^2) + 5(1) - 6 = {}^-2$.
  Hence $r = {}^-2$.

Example 2. If $\mathbf{p}(x) = x^3 - 2x^2 + 5x - 4$ and $x_1 = 1$, then $\mathbf{p}(x_1) = \mathbf{p}(1)$
$= 1^3 - 2(1^2) + 5(1) - 4 = 0$.
  Hence $r = 0$.

Example 3. If $\mathbf{p}(x) = x^4 - 2x^3 - 4x^2 - 16$ and $x_1 = {}^-2$, then $\mathbf{p}(x_1)$
$= \mathbf{p}({}^-2) = ({}^-2)^4 - 2({}^-2)^3 - 4({}^-2)^2 - 16 = 0$.
  Hence $r = 0$.

In order to state in the traditional terminology, a theorem which is motivated by Examples 2 and 3, we make the following definition.

DEFINITION 2.   Any root of the equation $f(x) = 0$ is called a *zero* of $f(x)$.

For example, 1 is a *zero* of $x^3 - 2x^2 + 5x - 4$ and a *root* of $x^3 - 2x^2 + 5x - 4 = 0$.

The following theorem is known as the *factor theorem*.

THEOREM 2.   *If* $p(x)$ *is a polynomial, then* $x - x_1$ *is a factor of* $p(x)$ *if and only if* x_1 *is a zero of* $p(x)$.

Proof.

Let $(x - x_1)$ be a factor of $p(x)$.
Then $p(x) = (x - x_1)\ q(x)$.
Hence $p(x_1) = 0$.
Thus x_1 is a zero of $p(x)$.

Let x_1 be a zero of $p(x)$.
Then $p(x_1) = 0$.
But $r = p(x_1)$.
Thus $r = 0$.
Hence $p(x) = (x - x_1)\ q(x)$.
Thus $x - x_1$ is a factor of $p(x)$.◇

It follows immediately from Theorem 2 that $x - x_1$ is a factor of $p(x)$ if and only if $p(x_1) = 0$. In other words, $x - x_1$ is a factor of $p(x)$ if and only if the remainder r is 0. We may employ synthetic division to compute r, as illustrated in the following example.

Example 4.   Is $x + 2$ a factor of $x^4 - 2x^3 - 4x^2 - 16$?

$$\begin{array}{r} 1 - 2 - 4 + 0 - 16 \ \underline{\lvert -2} \\ \underline{-2 + 8 - 8 + 16} \\ 1 - 4 + 4 - 8 + 0 \end{array}$$

Since $r = 0$, we conclude that $x + 2$ is a factor of $x^4 - 2x^3 - 4x^2 - 16$.

Exercise 9.2

I. Employ the factor theorem to determine whether the first expression is a factor of the second expression.

(1) $x - 1$, $x^4 + 3x^3 - 2x^2 - 4x + 2$
(2) $x + 3$, $x^3 - 4x^2 - 18x + 9$

(3) $x + 2$, $x^3 - 3x^2 - 4x + 12$
(4) $x - 5$, $x^3 + 2x^2 - 25x - 50$
(5) $x - 4$, $x^3 - x^2 + 3x + 8$
(6) $x - 2$, $x^4 - x^3 + 4x^2 + 6$
(7) $x + 3$, $3x^4 + 4x^3 - 6x^2 + 30x - 51$
(8) $x + 4$, $x^3 + 5x^2 + 3x - 4$

II. Compute $\mathbf{p}(a)$ in each of the following.

(1) $a = 2$, $\mathbf{p}(x) = x^3 - 3x^2 + 7x + 2$
(2) $a = {}^-3$, $\mathbf{p}(x) = 2x^3 + 3x^2 + 5$
(3) $a = {}^-5$, $\mathbf{p}(x) = x^3 + 4x^2 - 4x + 3$
(4) $a = {}^-1$, $\mathbf{p}(x) = 2x^4 + 3x^3 - 2x^2 + 2x + 4$
(5) $a = 4$, $\mathbf{p}(x) = x^4 - 2x^3 + 2x^2 - 3x + 1$
(6) $a = {}^-2$, $\mathbf{p}(x) = x^5 + x^4 + 2x^3 + 3x^2 - x + 8$

9.3 Fundamental Theorem of Algebra

By Definition 2, we know that a *zero* of the polynomial $\mathbf{p}(x)$ is any *root* of the polynomial equation $\mathbf{p}(x) = 0$. However, we cannot be certain from the definition that every polynomial has at least one zero. An important theorem, known as the *fundamental theorem of algebra*, guarantees that every polynomial of positive degree has a zero. The fundamental theorem of algebra was first proved by Karl Friedrich Gauss (1777–1855) when he was only 22 years old. Although the statement is simple, there is no known simple, elementary proof. For this reason, the theorem is stated without proof.

THEOREM 3. (*Fundamental Theorem of Algebra*) *Every polynomial of positive degree has (at least) one zero in the set of complex numbers.*

Since every complex number is either a real number or an imaginary number, it follows that each zero of a polynomial is either real or imaginary. The following theorem, which we state without proof, asserts that the conjugate of any imaginary zero of a polynomial is also a zero of the polynomial.

THEOREM 4. *If the imaginary number* $a + bi$ *is a zero of the polynomial* $\mathbf{p}(x)$, *then its conjugate* $a - bi$ *is also a zero of* $\mathbf{p}(x)$.

Theorem 4 is a generalization of a similar result for quadratic functions. In Chapter 7 we learned that if one root of a quadratic equation is imaginary, then the second root is its conjugate.

The following theorem, which we state without proof, relates the number of zeros of a polynomial to the degree of the polynomial.

THEOREM 5.   *If $a_mx^m + \cdots + a_1x + a_0$ is any polynomial whose degree m is positive $(a_m \neq 0)$, then there exist complex numbers, $x_1, x_2, \ldots, x_m$, such that $a_mx^m + \cdots + a_1x + a_0 = a_m(x - x_1)(x - x_2) \ldots (x - x_m)$.*

Observe that $x_1, x_2, \ldots, x_m$ are the zeros of the polynomial $a_mx^m + \cdots + a_1x + a_0$. In classical terminology we say that any polynomial of degree m has m zeros. However, the zeros need not all be distinct. For example, the zeros of $x^3 - 2x^2 + x$ are 0, 1, and 1. Because $x^3 - 2x^2 + x = x(x - 1)^2$, and thus $(x - 1)$ occurs *twice* as a factor of $x^3 - 2x^2 + x$, we say that 1 is a zero of *multiplicity* 2.

Theorem 5 asserts the *existence* of m factors of any polynomial of positive degree m and thus the existence of m zeros. If $m = 1$, we can compute the zero by the methods of Chapter 3. If $m = 2$, we can compute the zeros by the methods of Chapters 6 and 7. In 1545 Cardan published general formulas, known as *Cardan's formulas*, for computing the zeros of the third-degree polynomial.

In 1540 Ferrari (1522–1565) derived general formulas for computing the zeros of the fourth-degree polynomial. His professor, Cardan, later published Ferrari's solution to the quartic. However, early in the 19th century, Abel published a proof that no general formula exists for computing the zeros of a polynomial whose degree is greater than 4.

Although there is no general formula for computing the zeros of a polynomial whose degree is greater than 4, we can compute the *rational* zeros and approximate the *irrational* zeros. The following theorem enables us to compute the rational roots of any polynomial equation.

THEOREM 6.   *If the nonzero rational number a/b, expressed in lowest terms, is a root of the mth-degree polynomial equation $a_mx^m + \cdots + a_1x + a_0 = 0$, in which $a_0, a_1, \ldots, a_m$ are integers, then $a|a_0$ and $b|a_m$.*

Proof. $a_m(a/b)^m + \cdots + a_1(a/b) + a_0 = 0$
$a_m(a^m/b^m) + \cdots + a_1(a/b) = {}^-a_0$
$a_ma^m + \cdots + a_1ab^{m-1} = {}^-a_0b^m$
$a_ma^{m-1} + \cdots + a_1b^{m-1} = {}^-a_0b^m/a$

The left member is an integer. Hence the right member, ${}^-a_0b^m/a$, is an integer. Thus $a|a_0b^m$. But $a \nmid b^m$. Hence $a|a_0$. Similarly, $b|a_m$.◇

The following theorem is an immediate consequence of Theorem 6. Hence we omit the proof.

THEOREM 7. *Every rational root of the polynomial equation* x^m $+ a_{m-1}x^{m-1} + \cdots + a_1x + a_0 = 0$, *in which* $a_0, a_1, \ldots, a_{m-1}$ *are integers and* $a_0 \neq 0$, *is an integer which divides* a_0.

The following examples illustrate a procedure for computing the rational roots of a polynomial equation.

Example 1. Solve the equation $x^4 - 15x^2 + 10x + 24 = 0$.

By Theorem 7, the only possible rational roots are the integers 1, 2, 3, 4, 6, 8, 12, 24, $^-1$, $^-2$, $^-3$, $^-4$, $^-6$, $^-8$, $^-12$, and $^-24$.

To determine whether these are roots of the given equation, we employ synthetic division as follows:

$$
\begin{array}{r}
1 + 0 - 15 + 10 + 24 \;\underline{|1} \\
\underline{1 + 1 - 14 - 4} \\
1 + 1 - 14 - 4 + 20
\end{array}
$$

[Since $r = 20$, 1 is *not* a root.]

$$
\begin{array}{r}
1 + 0 - 15 + 10 + 24 \;\underline{|2} \\
\underline{2 + 4 - 22 - 24} \\
1 + 2 - 11 - 12 + 0
\end{array}
$$

[Since $r = 0$, 2 *is* a root. Hence $x^4 - 15x^2 + 10x + 24 = (x - 2)$ $(x^3 + 2x^2 - 11x - 12)$. The remaining roots of $x^4 - 15x^2 + 10x + 24 = 0$ are roots of $x^3 + 2x^2 - 11x - 12 = 0$.]

$$
\begin{array}{r}
1 + 2 - 11 - 12 \;\underline{|3} \\
\underline{3 + 15 + 12} \\
1 + 5 + 4 + 0
\end{array}
$$

[Since $r = 0$, 3 is a root. Hence $x^3 + 2x^2 - 11x - 12 = (x - 3)$ $(x^2 + 5x + 4)$. The remaining roots of $x^3 + 2x^2 - 11x - 12 = 0$ are roots of $x^2 + 5x + 4 = 0$. To determine the remaining roots, we could employ synthetic division; however, it is simpler to solve the quadratic equation $x^2 + 5x + 4 = 0$.]

$x^2 + 5x + 4 = 0$
$(x + 1)(x + 4) = 0$
$x + 1 = 0$ or $x + 4 = 0$
$x = {}^-1$ or $x = {}^-4$

The four roots of the fourth-degree equation $x^4 - 15x^2 + 10x + 24 = 0$ are 2, 3, $^-1$, and $^-4$.

The factorization specified in Theorem 5 is $(x - 2)(x - 3)(x + 1)$ $(x + 4)$.

Example 2. Solve the equation $x^5 - 4x^4 + 3x^3 - x^2 + 4x - 3 = 0$.

By Theorem 7, the only possible rational roots are the integers $1, 3, {}^-1$, and $^-3$. To determine whether these are roots of the given equation, we employ synthetic division as follows:

$$\begin{array}{l} 1 - 4 + 3 - 1 + 4 - 3 \ \underline{|1} \\ \ \underline{1 - 3 + 0 - 1 + 3} \\ 1 - 3 + 0 - 1 + 3 + 0 \end{array}$$

[1 is a root.]

$$\begin{array}{l} 1 - 3 + 0 - 1 + 3 \ \underline{|3} \\ \ \underline{+ 3 + 0 + 0 - 3} \\ 1 + 0 + 0 - 1 + 0 \end{array}$$

[3 is a root.]

$$\begin{array}{l} 1 + 0 + 0 - 1 \ \underline{|^-1} \\ \ \underline{{}^-1 + 1 - 1} \\ 1 - 1 + 1 - 2 \end{array}$$

[Since $r = {}^-2$, $^-1$ is *not* a root. Since $^-3$ does not divide $^-1$, $^-3$ is *not* a root.]

$$\begin{array}{l} 1 + 0 + 0 - 1 \ \underline{|1} \\ \ \underline{1 + 1 + 1} \\ 1 + 1 + 1 + 0 \end{array}$$

[1 is a root of $x^3 - 1 = 0$. Hence $x^3 - 1 = (x - 1)(x^2 + x + 1)$. We solve the quadratic equation $x^2 + x + 1 = 0$ by the quadratic formula.]

$$x^2 + x + 1 = 0$$

$$x = \left[\frac{-1 \pm \sqrt{1 - 4(1)(1)}}{2(1)}\right]$$

$$x = \left(\frac{-1 \pm \sqrt{3}\,i}{2}\right).$$

The five roots of the fifth-degree equation $x^5 - 4x^4 + 3x^3 - x^2 + 4x - 3 = 0$ are $1, 3, 1, \left(\frac{-1 + \sqrt{3}\,i}{2}\right), \left(\frac{-1 - \sqrt{3}\,i}{2}\right)$. Notice that 1 is a root of multiplicity 2. The factorization specified in Theorem 5 is

$$(x - 1)^2(x - 3)\left(x - \frac{-1 + \sqrt{3}\,i}{2}\right)\left(x - \frac{-1 - \sqrt{3}\,i}{2}\right).$$

Example 3. Compute the roots of $6x^3 + 11x^2 - 3x - 2 = 0$.

By Theorem 6, the only possible numerators of the only possible rational roots are $1, 2, {}^-1$, and $^-2$, and the only possible denominators are 1, 2, 3, 6, ⁻1, ⁻2, ⁻3, and ⁻6. Hence the only possible rational roots are 1, ⁻1, 2, ⁻2, $\frac{1}{2}$, $\frac{-1}{2}$, $\frac{1}{3}$, $\frac{-1}{3}$, $\frac{1}{6}$, $\frac{-1}{6}$, $\frac{2}{3}$, and $\frac{-2}{3}$. By synthetic division we learn that 1, ⁻1, 2 and ⁻2 are not roots. To determine whether $\frac{1}{2}$ is a root we employ synthetic division as follows:

$$6 + 11 - 3 - 2 \ \lfloor\tfrac{1}{2}$$
$$\underline{3 + 7 + 2}$$
$$6 + 14 + 4 + 0$$

$\qquad \times (-2)$

[Hence $\frac{1}{2}$ is a root, and $6x^3 + 11x^2 - 3x - 2$

$$= (x - \tfrac{1}{2})(6x^2 + 14x + 4)$$
$$= 2(x - \tfrac{1}{2})(3x^2 + 7x + 2)$$
$$= 2(x - \tfrac{1}{2})(3x + 1)(x + 2)$$
$$= (2x - 1)(3x + 1)(x + 2).]$$

The three roots of the third-degree equation $6x^3 + 11x^2 - 3x - 2 = 0$ are $\frac{1}{2}$, $\frac{-1}{3}$, and ⁻2.

The following theorem, whose proof is omitted, is useful in the computation of the roots of a polynomial equation.

THEOREM 8.   *Let the following diagram represent the synthetic division of* $a_m x^m + a_{m-1} x^{m-1} + \cdots + a_1 x + a_0$ *by* $x - x_1$, *in which* a_m *is positive.*

$$a_m + a_{m-1} + \cdots + a_1 + a_0 \qquad \lfloor x_1$$
$$\underline{ a_m x_1 + \cdots + b_2 x_1 + b_1 x_1}$$
$$a_m + b_{m-1} + \cdots + b_1 + r$$

(a) *If* x_1, a_m, b_{m-1}, $\cdots$, b_1, *and* r *are all positive, then* x_1 *is an upper bound for the positive zeros of* $a_m x^m + a_{m-1} x^{m-1} + \cdots a_1 x + a_0$.
(b) *If* x_1 *is negative and the signs of* a_m, b_{m-1}, $\cdots$, b_1, *and* r *alternate, then* x_1 *is a lower bound for the negative zeros of* $a_m x^m + a_{m-1} x^{m-1} + \cdots + a_1 x + a_0$.

The following example illustrates Theorem 8.

Example 4.   Determine an upper bound for the positive roots of $x^3 - x^2 + x + 6 = 0$, and determine a lower bound for the negative roots of $x^3 - x^2 + x + 6 = 0$.

$$1 - 1 + 1 + 6 \ \lfloor 1$$
$$\underline{ 1 + 0 + 1}$$
$$1 + 0 + 1 + 7$$

Hence 1 is an upper bound for the positive roots.
Thus 2, 3, and 6 cannot be roots.

$1 - 1 + 1 + 6 \underline{\big|^-2}$
$ \quad {}^-2 + 6 - 14$
$\overline{1 - 3 + 7 - 8}$

Hence $^-2$ is a lower bound for the negative roots.

Thus $^-3$ and $^-6$ cannot be roots.

Exercise 9.3

I. Determine the zeros and multiplicity of each zero in each of the following polynomials.

(1) $(x - 1)^3(x + 2)^2(x + 3)$
(2) $(x^2 - 6x - 9)(x - 3)^2(x - 2)^5$
(3) $(x - 3)^4(x + 2)^3$
(4) $(x + 3)^2(x + 5)(x - 2)$
(5) $(x - 7)(x + 2)^2(x + 1)^3 \, x^2$
(6) $x^3(x + 1)^2(x - 1)^2$

II. List the only possible rational zeros of each of the following polynomials.

(1) $2x^3 - 3x^2 + 4x + 3$
(2) $6x^3 + 2x^2 - x + 1$
(3) $5x^4 + 3x^2 - 3x - 2$
(4) $x^3 + x^2 - 3x + 6$
(5) $x^4 - 5x^2 + 12$
(6) $x^5 - 3x^4 + 5x^3 + 2x$

III. Compute the roots of each of the following polynomial equations.

(1) $x^3 + 2x^2 - x - 2 = 0$
(2) $x^3 + x^2 + 2x + 8 = 0$
(3) $2x^3 + 9x^2 + 5x - 2 = 0$
(4) $x^4 - x^3 - 19x^2 + 49x - 30 = 0$
(5) $2x^4 + x^3 - 2x^2 - 4x - 3 = 0$
(6) $12x^3 - 4x^2 - 3x + 1 = 0$
(7) $x^4 + x^3 + 2x^2 + 4x - 8 = 0$
(8) $x^4 + 4x^3 + 6x^2 + 8x + 8 = 0$
(9) $10x^4 + 4x^3 - 6x^2 - 8x = 0$
(10) $x^5 - 2x^4 - 3x^3 - x^2 = 0$

IV. Compute an upper bound and a lower bound for the zeros of each polynomial in Exercise II.

V. (1) Does $x^5 + 2x^4 + 5x^3 + x^2 + 7x + 3$ have any positive zeros? Why?

(2) Does $x^8 + x^6 + x^5 + 3x^2 + x + 2$ have any positive zeros? Why?

(3) Does $x^5 - x^4 + 2x^3 - 7x^2 + 5x - 8$ have any negative zeros? Why?

(4) Does $x^6 - 4x^5 + 3x^4 - 2x^3 + 7x^2 - 6x + 17$ have any negative zeros? Why?

VI. (1) One zero of $x^2 - 4x + 1$ is $2 - \sqrt{3}$.
Prove that $2 + \sqrt{3}$ is also a zero of $x^2 - 4x + 1$.

(2) One zero of $x^2 - 2x - 6$ is $1 + \sqrt{7}$.
Prove that $1 - \sqrt{7}$ is also a zero of $x^2 - 2x - 6$.

(3) Two zeros of $x^4 - 10x^2 + 16x + 5$ are $^-2 + \sqrt{3}$ and $2 - i$.
Prove that $^-2 - \sqrt{3}$ and $2 + i$ are also zeros.

(4) Two zeros of $x^4 - 12x^3 + 24x^2 - 20x + 35$ are $3 - \sqrt{2}$ and $1 + 2i$. Prove that $3 + \sqrt{2}$ and $1 - 2i$ are also zeros.

9.4 Graphing of Polynomials

Recall that the zeros of the polynomial $\mathbf{p}(x)$ are the roots of the polynomial equation $\mathbf{p}(x) = 0$; i.e., $\{x: \mathbf{p}(x) = 0\}$ is the set of all zeros of $\mathbf{p}(x)$. In Chapter 6 we learned that the real roots of the quadratic equation $ax^2 + bx + c = 0$ correspond to the points of intersection of the graph of the quadratic function $y = ax^2 + bx + c$ and the X-axis. We observe also that the real roots of any polynomial equation correspond to the points of intersection of the graph of the polynomial and the X-axis. The graph of a polynomial function is useful in the approximation of the irrational zeros of the function. We observe *from the graph* (a partial, approximate graph) the points of intersection of the graph and the X-axis. The following examples illustrate a procedure for determining two integers between which a real zero of a polynomial lies. In the next section we shall give a procedure for approximating the real zeros of any polynomial to any desired number of decimal places.

Example 1. Graph the polynomial function $\mathbf{p}(x) = x^3 + 3x^2 - x - 4$, and *isolate* the zeros (that is, determine two integers between which each of the real zeros lies).

By synthetic division or direct substitution, we compute images and display some ordered pairs and the graph in the accompanying figure. The graph intersects the X-axis between $^-3$ and $^-2$, between $^-2$ and $^-1$, and between 1 and 2. Thus there are three real zeros of $x^3 + 3x^2 - x - 4$. One zero lies between $^-3$ and $^-2$, one zero lies between $^-2$ and $^-1$, and the remaining zero lies between 1 and 2.

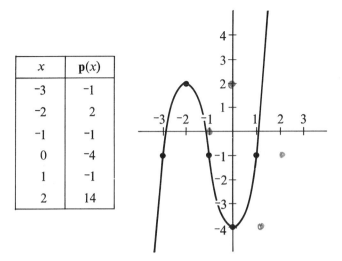

x	$p(x)$
-3	-1
-2	2
-1	-1
0	-4
1	-1
2	14

Example 2.   Graph the polynomial function

$p(x) = x^4 - 2x^3 - 7x^2 + 10x + 10$, and isolate the real zeros.

We compute images and display some ordered pairs and the graph in the accompanying figure.

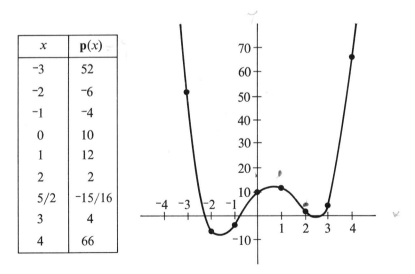

x	$p(x)$
-3	52
-2	-6
-1	-4
0	10
1	12
2	2
5/2	-15/16
3	4
4	66

There are four real zeros; one of them lies between ⁻3 and ⁻2, one of them lies between ⁻1 and 0, and two of them lie between 2 and 3.

Example 3. Sketch the graph of the polynomial function $\mathbf{p}(x) = x^4 + x^3 - 4x^2 - 5x - 5$, and isolate the real zeros.

We compute images and display some ordered pairs and the graph in the accompanying figure.

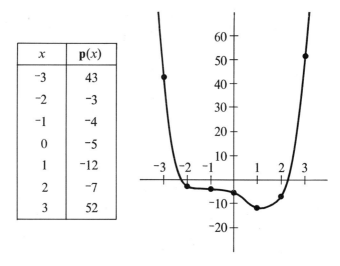

x	$\mathbf{p}(x)$
$^-3$	43
$^-2$	$^-3$
$^-1$	$^-4$
0	$^-5$
1	$^-12$
2	$^-7$
3	52

There are *two* real zeros; one of them lies between $^-3$ and $^-2$, and the other lies between 2 and 3. The other two zeros are *imaginary* (complex conjugates).

In sketching the graphs of the polynomial functions in the above examples, we have assumed that each polynomial function is *continuous*. Intuitively, a continuous function is one whose graph is not broken. The actual *proof* that every polynomial is continuous is beyond the scope of this text.

Exercise 9.4

I. Sketch the graph of each of the following cubic polynomial functions, and isolate the real zeros.

(1) $\mathbf{p}(x) = x^3 - 4x - 1$
(2) $\mathbf{p}(x) = x^3 - 5x + 2$
(3) $\mathbf{p}(x) = 2x^3 - 3x - 1$
(4) $\mathbf{p}(x) = x^3 - 3x^2 - 2x + 5$
(5) $\mathbf{p}(x) = x^3 - 3x^2 - 2x + 2$
(6) $\mathbf{p}(x) = x^3 - 3x^2 + 4x - 1$

(7) $\mathbf{p}(x) = x^3 + x^2 + 4$

(8) $\mathbf{p}(x) = x^3 - x^2 - x - 2$

(9) $\mathbf{p}(x) = 2x^3 + x - 1$

(10) $\mathbf{p}(x) = x^3 + 2x^2 + 4$

II. Sketch the graph of each of the following polynomial functions.

(1) $\mathbf{p}(x) = x^4 - 4x + 2$

(2) $\mathbf{p}(x) = x^4 - 3x + 1$

(3) $\mathbf{p}(x) = x^4 - 7x^2 - 6x - 2$

(4) $\mathbf{p}(x) = x^4 - x^3 - 4x^2 - 3x - 1$

(5) $\mathbf{p}(x) = x^4 - 4x^3 + 5x^2 - 2x - 2$

(6) $\mathbf{p}(x) = x^4 + 4x^3 - x^2 - 8x - 2$

(7) $\mathbf{p}(x) = 4x^4 - 28x^2 + 12x + 3$

(8) $\mathbf{p}(x) = 4x^4 - 32x^2 + 24x - 3$

(9) $\mathbf{p}(x) = 4x^5 - 24x^3 + 8x^2 + 3x$

(10) $\mathbf{p}(x) = 4x^5 - 32x^3 + 24x^2 - 3x$

III. Sketch the graph of each of the following polynomial functions.

(1) $\mathbf{p}(x) = x^2(x + 3)$

(2) $\mathbf{p}(x) = (x - 2)^2(x + 3)$

(3) $\mathbf{p}(x) = (x - 2)^2(x + 3)^2$

(4) $\mathbf{p}(x) = x^3$

(5) $\mathbf{p}(x) = x^3(x + 1)$

(6) $\mathbf{p}(x) = (x + 1)^3(x - 3)$

(7) $\mathbf{p}(x) = (2x + 1)^3(3x - 2)^4(5x + 2)^5$

(8) $\mathbf{p}(x) = (2x + 1)^3(3x - 2)^5(5x + 2)^4$

9.5   Approximation of the Irrational Zeros of a Polynomial

We have already learned how to *isolate* the real zeros of a polynomial. In this section we learn how to *approximate* the irrational zeros which have been isolated. There are several well-known methods for approximating the irrational zeros of a polynomial, such as the *bisector method*, the *linear-interpolation method, Graeffe's method, Horner's method*, and *Newton's method*. In this text we consider only the first two methods.

The following example illustrates the bisector method.

Example 1.   Employ the bisector method to approximate, to one decimal place, the irrational zero of $x^3 + 3x^2 - x - 4$ which lies between 1 and 2.

The table and graph of $\mathbf{p}(x) = x^3 + 3x^2 - x - 4$, shown in the accompanying sketch, are those shown in Example 1 of Section 9.4.

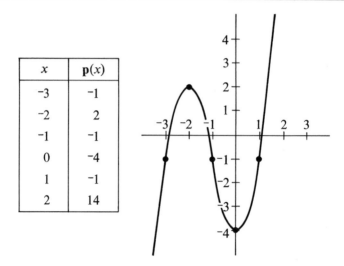

x	p(x)
⁻3	⁻1
⁻2	2
⁻1	⁻1
0	⁻4
1	⁻1
2	14

From the table we know that there *is* a real zero between 1 and 2. We bisect the segment from 1 to 2 and employ synthetic division to compute $p(1.5)$.

Since $p(1.5) = 4.625$, a positive number, and $p(1) = ⁻1$, a negative number, we know that the real zero is between 1 and 1.5.

We bisect the segment from 1 to 1.5 and employ synthetic division to compute $p(1.25)$.

Since $p(1.25) = 0.391$, a positive number, and $p(1) = ⁻1$, a negative number, we know that the real zero is between 1 and 1.25.

We bisect the segment from 1 to 1.25 and employ synthetic division to compute $p(1.125)$.

Since $p(1.125) = 0.096$, a positive number, and $p(1) = ⁻1$, a negative number, we know that the real zero is between 1 and 1.125.

We bisect the segment from 1 to 1.125 and employ synthetic division to compute $p(1.0625)$.

Since $p(1.0625) = ⁻0.476$, a negative number, and $p(1.125) = 0.096$, a positive number, we know that the real zero is between 1.0625 and 1.125.

We bisect the segment from 1.0625 to 1.125 and employ synthetic division to compute $p(1.09375)$.

Since $p(1.09375) = ⁻0.196$, a negative number, and $p(1.125) = 0.096$, a positive number, we know that the real zero is between 1.09375 and 1.125. Thus 1.1 is the approximation, to one decimal place, of the real zero between 1 and 2 of the polynomial $x^3 + 3x^2 - x - 4$.

The bisector method is especially adaptable to electronic digital computers. Moreover, after m bisections, the error in the approximation is less than $\frac{1}{2^m}$. However, the procedure is too time-consuming for desk calculation. For desk calculation one should employ all knowledge he can secure from the graph which will simplify the calculation. For example, if the graph indicates that the zero is nearer 1 than 2, his first approximation should be near 1. The linear interpolation method provides such an approximation.

The following example illustrates the linear interpolation method.

Example 2. Employ the linear interpolation method to approximate, to one decimal place, the irrational zero of $x^3 + 3x^2 - x - 4$ which lies between 1 and 2.

From the graph, which is shown in the figure of Example 1, we know that the zero is nearer 1 than 2. To obtain a first approximation, we *assume* that the graph is approximately a straight line (where it intersects the X-axis), and we compute the first approximation, $1 + h_1$, by means of the similar triangles indicated in the accompanying figure.

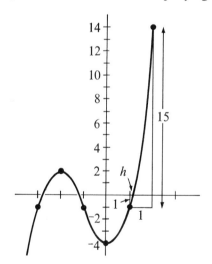

$$\frac{h_1}{1} = \frac{1}{15}$$
$$h_1 = \frac{1}{15}$$
$$h_1 = 0.07 \text{ (approximately)}$$
$$1 + h_1 = 1.07$$

Hence we assume a first approximation of 1.07 and, by synthetic division or direct substitution, we learn that $\mathbf{p}(1.07) = {}^{-}0.410$. Again, by similar triangles, we compute the second approximation, $1.07 + h_2$.

$$\frac{h_2}{0.139} = \frac{0.9}{14.139}$$

$h_2 = 0.026$ (approximately)

$1.07 + h_2 = 1.096$

Thus 1.1 is the approximation to one decimal place of the real zero between 1 and 2 of the polynomial $x^3 + 3x^2 - x - 4$.

Although the linear interpolation method usually provides an approximation to the zero in fewer iterations than the bisector method, the time difference on an electronic digital computer is negligible. Moreover, we can determine, in advance, the number of iterations in the bisector method which are required for a given accuracy in the approximation.

Exercise 9.5

I. Approximate, to two decimal places, the largest positive zero of $x^3 - x^2 - 3x + 1$.

II. Approximate, to two decimal places, the largest positive zero of $x^3 + 6x^2 + 6x - 5$.

III. Approximate, to two decimal places, all real zeros of $x^3 + 3x^2 + 6$.

IV. Approximate, to two decimal places, all real zeros of $x^4 - x^3 + 2x^2 - 3x - 3$.

V. Approximate, to two decimal places, all real zeros of $x^4 - 4x^3 - 4x + 12$.

Finite Number Systems

10.1 Calendar Number System

Recall that $(R_a, +, \times)$ and $(R, +, \times)$ are fields. Are there any other number systems which are fields? To answer this question, we consider a finite number system suggested by the set {Sunday, Monday, Tuesday, Wednesday, Thursday, Friday, Saturday}. For simplicity, we designate the days, in order, by 0, 1, 2, 3, 4, 5, 6 (called *calendar numbers*) as follows: $0 \leftrightarrow$ Sunday, $1 \leftrightarrow$ Monday, $2 \leftrightarrow$ Tuesday, $3 \leftrightarrow$ Wednesday, $4 \leftrightarrow$ Thursday, $5 \leftrightarrow$ Friday, $6 \leftrightarrow$ Saturday.

If you leave by car, on Friday, on a 4-day trip, when do you reach your destination? Looking at a calendar, you count 4 days from Friday; you reach your destination on Tuesday. You could count 4 days from 5 (for Friday): 6, 0, 1, 2. In this system $5 \oplus 4 = 2$. Similarly $2 \oplus 3 = 5$ and $5 \oplus 2 = 0$. Because of the above considerations, we define the binary operator $\oplus$, the operation of *addition*, and the *sum* of any two calendar numbers a and b as in Definition 1.

The symbol $\oplus$ denotes the binary operator in the calendar number system and the symbol $+$ denotes the binary operator in the system of integers, $(I, +, \times)$.

DEFINITION 1. The *sum* of any two calendar numbers a and b is the number $a \oplus b$ defined as follows:

(a) $a \oplus b = a + b$ if and only if $a + b \leq 6$,
(b) $a \oplus b = (a + b) - 7$ if and only if $6 < a + b$.

According to Definition 1, the sum of any two calendar numbers is a unique calendar number, as shown in Figure 10.1.

⊕	0	1	2	3	4	5	6
0	0	1	2	3	4	5	6
1	1	2	3	4	5	6	0
2	2	3	4	5	6	0	1
3	3	4	5	6	0	1	2
4	4	5	6	0	1	2	3
5	5	6	0	1	2	3	4
6	6	0	1	2	3	4	5

FIGURE 10.1

From Definition 1 (and Figure 10.1) we see that the calendar number system defined above possesses the closure property for addition. We now restate the first five field properties, which the calendar number system possesses.

CLOSURE PROPERTY FOR ADDITION OF CALENDAR NUMBERS

If a and b are any calendar numbers, then $a \oplus b$ is a unique calendar number.

ASSOCIATIVE PROPERTY FOR ADDITION OF CALENDAR NUMBERS

If a, b, and c are any calendar numbers, then
$(a \oplus b) \oplus c = a \oplus (b \oplus c)$.

IDENTITY PROPERTY FOR ADDITION OF CALENDAR NUMBERS

If a and z are any calendar numbers, then $a \oplus z = a$ if and only if $z = 0$.

INVERSE PROPERTY FOR ADDITION OF CALENDAR NUMBERS

If a is any calendar number, then there exists exactly one calendar number a' (called the *additive inverse of a*) such that $a \oplus a' = 0$.

COMMUTATIVE PROPERTY FOR ADDITION OF CALENDAR NUMBERS

If a and b are any calendar numbers, then $a \oplus b = b \oplus a$.

The proofs of all but the associative property follow immediately from Definition 1. We can prove the associative property either by using

Definition 1 and considering the various cases, or by using the addition table in Figure 10.1. However, there are 7^3 sums $(a \oplus b) \oplus c$ and 7^3 sums $a \oplus (b \oplus c)$ to compute if we use the table. In the exercises you will *verify* the associative property for a few of these sums and will *prove* the identity property, inverse property, and commutative property.

Since the additive inverse of each calendar number is a calendar number, the open sentence $a \oplus x = 0$, for any calendar number a, may be converted to a true sentence by replacement of the variable x by a calendar number. For example, the open sentence $5 \oplus x = 0$ may be converted to a true sentence by replacement of the variable x by the calendar number 2; that is, in classical terminology, the *solution* of the *equation* $5 \oplus x = 0$ is 2. Recall that an *equation* is a sentence or open sentence which involves the relation $=$. Any replacement of the variable in an equation which converts that equation to a true sentence is called a *solution* or *root* of the equation. The set of all roots of an equation is called the *solution set* of the equation. Recall that no equation of the form $a + x = 0$, for any nonzero counting number a, has a root in the system of counting numbers. In fact, every equation $a \oplus x = b$, for any calendar numbers a and b, has a root which is a calendar number, but there are some equations $a + x = b$, for counting numbers a and b, which do not have roots.

However, since every integer has an additive inverse, we see that the equation $a + x = 0$, for any integer a, has a root which is an integer. Thus it appears that the calendar number system, which at first appeared to be more like the counting number system, is actually more like the system of integers. Does the system of integers possess the five properties of the calendar number system? In Chapter 2 we learned that the system of integers does possess these five properties. Although the calendar number system is a *finite* number system, it has these five properties in common with the *infinite* system of integers. In fact, the system of integers, the clock number system,* and the calendar number system are three different number systems which all possess these same five properties. Because many other systems, some from the physical and social sciences, also possess these same five properties, it is advantageous to study an abstract (rather than a specific) system which has these five properties. Then any theorem which is provable from *these five properties* is immediately available for application to any one of the particular systems. Thus it is unnecessary to prove the same theorem in all of these systems; it is sufficient to prove it *once* in the abstract system.

Any abstract system $(G, \oplus)$ which possesses the above-mentioned properties is given a special name.

---

* The clock number system, whose elements are 0, 1, 2, . . . , 11, is similar to the calendar number system.

DEFINITION 2. A system $(G, \oplus)$ is called a *commutative group* if and only if it possesses all of the following properties.

(a) If a and b are any elements of G, then $a \oplus b$ is a unique element of G (*closure property*).
(b) If a, b, and c are any elements of G, then $(a \oplus b) \oplus c = a \oplus (b \oplus c)$ (*associative property*).
(c) There exists a unique element i in G such that $a \oplus i = a$ for all a in G (*identity property*).
(d) If a is any element of G, then there exists a unique element a' in G such that $a \oplus a' = i$ (*inverse property*).
(e) If a and b are any elements of G, then $a \oplus b = b \oplus a$ (*commutative property*).

The following theorem, which states that the additive inverse of the sum of any two elements is equal to the sum of the additive inverses, is an example of a theorem which may be proved from the definition of a commutative group. Observe that no properties other than the five properties of Definition 2 are used in the proof.

THEOREM 1.   *If a and b are any elements of a commutative group $(G, \oplus)$, then $(a \oplus b)' = a' \oplus b'$.*

Proof.
$$
\begin{aligned}
(a \oplus b) \oplus (a' \oplus b') &= (b \oplus a) \oplus [a' \oplus b'] \\
&= [(b \oplus a) \oplus a'] \oplus b' \\
&\qquad \text{(by the associative property)} \\
&= [b \oplus (a \oplus a')] \oplus b' \\
&= [b \oplus i] \oplus b' \\
&= b \oplus b' \\
&= i.
\end{aligned}
$$

Thus $a' \oplus b'$ is the additive inverse of $a \oplus b$. But $(a \oplus b)'$ is the additive inverse of $a \oplus b$. Since the additive inverse is unique, it follows that $(a \oplus b)' = a' \oplus b'. \diamond$

Observe that the sign property proved in Chapter 2 is a special case of Theorem 1. If Theorem 1 had been available in Chapter 2, it would have been unnecessary to prove the sign property. Moreover, since Theorem 1 applies to *any* commutative group, it applies, in particular, to the clock number system and to the calendar number system, and, in fact, to every particular commutative group regardless of the binary operator and the number of elements in the group.

Exercise 10.1

I. Prove that the calendar number system possesses each of the following properties.

  (1) Identity property for addition
  (2) Inverse property for addition
  (3) Commutative property for addition

II. Verify the associative property for addition of calendar numbers in each of the following cases.

  (1) $a = 3$, $b = 1$, $c = 4$
  (2) $a = 1$, $b = 4$, $c = 5$
  (3) $a = 6$, $b = 0$, $c = 6$
  (4) $a = 0$, $b = 5$, $c = 5$
  (5) $a = 6$, $b = 4$, $c = 4$
  (6) $a = 5$, $b = 5$, $c = 4$

III. Complete the following addition table so that the system will be commutative.

⊕	0	1	2	3	4
0	0	1	2	3	4
1		2	3	4	0
2			4	0	1
3				1	2
4					3

IV. (1) Complete the following table so that the system will be a commutative group. What is the identity of the group?

⊕	a	b	c
a	a	b	c
b		c	
c			b

(2) Complete the following table so that the system will be a commutative group. What is the identity of the group?

$\oplus$	a	b	c	d
a	b		d	a
b	c			b
c			b	
d				d

V. Supply the reason for each step in the proof of Theorem 1.

10.2   Calendar Number System (continued)

We can define the product of two calendar numbers as repeated addition. For example, $2 \odot 3 = 3 \oplus 3 = 6$, $3 \odot 2 = 2 \oplus 2 \oplus 2 = (2 \oplus 2) \oplus 2 = 4 \oplus 2 = 6$. In general, we define the binary operator $\odot$, the operation *multiplication*, and the *product* of any calendar numbers a and b as in Definition 3.

DEFINITION 3.   The product, $a \odot b$, of any calendar numbers a and b is the remainder when $a \times b$ is divided by 7.

According to Definition 3, the product of any two calender numbers is a unique calendar number, as shown in Figure 10.2.

$\odot$	0	1	2	3	4	5	6
0	0	0	0	0	0	0	0
1	0	1	2	3	4	5	6
2	0	2	4	6	1	3	5
3	0	3	6	2	5	1	4
4	0	4	1	5	2	6	3
5	0	5	3	1	6	4	2
6	0	6	5	4	3	2	1

FIGURE 10.2

From Definition 3 (and Figure 10.2) we see that the calendar number system possesses the closure property for multiplication. We now restate the second five field properties (properties $F6$-$F10$), which the calendar number system possesses.

CLOSURE PROPERTY FOR MULTIPLICATION OF CALENDAR NUMBERS

If a and b are any calendar numbers, then $a \odot b$ is a unique calendar number.

ASSOCIATIVE PROPERTY FOR MULTIPLICATION OF CALENDAR NUMBERS

If a, b, and c are any calendar numbers, then $(a \odot b) \odot c = a \odot (b \odot c)$.

IDENTITY PROPERTY FOR MULTIPLICATION OF CALENDAR NUMBERS

If a and u are any calendar numbers, then $a \odot u = a$ if and only if $u = 1$.

INVERSE PROPERTY FOR MULTIPLICATION OF CALENDAR NUMBERS

If a is any calendar number, then there exists exactly one calendar number $\bar{a}$ (*called the multiplicative inverse of a*) such that $a \odot \bar{a} = 1$.

COMMUTATIVE PROPERTY FOR MULTIPLICATION OF CALENDAR NUMBERS

If a and b are any calendar numbers, then $a \odot b = b \odot a$.

Since the multiplicative inverse of each calendar number except 0 is a unique calendar number, the open sentence $a \odot x = 1$, for any calendar number a except 0, can be converted to a true sentence by replacement of the variable x by a calendar number. For example, the open sentence $5 \odot x = 1$ can be converted to a true sentence by replacement of the variable x by the calendar number 3; that is, the *solution* of the *equation* $5 \odot x = 1$ is 3. Recall that no equation of the form $a \odot x = 1$, in which a is a counting number greater than 1, has a solution in the system of counting numbers. However, every equation $a \odot x = 1$, for any nonzero calendar number a, has a solution which is a calendar number. The calendar number system, which is a *finite* system, now appears to be more like the rational number system than like the system of counting numbers or the system of integers.

Is the calendar number system a field? That is, does the calendar number system possess all the field properties? Since we can prove that the calendar number system possesses the distributive property (for multiplication over addition), we conclude that the calendar number system is a field.

DISTRIBUTIVE PROPERTY (FOR CALENDAR NUMBERS)

If a, b, and c are any calendar numbers, then $a \odot (b \oplus c) = a \odot b \oplus a \odot c$.

Exercise 10.2

I. Prove that the calendar number system possesses each of the following properties.

(1) Identity property for multiplication
(2) Inverse property for multiplication
(3) Commutative property for multiplication

II. Verify the associative property for multiplication of calendar numbers in each of the following cases.

(1) $a = 3$, $b = 1$, $c = 4$
(2) $a = 1$, $b = 4$, $c = 5$
(3) $a = 6$, $b = 0$, $c = 6$
(4) $a = 0$, $b = 5$, $c = 5$
(5) $a = 6$, $b = 4$, $c = 4$
(6) $a = 5$, $b = 5$, $c = 4$

III. The *reduced calendar number system* is that system whose elements are 1, 2, 3, 4, 5, 6 and whose binary operators are $\oplus$ and $\odot$ of the calendar number system. Assuming the associative property for multiplication, prove that the reduced calendar number system is a commutative group with the operator $\odot$.

10.3 System of Integers Modulo m

The calendar number system is an example of a more general number system known as *the system of integers modulo m*, or more briefly, the *mod m number system*. Another example of a *modular number system* is the mod 6 number system, in which the elements are 0, 1, 2, 3, 4, 5 and the binary operators $\oplus$ and $\odot$ are defined in Definitions 4 and 5, respectively.

DEFINITION 4.   The *sum* of any mod 6 numbers a and b is the number $a \oplus b$ defined as follows:
(a) $a \oplus b = a + b$ if and only if $a + b \leq 5$,
(b) $a \oplus b = (a + b) - 6$ if and only if $5 < a + b$.

DEFINITION 5.   *The product, $a \odot b$, of any mod 6 numbers a and b is the remainder when $a \times b$ is divided by 6.*

According to Definition 4, the sum of any two mod 6 numbers is a unique mod 6 number; according to Definition 5, the product of any two mod 6 numbers is a unique mod 6 number. The addition and multiplication tables are shown in Figure 10.3.

$\oplus$	0	1	2	3	4	5
0	0	1	2	3	4	5
1	1	2	3	4	5	0
2	2	3	4	5	0	1
3	3	4	5	0	1	2
4	4	5	0	1	2	3
5	5	0	1	2	3	4

$\odot$	0	1	2	3	4	5
0	0	0	0	0	0	0
1	0	1	2	3	4	5
2	0	2	4	0	2	4
3	0	3	0	3	0	3
4	0	4	2	0	4	2
5	0	5	4	3	2	1

(*a*)   (*b*)

FIGURE 10.3

From Definition 4 (and Figure 10.3) we see that the mod 6 number system possesses the closure property for addition. In fact, it is easy to verify that the mod 6 number system possesses the first five field properties (properties *F*1 to *F*5).

*F*1.   If a and b are any mod 6 numbers, then $a \oplus b$ is a unique mod 6 number.

*F*2.   If a, b, and c are any mod 6 numbers, then $(a \oplus b) \oplus c = a \oplus (b \oplus c)$.

*F*3.   If a and z are any mod 6 numbers, then $a \oplus z = a$ if and only if $z = 0$.

*F*4.   If a is any mod 6 number, then there exists exactly one mod 6 number a' (called the *additive inverse of a*) such that $a \oplus a' = 0$.

*F*5.   If a and b are any mod 6 numbers, then $a \oplus b = b \oplus a$.

Observe that the additive identity is 0, the additive inverse of 0 is 0, the additive inverse of 1 is 5, the additive inverse of 2 is 4, and the additive inverse of 3 is 3.

From Definition 5 (and Figure 10.3) we see that the mod 6 number system possesses the closure property for multiplication. In fact, it is easy to verify that the mod 6 number system possesses field properties *F*6, *F*7, *F*8, *F*10, and *F*11, but does not possess field property *F*9.

*F*6.   If a and b are any mod 6 numbers, then $a \odot b$ is a unique mod 6 number.

*F*7.   If a, b, and c are any mod 6 numbers, then $(a \odot b) \odot c = a \odot (b \odot c)$.

*F*8.   If a is any mod 6 number, then $a \odot 1 = a$. Moreover, if $a \odot u = a$ for all a and some u in the mod 6 number system, then $u = 1$.

F10. If a and b are any mod 6 numbers, then $a \odot b = b \odot a$.
F11. If a, b, and c are any mod 6 numbers, then $a \odot (b + c) = a \odot b + a \odot c$.

Observe that the multiplicative identity is 1, the multiplicative inverse of 1 is 1, and the multiplicative inverse of 5 is 5. However, 2 does not have a multiplicative inverse, 3 does not have a multiplicative inverse, and 4 does not have a multiplicative inverse. Observe also that the gcd of 1 and 6 is 1, the gcd of 5 and 6 is 1, but the gcd of 2 and 6 is 2, the gcd of 3 and 6 is 3, and the gcd of 4 and 6 is 2.

Since the mod 6 number system does not possess field property F9, we conclude that the mod 6 number system is *not* a field. Recall from Section 10.2 that the mod 7 number system (the calendar number system), whose elements are 0, 1, 2, 3, 4, 5, 6, is a field. Observe the essential differences between the multiplication table of the calendar number system and the multiplication table of the mod 6 number system. The following exercises will afford you an opportunity to study other modular number systems. The operations of addition and multiplication are defined, in general, as in Definitions 6 and 7.

DEFINITION 6. The *sum* of any mod m numbers a and b is the number $a \oplus b$ defined as follows:
(a) $a \oplus b = a + b$ if and only if $a + b \le m - 1$,
(b) $a \oplus b = (a + b) - m$ if and only if $m - 1 < a + b$.

DEFINITION 7. The product, $a \odot b$, of any mod m numbers a and b is the remainder when $a \times b$ is divided by m.

The mod m number system will be denoted by $(I_m, \oplus, \odot)$. For example, $(I_4, \oplus, \odot)$ denotes the mod 4 number system, and $(I_9, \oplus, \odot)$ denotes the mod 9 number system.

Exercise 10.3

I. Construct the addition table and multiplication table for each of the following number systems.

(1) mod 4
(2) mod 5
(3) mod 10
(4) mod 11
(5) mod 12
(6) mod 13
(7) mod 2
(8) mod 9

II. Which modular number systems in Exercise I are fields?

III. State which elements of each of the modular number systems in Exercise I possess multiplicative inverses.

10.4 Properties of the System of Integers Modulo a Prime

Recall that the system $(I, + \times)$ of integers possesses all field properties except $F9$, and recall also that the system $(I_m, \oplus, \odot)$, for any composite integer m, possesses all field properties except $F9$. Do all of the properties of $(I, +, \times)$ follow from $F1$ to $F8$, $F10$, $F11$? If they do, then for every property of $(I, +, \times)$ there is a corresponding property of $(I_m, \oplus, \odot)$. For example, *under this assumption*, since $(I, +, \times)$ has the multiplication property of 0, then the system $(I_m, \oplus, \odot)$ must also have this property. However, the following theorem states that $(I_m, \oplus, \odot)$ does not possess the multiplication property of 0. As a consequence, we see that the multiplication property of zero does not follow from the properties $F1$ to $F8$, $F10$, $F11$.

THEOREM 2. *If m is any composite number, then the system* $(I_m, \oplus, \odot)$ *does not possess the multiplication property of 0.*

For example, consider the mod 6 number system. Although $2 \neq 0$ and $3 \neq 0$, we see that $2 \times 3 = 0$. In $(I, +, \times)$, $a \times b = 0$ if and only if $a = 0$ or $b = 0$. However, in $(I_m, \oplus, \odot)$, $a \odot b$ may be equal to 0 even if $a \neq 0$ and $b \neq 0$.

Recall the cancellation property for multiplication of integers: if a, b, and c are any integers such that $a \neq 0$ and $ab = ac$, then $b = c$. If m is a composite, does $(I_m, \oplus, \odot)$ possess the cancellation property for multiplication? To answer this question, we observe that $4 \times 2 = 1 \times 2$ but $4 \neq 1$ in the mod 6 number system.

The following theorem assures us that $(I_m, \oplus, \odot)$, for any composite m, does not possess the cancellation property for multiplication. The proof is an immediate consequence of Theorem 2.

THEOREM 3. *If m is any composite number, then the system* $(I_m, \oplus, \odot)$ *does not possess the cancellation property for multiplication.*

We know that the system $(I_m, \oplus, \odot)$ does not possess property $F9$ if m is composite. The following theorem states that $(I_p, \oplus, \odot)$ does possess property $F9$ if p is a prime. That is, every equation of the form $ax = 1$ for any $a \neq 0$, has a unique solution in the mod p number system. The following examples illustrate the method of proof. The proof of the theorem is omitted.

Example 1. Solve the equation $6x = 1$ in the mod 7 number system.

Of course, we can solve the given equation by actually replacing the variable x by each of the integers 0, 1, 2, 3, 4, 5, 6. By this method, we see that $6 \times 6 = 1$ and hence that the equation $6x = 1$ has the unique solution 6; that is, the multiplicative inverse of 6 is 6.

Example 2. Solve the equation $4x = 1$ in the mod 11 number system.

Replacing the variable successively by 1, 2, 3, . . . , 10, we see that $4 \times 3 = 1$ and, moreover, that 3 is the only solution.

Since 11 is a prime, we are certain that there are no nonzero integers, a and b, in the mod 11 number system such that $a \times b = 0$. Moreover, if $4 \times r = 1$ and $4 \times s = 1$, mod 11, then $r = s$, mod 11. Hence we are assured that the equation $4x = 1$, mod 11, has a unique solution in the set $\{0, 1, 2, 3, \ldots, 10\}$.

THEOREM 4. *If p is any prime and a is any positive integer less than p, then there exists a unique positive integer $b < p$ such that $ab = 1$ (mod p).*

By Theorem 4, if p is any prime and a is any element of $\{1, 2, \ldots, p - 1\}$, then there exists a unique element b of $\{1, 2, \ldots, p - 1\}$ such that $ab = 1$. That is, if p is any prime, then $(I_p, \oplus, \odot)$ possesses field property $F9$. Since $(I_p, \oplus, \odot)$ possesses all other field properties, we see that $(I_p, \oplus, \odot)$ is a field. For reference, we state this result as a theorem.

THEOREM 5. *If p is any prime, then $(I_p, \oplus, \odot)$ is a field.*

Since $(I_p, \oplus, \odot)$ is a field, we can solve any equation of the form $ax = b$, mod p. For example, to solve the equation $3x = 4$, mod 7, we multiply both sides by 5 (the multiplicative inverse of 3). Thus $5(3x) = 5(4)$; that is, $x = 6$, mod 7.

In summary we observe the following:
In $(I, +, \times)$, every equation $a + x = b$ has a solution.
In $(I_m, \oplus, \odot)$ every equation $a + x = b$ has a solution.
In $(I, +, \times)$, not every equation $ax = b$ has a solution (even if $a \neq 0$).
In $(R_a, +, \times)$, every equation $ax = b$ has a solution if $a \neq 0$.
In $(I_p, \oplus, \odot)$, every equation $ax = b$ has a solution if $a \neq 0$.

Exercise 10.4

I. Solve each of the following equations.

(1) $2x = 1$ (mod 3)   (6) $3x = 2$ (mod 11)
(2) $2x = 1$ (mod 5)   (7) $9x = 10$ (mod 11)
(3) $8x = 4$ (mod 17)   (8) $10x = 9$ (mod 11)
(4) $8x = 6$ (mod 17)   (9) $3x = 11$ (mod 13)
(5) $2x = 3$ (mod 11)   (10) $4x = 11$ (mod 13)

II. Illustrate Theorem 3 in each of the following.

(1) $(I_8, \oplus, \odot)$ (6) $(I_{15}, \oplus, \odot)$
(2) $(I_6, \oplus, \odot)$ (7) $(I_{21}, \oplus, \odot)$
(3) $(I_9, \oplus, \odot)$ (8) $(I_{25}, \oplus, \odot)$
(4) $(I_{10}, \oplus, \odot)$ (9) $(I_{49}, \oplus, \odot)$
(5) $(I_{14}, \oplus, \odot)$ (10) $(I_{81}, \oplus, \odot)$

Algebraic Structures

11.1 Groups

Recall from Chapter 10 that the system $(I, +)$ and the system $(I_m, +)$ are commutative groups. In Definition 2 of Chapter 10, we required that the identity element of the group be *unique* and that the inverse of each element be *unique*. The following definition of *commutative group* is less restrictive than Definition 2 of Chapter 10.

DEFINITION 1. A system $(G, \odot)$ is called a *commutative group* if and only if it possesses all of the following properties:

(a) If a and b are any elements of G, then $a \odot b$ is a unique element of G (closure property).
(b) If a, b, and c are any elements of G, then $(a \odot b) \odot c = a \odot (b \odot c)$ (associative property).
(c) There exists an element i in G such that $a \odot i = a$ for all a in G (identity property).
(d) If a is any element of G, then there exists an element a' in G such that $a \odot a' = i$ (inverse property).
(e) If a and b are any elements of G, then $a \odot b = b \odot a$ (commutative property).

Notice the difference between the above definition and Definition 2 of Chapter 10. There is no requirement that G shall have a *unique* identity, and there is no requirement in the above definition that each element shall have a *unique* inverse. In fact, according to Definition 1, it appears possible that G may have more than one identity and that each element may have more than one inverse. If there is actually more than one identity or if some element actually has more than one inverse,

286

then Definition 1 does not agree with the previous definition of commutative group. The following theorems assert that there is only one identity in G and that each element of G has only one inverse. Consequently Definition 1 of this section is equivalent to Definition 2 of Chapter 10.

THEOREM 1. *The identity element i of any commutative group $(G, \odot)$ is unique.*

Proof. Assume that i and u are both identities in G.
Then $a \odot i = a$ and $a \odot u = a$ for all a in G.
Thus $a \odot u = a \odot i$.

$a' \odot (a \odot u) = a' \odot (a \odot i)$	(by closure property)
$(a' \odot a) \odot u = (a' \odot a) \odot i$	(by associative property)
$(a \odot a') \odot u = (a \odot a') \odot i$	(by commutative property)
$i \odot u = i \odot i$	(by inverse property)
$u \odot i = i \odot i$	(by commutative property)
$u = i$	(by identity property)

Hence there is exactly one identity element in G. ◇

THEOREM 2. *Each element a of any commutative group $(G, \odot)$ has a unique inverse.*

Proof. Let $a \in G$.
Assume that a' and a'' are both inverses of a.
Then $a \odot a' = i$ and $a \odot a'' = i$.
Thus $a \odot a' = a \odot a''$.

$a' \odot (a \odot a') = a' \odot (a \odot a'')$	(by closure property)
$(a' \odot a) \odot a' = (a' \odot a) \odot a''$	(by associative property)
$(a \odot a') \odot a' = (a \odot a') \odot a''$	(by commutative property)
$i \odot a' = i \odot a''$	(by inverse property)
$a' \odot i = a'' \odot i$	(by commutative property)
$a' = a''$	(by identity property)

Hence each element a of $(G, \odot)$ has exactly one inverse a' in $(G, \odot)$. ◇

Recall that the rational number system $(R_a, +, \times)$ is a field and hence $(R_a, +)$ is a commutative group. Again, if Definition 1, Theorem 1, and Theorem 2 had been available when we developed the rational number system,* it would have been unnecessary to prove the uniqueness of the identity and the inverses. The reader will observe that studying an abstract system has definite advantages.

---

* Ohmer, Aucoin, and Cortez. *Elementary Contemporary Mathematics* (Massachusetts: Blaisdell Publishing Company, 1964).

Is $(C_0, +)$ a commutative group? Since $(C_0, +)$ does not possess the inverse property, we see that it is not a commutative group. For example, the element 3 does not have an inverse. In fact, we invented the set of integers because of this defect of $(C_0, +)$.

There are abstract systems which possess the closure property, associative property, identity property, and inverse property, but not the commutative property. For this reason, mathematicians study a more general system known as a *group*.

DEFINITION 2.   A system $(G, \odot)$ is called a *group* if and only if it possesses all of the following properties:

(a) If a and b are any elements of G, then $a \odot b$ is a unique element of G (closure property).
(b) If a, b, and c are any elements of G, then $(a \odot b) \odot c = a \odot (b \odot c)$ (associative property).
(c) There exists an element i of G such that $a \odot i = a$ for all a in G (identity property).
(d) If a is any element of G, then there exists an element a' of G such that $a \odot a' = i$ (inverse property).

Later we shall study a particular system, known as a *permutation group*, which is not commutative. The remainder of this section will be concerned with some general theorems and comments about groups.

The following theorems are stated without proof.

THEOREM 3.   *If a is any element of G, then $i \odot a = a \odot i = a$.*

THEOREM 4.   *If a is any element of G and a' is an inverse of a, then $a' \odot a = a \odot a' = i$.*

THEOREM 5.   *The identity element i of Definition 2 is unique.*

THEOREM 6.   *Each element a of any group G has a unique inverse.*

Henceforth when we refer to the *identity property*, we mean $i \odot a = a \odot i = a$, and when we refer to the *inverse property* we mean $a' \odot a = a \odot a' = i$.

A group is a beautiful example of a mathematical system which is interesting to pure mathematicians for its own sake. Perhaps it seems to you that no important theory can be developed from such a simple system as a group. However, many interesting and important theorems in modern mathematics have resulted from the study of groups. In fact, group theory has been applied to geometry, nuclear physics, chemistry, thermodynamics, and other fields. This is a frequent occurrence in mathematics: mathematicians develop abstract theory for its own elegance; later, the theory is applied to physical problems and society is advanced thereby.

Several famous mathematicians (Lagrange, Legendre, Abel, and Galois) were responsible for the origin and the preliminary developments of group theory. One of the main problems which occupied the attention of mathematicians during their lives was that of deriving a formula in terms of the coefficients (similar to the quadratic formula) for computing the roots of the equation $a_0 + a_1x + a_2x^2 + \ldots + a_mx^m = 0$ for any positive integer m. Instead of trying to derive such a formula, the above-named mathematicians tried to prove that no such formula exists if $5 \leq m$. They showed great ingenuity when they focused their attention on the *abstract* structure rather than the particular aspects of the number system. The formidable result, credited to Abel, Galois, and Ruffine is that no formula exists for solving the equation $a_0 + a_1x + a_2x^2 + \ldots + a_mx^m = 0$ for $5 \leq m$. These mathematicians developed the fundamentals of group theory as the principal tool in the solution of this problem. Later mathematicians extended the theory for its own beauty.

Exercise 11.1

I. Let $S = \{a + b\sqrt{3}: a \in R \land b \in R\}$.
Prove that $(S, +)$ is a commutative group.

II. Prove that $(C, +)$ is a commutative group.

III. Determine whether each of the following systems is a group; if it is a group, determine whether it is a commutative group.

(1)

$\odot$	i	a	b	c
i	i	a	b	c
a	a	b	c	i
b	b	c	i	a
c	c	i	a	b

(3)

$\odot$	a	b	c	d
a	a	b	c	d
b	b	a	c	d
c	c	d	a	c
d	d	a	b	c

(2)

$\odot$	a	b	c	d
a	a	b	c	d
b	b	c	d	a
c	c	d	a	b
d	d	a	b	c

(4)

$\odot$	i	a	b	c
i	i	a	b	c
a	a	i	c	b
b	b	c	i	a
c	c	b	a	i

(5) $\odot$	a	b	c	d
a	a	b	c	d
b	b	a	d	c
c	c	d	a	b
d	d	c	b	a

(6) $\odot$	a	b	c	d
a	b	c	a	d
b	c	a	d	b
c	a	d	b	c
d	d	a	c	b

IV. (1) Prove: if a and b are any elements of a group, then $(a \odot b)' = b' \odot a'$.

(2) Prove: if a, b, and c are any elements of a group, then $(a \odot b \odot c)' = c' \odot b' \odot a'$. [Because of the associative property, $a \odot b \odot c = (a \odot b) \odot c = a \odot (b \odot c)$].

11.2 Permutations

In the preceding section we defined *group* and remarked that not every group is commutative. In this section we shall give an example of a non-commutative group, called a *permutation group*. We have already mentioned the advantages of studying abstract systems. Frequently when the mathematical model of a physical problem involves a group $(G, \odot)$ the elements of G are not numbers, and the group operator $\odot$ is not one of the familiar operators. The permutation group is a simple example of such a group.

A teacher sends three pupils p_1, p_2, and p_3 to the board to work an arithmetic problem. These three pupils occupy their usual seats. We indicate this fact by writing $\binom{p_1 p_2 p_3}{p_1 p_2 p_3}$; i.e., pupil p_1 occupies his own seat, pupil p_2 occupies his own seat, and pupil p_3 occupies his own seat. When they complete their work at the board, they return to their seats. However, p_2 now occupies p_3's seat, and p_3 now occupies p_2's seat. We indicate this new position by $\binom{p_1 p_2 p_3}{p_1 p_3 p_2}$. The teacher then begins to wonder how many different seating arrangements of p_1, p_2, and p_3 there are. Consequently she calls the class's attention to the new seating arrangement, writes the symbols $\binom{p_1 p_2 p_3}{p_1 p_2 p_3}$ and $\binom{p_1 p_2 p_3}{p_1 p_3 p_2}$ on the board, and explains that the first symbol represents the first (original) seating arrangement of the three pupils and the second symbol represents the second (new) seating arrangement. Then she invites the class to write the symbols for other seating arrangements. One pupil writes $\binom{p_1 p_2 p_3}{p_3 p_2 p_1}$, and another writes $\binom{p_1 p_2 p_3}{p_2 p_1 p_3}$. Finally one pupil writes $\binom{p_1 p_2 p_3}{p_2 p_3 p_1}$ and $\binom{p_1 p_2 p_3}{p_3 p_1 p_2}$ and then says that there are no more arrangements. When the teacher and other pupils agree that these are the only six arrangements, she writes them all on the board, calls them *permutations*, and simplifies the notation as follows:

$$i = \binom{1\,2\,3}{1\,2\,3}, \quad a = \binom{1\,2\,3}{1\,3\,2}, \quad b = \binom{1\,2\,3}{3\,2\,1}, \quad c = \binom{1\,2\,3}{2\,1\,3}, \quad d = \binom{1\,2\,3}{2\,3\,1}, \quad e = \binom{1\,2\,3}{3\,1\,2}.$$

Then she explains that $\left(\begin{smallmatrix}1&2&3\\1&3&2\end{smallmatrix}\right)$, for example, indicates that p_1's seat is occupied by p_1, p_2's seat is occupied by p_3, and p_3's seat is occupied by p_2. Next she asks the class to consider the problem of *a followed by b*; i.e., to begin with arrangement *a* and then to follow this with the arrangement *b*. As a hint she writes $a = \left(\begin{smallmatrix}1&2&3\\1&3&2\end{smallmatrix}\right)$, $b = \left(\begin{smallmatrix}1&2&3\\3&2&1\end{smallmatrix}\right) = \left(\begin{smallmatrix}1&3&2\\3&1&2\end{smallmatrix}\right)$. One pupil immediately remarks that *a followed by b is equal to* $\left(\begin{smallmatrix}1&2&3\\3&1&2\end{smallmatrix}\right)$. The teacher asks him to explain the reason for his answer. He answers "*a* tells us that 1 is replaced by 1, and *b* tells us that 1 is replaced by 3, and hence *a followed by b* tells us that 1 is replaced by 3." Then he says, "*a* tells us that 2 is replaced by 3, and *b* tells us that 3 is replaced by 1, and hence *a followed by b* tells us that 2 is replaced by 1." Then he makes a similar remark that *a followed by b* tells us that 3 is replaced by 2.

Then the teacher introduces the symbol $\odot$ to indicate *followed by* and writes $a = \left(\begin{smallmatrix}1&2&3\\1&3&2\end{smallmatrix}\right)$, $b = \left(\begin{smallmatrix}1&3&2\\3&1&2\end{smallmatrix}\right)$, $a \odot b = \left(\begin{smallmatrix}1&2&3\\3&1&2\end{smallmatrix}\right) = e$. In a similar manner, the teacher and pupils discover that any permutation of the set $\{i, a, b, c, d, e\}$ followed by a permutation of this set is one of these permutations.

From the above classroom episode we observe that $\odot$ is a *binary* operator defined between any *two* of the permutations i, a, b, c, d, e. For simplicty, we shall refer to $a \odot b$, for example, as the *product of a and b* and read $a \odot b$ as *a times b*. The following table exhibits all multiplication facts of this set of permutations.

$\odot$	i	a	b	c	d	e
i	i	a	b	c	d	e
a	a	i	e	d	c	b
b	b	d	i	e	a	c
c	c	e	d	i	b	a
d	d	b	c	a	e	i
e	e	c	a	b	i	d

FIGURE 11.1

We read the table from *left* to *right*; for example $a \odot b = e$ but $b \odot a = d$. Hence $a \odot b \neq b \odot a$, and the binary operator $\odot$ is *not* commutative. Let $P_3 = \{i, a, b, c, d, e\}$. Although $(P_3, \odot)$ is not a commutative group, $(P_3, \odot)$ is a group; i.e., $(P_3, \odot)$ possesses the closure, associative, identity, and inverse properties. The closure property is evident from Figure 10.1. As the proof of the associative property is tedious, it will not be given here. In the exercise you will have an opportunity to *verify* the associative property for a few triplets of permutations. From the table we see that the identity is i (and is unique). Also from the table we see that $i' = i$, $a' = a$, $b' = b$, $c' = c$, $d' = e$, and $e' = d$; i.e., each element of P_3 has a unique inverse.

In summary, we see that $(P_3, \odot)$ *is a group but not a commutative group*, its elements are permutations rather than numbers, and the operator $\odot$, is not one of the familiar operators. The group $(P_3, \odot)$ is called the *symmetric group on three symbols.*

If the number of symbols is *four* rather than *three*, there are 24 permutations. Four of these permutations are $\left(\begin{smallmatrix}1&2&3&4\\1&2&3&4\end{smallmatrix}\right)$, $\left(\begin{smallmatrix}1&2&3&4\\2&3&4&1\end{smallmatrix}\right)$, $\left(\begin{smallmatrix}1&2&3&4\\3&4&1&2\end{smallmatrix}\right)$, and $\left(\begin{smallmatrix}1&2&3&4\\4&1&2&3\end{smallmatrix}\right)$. The binary operator $\odot$ between permutations on 4 symbols is defined as it was between permutations on 3 symbols. For example $\left(\begin{smallmatrix}1&2&3&4\\2&3&4&1\end{smallmatrix}\right) \odot \left(\begin{smallmatrix}1&2&3&4\\3&4&1&2\end{smallmatrix}\right) = \left(\begin{smallmatrix}1&2&3&4\\2&3&4&1\end{smallmatrix}\right) \odot \left(\begin{smallmatrix}2&3&4&1\\4&1&2&3\end{smallmatrix}\right) = \left(\begin{smallmatrix}1&2&3&4\\4&1&2&3\end{smallmatrix}\right)$. Letting P_4 be equal to the set of all 24 permutations on 4 symbols, we can prove that $(P_4, \odot)$ is a group. Similarly, letting P_k be equal to the set of all permutations on k symbols, we can prove that $(P_k, \odot)$ is a group. It is easy to prove that $\mathbf{n}(P_k) = (k)(k-1) \ldots (2)(1) = (1)(2) \ldots (k-1)(k)$. For example, the number of permutations on 5 symbols $= \mathbf{n}(P_5) = 5(4)$ $(3)(2)(1) = 120$.

Next we consider another group which we call the *group of rotations of a square.* You can actually construct the model by cutting out a square sheet of cardboard and labeling the vertices, clockwise, 1, 2, 3, 4, as shown in Figure 11.2.

FIGURE 11.2

The elements of this group are *counterclockwise rotations* of the square about its center. The four possible positions of the square are: $\begin{smallmatrix}1&2\\4&3\end{smallmatrix}$, $\begin{smallmatrix}2&3\\1&4\end{smallmatrix}$, $\begin{smallmatrix}3&4\\2&1\end{smallmatrix}$, and $\begin{smallmatrix}4&1\\3&2\end{smallmatrix}$. The rotation which changes the position $\begin{smallmatrix}1&2\\4&3\end{smallmatrix}$ to the position $\begin{smallmatrix}1&2\\4&3\end{smallmatrix}$ is designated by $\left(\begin{smallmatrix}1&2&3&4\\1&2&3&4\end{smallmatrix}\right)$. This is a counterclockwise rotation of $0°$ (or $360°$). The rotation which changes the position $\boxed{\begin{smallmatrix}1&2\\4&3\end{smallmatrix}}$ to the position $\boxed{\begin{smallmatrix}2&3\\1&4\end{smallmatrix}}$ is designated by $\left(\begin{smallmatrix}1&2&3&4\\2&3&4&1\end{smallmatrix}\right)$. This is a counter-clockwise rotation of 90°. The rotation which changes the position $\boxed{\begin{smallmatrix}1&2\\4&3\end{smallmatrix}}$ to the position $\boxed{\begin{smallmatrix}3&4\\2&1\end{smallmatrix}}$ is designated by $\left(\begin{smallmatrix}1&2&3&4\\3&4&1&2\end{smallmatrix}\right)$. This is a counterclockwise rotation of 180°. The rotation which changes the position $\boxed{\begin{smallmatrix}1&2\\4&3\end{smallmatrix}}$ to the position $\boxed{\begin{smallmatrix}4&1\\3&2\end{smallmatrix}}$ is designated by $\left(\begin{smallmatrix}1&2&3&4\\4&1&2&3\end{smallmatrix}\right)$. This is a counterclockwise rota-tion of 270°.

For simplicity, we let $i = \left(\begin{smallmatrix}1&2&3&4\\1&2&3&4\end{smallmatrix}\right)$, $a = \left(\begin{smallmatrix}1&2&3&4\\2&3&4&1\end{smallmatrix}\right)$, $b = \left(\begin{smallmatrix}1&2&3&4\\3&4&1&2\end{smallmatrix}\right)$, and $c = \left(\begin{smallmatrix}1&2&3&4\\4&1&2&3\end{smallmatrix}\right)$.

The multiplication table is given in Figure 11.3. Notice that $a \odot b$ means a counterclockwise rotation of $\boxed{\begin{smallmatrix}1&2\\4&3\end{smallmatrix}}$ through 90° *followed by* a counterclockwise rotation through 180°. Thus $a \odot b = c$, a counter-clockwise rotation through 270°.

$\odot$	i	a	b	c
i	i	a	b	c
a	a	b	c	i
b	b	c	i	a
c	c	i	a	b

FIGURE 11.3

Denoting the set $\{i, a, b, c\}$ by S, we see from Figure 11.3 that $(S, \odot)$ possesses the closure property. The proof that $(S, \odot)$ possesses the associative property follows from the fact that multiplication of per-mutations, in general, is associative. The identity is i. As $i' = i$, $a' = c$, $b' = b$, and $c' = a$, we see that $(S, \odot)$ possesses the inverse property. The commutative property is evident from Figure 11.3. Con-sequently, $(S, \odot)$ *is a commutative group.*

Exercise 11.2

I. Verify the associative property in each of the following.

(1) $a = \left(\begin{smallmatrix}1&2&3\\1&3&2\end{smallmatrix}\right)$, $b = \left(\begin{smallmatrix}1&2&3\\3&2&1\end{smallmatrix}\right)$, $c = \left(\begin{smallmatrix}1&2&3\\2&1&3\end{smallmatrix}\right)$
(2) $a = \left(\begin{smallmatrix}1&2&3\\1&3&2\end{smallmatrix}\right)$, $b = \left(\begin{smallmatrix}1&2&3\\3&2&1\end{smallmatrix}\right)$, $e = \left(\begin{smallmatrix}1&2&3\\3&1&2\end{smallmatrix}\right)$
(3) $a = \left(\begin{smallmatrix}1&2&3\\1&3&2\end{smallmatrix}\right)$, $b = \left(\begin{smallmatrix}1&2&3\\3&2&1\end{smallmatrix}\right)$, $d = \left(\begin{smallmatrix}1&2&3\\2&3&1\end{smallmatrix}\right)$
(4) $b = \left(\begin{smallmatrix}1&2&3\\3&2&1\end{smallmatrix}\right)$, $c = \left(\begin{smallmatrix}1&2&3\\2&1&3\end{smallmatrix}\right)$, $e = \left(\begin{smallmatrix}1&2&3\\3&1&2\end{smallmatrix}\right)$

II. Compute each of the following products.

(1) $\begin{pmatrix} 1 & 2 & 3 & 4 \\ 3 & 2 & 1 & 4 \end{pmatrix} \odot \begin{pmatrix} 1 & 2 & 3 & 4 \\ 1 & 3 & 2 & 4 \end{pmatrix}$

(2) $\begin{pmatrix} 1 & 2 & 3 & 4 \\ 1 & 3 & 2 & 4 \end{pmatrix} \odot \begin{pmatrix} 1 & 2 & 3 & 4 \\ 3 & 2 & 1 & 4 \end{pmatrix}$

(3) $\begin{pmatrix} 1 & 2 & 3 & 4 & 5 \\ 2 & 3 & 4 & 5 & 1 \end{pmatrix} \odot \begin{pmatrix} 1 & 2 & 3 & 4 & 5 \\ 1 & 4 & 3 & 2 & 5 \end{pmatrix}$

(4) $\begin{pmatrix} 1 & 2 & 3 & 4 & 5 \\ 1 & 4 & 3 & 2 & 5 \end{pmatrix} \odot \begin{pmatrix} 1 & 2 & 3 & 4 & 5 \\ 2 & 3 & 4 & 5 & 1 \end{pmatrix}$

(5) $\begin{pmatrix} 1 & 2 & 3 & 4 & 5 & 6 \\ 4 & 5 & 6 & 1 & 2 & 3 \end{pmatrix} \odot \begin{pmatrix} 1 & 2 & 3 & 4 & 5 & 6 \\ 6 & 5 & 4 & 3 & 2 & 1 \end{pmatrix}$

(6) $\begin{pmatrix} 1 & 2 & 3 & 4 & 5 & 6 \\ 6 & 5 & 4 & 3 & 2 & 1 \end{pmatrix} \odot \begin{pmatrix} 1 & 2 & 3 & 4 & 5 & 6 \\ 4 & 5 & 6 & 1 & 2 & 3 \end{pmatrix}$

III. Prove that each of the following systems is a commutative group with operator $\odot$.

(1) $\left\{ \begin{pmatrix} 1 & 2 & 3 \\ 1 & 2 & 3 \end{pmatrix}, \begin{pmatrix} 1 & 2 & 3 \\ 3 & 1 & 2 \end{pmatrix}, \begin{pmatrix} 1 & 2 & 3 \\ 2 & 3 & 1 \end{pmatrix} \right\}$

(2) $\left\{ \begin{pmatrix} 1 & 2 & 3 & 4 \\ 1 & 2 & 3 & 4 \end{pmatrix}, \begin{pmatrix} 1 & 2 & 3 & 4 \\ 2 & 1 & 4 & 3 \end{pmatrix} \right\}$

IV. Triangle *ABC* is an equilateral triangle with altitudes *AD*, *BE*, and *CF* which intersect at point *P*.

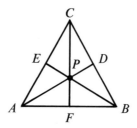

Let $S = \{i, a, b, c, d, e\}$ defined as follows:
i = rotation through 0° about *P*   (identity),
a = rotation through 180° about *AD*,
b = rotation through 180° about *BE*,
c = rotation through 180° about *CF*,
d = counterclockwise rotation through 120° about *P*,
e = counterclockwise rotation through 240° about *P*.

Let the operator $\odot$ designate *followed by*.
Thus $a \odot b$ means *rotation a followed by rotation b*.
   (1) Write the multiplication table.
   (2) Prove that $(S, \odot)$ is a group.
   (3) Compare $(S, \odot)$ with the group $(P_3, \odot)$.

V. Let π_1 be a permutation which replaces α by β, let π_2 be a permutation which replaces β by γ, and let π_3 be a permutation which replaces γ by δ. Prove $(\pi_1 \odot \pi_2) \odot \pi_3 = \pi_1 \odot (\pi_2 \odot \pi_3)$.

11.3   Theorems on Groups

We have already learned that *every* group $(G, \odot)$ possesses the closure, associative, identity, and inverse properties, and some groups possess the commutative property. In this section we shall investigate some theorems which are immediate consequences of the definition of a group and some which are not. The first property which we investigate is the cancellation property. The following theorem states that any group $(G, \odot)$ possesses the cancellation property.

THEOREM 7.   *If a, b, and c are any elements of a group $(G, \odot)$ and $c \odot a = c \odot b$, then $a = b$.*

Proof.   Let $c \odot a = c \odot b$.
   Then $c' \odot (c \odot a) = c' \odot (c \odot b)$ (by closure property).
   $(c' \odot c) \odot a = (c' \odot c) \odot b$ (by associative property).
   $i \odot a = i \odot b$ (by inverse property).
   Hence $a = b$ (by identity property). $\diamondsuit$

The following theorem states that the equation $a \odot x = b$ has a unique solution.

THEOREM 8.   *If a and b are any elements of a group $(G, \odot)$, then the equation $a \odot x = b$ has the unique solution $a' \odot b$.*

Proof.   Now $a \odot x = b \rightarrow a' \odot (a \odot x) = a' \odot b$ (by closure property)
$ \rightarrow (a' \odot a) \odot x = a' \odot b$ (by associative property)
$ \rightarrow i \odot x = a' \odot b$ (by inverse property)
$ \rightarrow x = a' \odot b$ (by identity property)
Moreover, $x = a' \odot b \rightarrow i \odot x = a' \odot b$ (by identity property)
$ \rightarrow (a' \odot a) \odot x = a' \odot b$ (by inverse property)
$ \rightarrow a' \odot (a \odot x) = a' \odot b$ (by associative property)
$ \rightarrow a \odot x = b$ (by cancellation property).
Thus $a \odot x = b$ if and only if $x = a' \odot b$.
Hence $a' \odot b$ is the unique solution of the equation $a \odot x = b$. $\diamondsuit$

The following theorem, which we shall not prove, is a statement of the *generalized associative property* in any group $(G, \odot)$.

THEOREM 9. *If $a_1, a_2, \ldots, a_k$ are any elements of a group $(G, \odot)$, then all punctuations of $a_1 \odot a_2 \odot \ldots \odot a_k$ yield the same element of $(G, \odot)$.*

The following theorem is a statement of the *generalized commutative and associative property* in any *commutative* group $(G, \odot)$.

THEOREM 10. *If $a_1, a_2, \ldots, a_k$ are any elements of a commutative group $(G, \odot)$, then all arrangements and punctuations of $a_1 \odot a_2 \odot \ldots \odot a_k$ yield the same element of $(G, \odot)$.*

The proofs of Theorems 9 and 10 depend on the *postulate of finite induction*, which we have not included in this text.

Recall that $(P_3, \odot)$ is a group with the six elements $i = \left(\begin{smallmatrix} 1 & 2 & 3 \\ 1 & 2 & 3 \end{smallmatrix}\right)$, $a = \left(\begin{smallmatrix} 1 & 2 & 3 \\ 1 & 3 & 2 \end{smallmatrix}\right)$, $b = \left(\begin{smallmatrix} 1 & 2 & 3 \\ 3 & 2 & 1 \end{smallmatrix}\right)$, $c = \left(\begin{smallmatrix} 1 & 2 & 3 \\ 2 & 1 & 3 \end{smallmatrix}\right)$, $d = \left(\begin{smallmatrix} 1 & 2 & 3 \\ 2 & 3 & 1 \end{smallmatrix}\right)$, $e = \left(\begin{smallmatrix} 1 & 2 & 3 \\ 3 & 1 & 2 \end{smallmatrix}\right)$. Recall also that the three elements $i = \left(\begin{smallmatrix} 1 & 2 & 3 \\ 1 & 2 & 3 \end{smallmatrix}\right)$, $d = \left(\begin{smallmatrix} 1 & 2 & 3 \\ 2 & 3 & 1 \end{smallmatrix}\right)$, and $e = \left(\begin{smallmatrix} 1 & 2 & 3 \\ 3 & 1 & 2 \end{smallmatrix}\right)$ form a group with operator $\odot$. Observe that $\{i, d, e\} \subset \{i, a, b, c, d, e\}$. Whenever a group contains a subset which is itself a group, we give this subset a special name.

DEFINITION 3. *$(S, \odot)$ is said to be a *subgroup* of the group $(G, \odot)$ if and only if $S \subset G$ and $(S, \odot)$ is a group.*

For example, denoting the set $\{i, d, e\}$ by A, we see that $(A, \odot)$ is a subgroup of $(P_3, \odot)$. Notice that $\mathbf{n}(A) = 3$ and $\mathbf{n}(P_3) = 6$ and hence $\mathbf{n}(A) | \mathbf{n}(P_3)$. As another example, consider the set $S = \{i, a, b, c\} = \{\left(\begin{smallmatrix} 1 & 2 & 3 & 4 \\ 1 & 2 & 3 & 4 \end{smallmatrix}\right), \left(\begin{smallmatrix} 1 & 2 & 3 & 4 \\ 2 & 3 & 4 & 1 \end{smallmatrix}\right), \left(\begin{smallmatrix} 1 & 2 & 3 & 4 \\ 3 & 4 & 1 & 2 \end{smallmatrix}\right), \left(\begin{smallmatrix} 1 & 2 & 3 & 4 \\ 4 & 1 & 2 & 3 \end{smallmatrix}\right)\}$ of Section 11.2. Recall that $(S, \odot)$ is a group. Moreover, recall that $(P_4, \odot)$ is a group. Since $S \subset P_4$, we see that $(S, \odot)$ is a *subgroup* of $(P_4, \odot)$. Notice that $\mathbf{n}(S) = 4$ and $\mathbf{n}(P_4) = 24$ and hence $\mathbf{n}(S) | \mathbf{n}(P_4)$. The following theorem, known as *Lagrange's Theorem*, states that the number of elements of any subgroup of a finite group divides the number of elements of the group. We do not include the proof.

THEOREM 11. *If $(G, \odot)$ is a finite group and $(S, \odot)$ is a subgroup of $(G, \odot)$, then $\mathbf{n}(S) | \mathbf{n}(G)$.*

Another important theorem in abstract algebra is a theorem known as *Cayley's Theorem*. Before we state Cayley's theorem, we shall consider two apparently different groups and show that they are abstractly identical. We consider the subset $B = \{1_{17}, 4_{17}, 16_{17}, 13_{17}\}$ of the mod 17 system and write the multiplication table shown in Figure 11.4.

$\otimes$	1	4	16	13
1	1	4	16	13
4	4	16	13	1
16	16	13	1	4
13	13	1	4	16

FIGURE 11.4

It is easy to prove that $(B, \otimes)$ is a group with identity 1. Next we reconsider the group $(S, \odot)$ consisting of the elements $i = \binom{1\,2\,3\,4}{1\,2\,3\,4}$, $a = \binom{1\,2\,3\,4}{2\,3\,4\,1}$, $b = \binom{1\,2\,3\,4}{3\,4\,1\,2}$, and $c = \binom{1\,2\,3\,4}{4\,1\,2\,3}$. *Since* $\mathbf{n}(B) = \mathbf{n}(S)$, we see that $B \approx S$ (i.e., B is equivalent to S). Is the group $(B, \otimes)$ *abstractly identical* with the group $(S, \odot)$? That is, is the group $(B, \otimes)$ *identical with the group* $(S, \odot)$ *except for notation*? To answer this question, we compare the table in Figure 11.3 with the table in Figure 11.4. For convenience, we reproduce both tables in Figure 11.5.

$\odot$	i	a	b	c
i	i	a	b	c
a	a	b	c	i
b	b	c	i	a
c	c	i	a	b

$\otimes$	1	4	16	13
1	1	4	16	13
4	4	16	13	1
16	16	13	1	4
13	13	1	4	16

(a)   (b)

FIGURE 11.5

Observe that Figure 11.5(a) is identical with Figure 11.5(b) *except for notation*. That is, in Figure 11.5(a) if we replace $\odot$ by $\otimes$, i by 1_{17}, a by 4_{17}, b by 16_{17}, and c by 13_{17}, we obtain Figure 11.5(b). In other words, the one-to-one correspondence

$$i \leftrightarrow 1_{17}$$
$$a \leftrightarrow 4_{17}$$
$$b \leftrightarrow 16_{17}$$
$$c \leftrightarrow 13_{17}$$

is operation-preserving; i.e., $a \odot b \leftrightarrow 4_{17} \otimes 16_{17}$, $a \odot c \leftrightarrow 4_{17} \otimes 13_{17}$, $b \odot c \leftrightarrow 16_{17} \otimes 13_{17}$, etc. In general, a one-to-correspondence between two groups $(A, \odot)$ and $(B, \otimes)$ is *operation-preserving* if and only if $(a_i \odot a_j \leftrightarrow b_i \otimes b_j)$ whenever $a_i \leftrightarrow b_i$ and $a_j \leftrightarrow b_j$. We are now prepared to give precise meaning to the term *abstractly identical*.

DEFINITION 4. Two groups are said to be *abstractly identical* (or *isomorphic*) if and only if there exists an operation-preserving one-to-one correspondence between the groups.

Thus $(B, \otimes)$ is abstractly identical with the subgroup $(S, \odot)$ of $(P_4, \odot)$. Moreover, $\mathbf{n}(S) = 4$, and the elements of S are permutations on 4 symbols.

In summary, we observe that $(B, \otimes)$ is a group of four elements, and $(B, \otimes)$ is abstractly identical with a group of *four* permutations on *four* symbols. Moreover, the group of *four* permutations on *four* symbols is a subgroup of $(P_4, \odot)$. *Cayley's theorem*, which we state without proof, tells us that this result is true in general.

THEOREM 12. *Every finite group consisting of k elements is abstractly identical with a subgroup of* $(P_k, \odot)$.

Since the theory of permutation groups has been investigated carefully, Cayley's theorem is extremely important to pure mathematicians. The reason for this is that any finite group of k elements may be replaced by a subgroup of $(P_k, \odot)$; the theory of permutation groups is then immediately applicable to the given finite group. Mathematicians appreciate the elegance of a theorem such as Cayley's theorem, which unifies the theory of finite groups. In addition, it is very useful in the applications of group theory to physical problems.

Exercise 11.3

I. Prove each of the following.
   (1) If a, b, and c are any elements of a group $(G, \odot)$ and $a \odot c = b \odot c$, then $a = b$.
   (2) If a and b are any elements of a group $(G, \odot)$, then the equation $x \odot a = b$ has the unique solution $b \odot a'$.
   (3) If a is any element of a group $(G, \odot)$, then $(a')' = a$.
   (4) If a and b are any elements of a commutative group $(G, \odot)$, then $a \odot (b \odot a') = b$.
   (5) If a and b are any elements of a (*not necessarily commutative*) group $(G, \odot)$, then $(a \odot b')' = b \odot a'$.

II. (1) Let $E = \{2n: n \in I\} = \{\dots, {}^-4, {}^-2, 0, 2, 4, \dots\}$. Prove
     that $(E, +)$ is a commutative group.

  (2) Let $O = \{2n + 1: n \in I\} = \{\dots, {}^-3, {}^-1, 1, 3, \dots\}$. Is
     $(O, +)$ a group? Is $(O, \times)$ a group?

III. (1) Give an example of a commutative subgroup of a noncommu-
     tative group.

  (2) List the subgroups of $(I_6, \oplus)$.

  (3) List the subgroups of $(I_7, \oplus)$.

  (4) Let $G = \{1_5, 2_5, 3_5, 4_5\}$. Prove that $(G, \otimes)$ is a commutative
     group.

IV. Prove that the group $(I_5, \oplus)$ is abstractly identical with the following subgroup $(S, \odot)$ of $(P_5, \odot)$:

$$S = \left\{ \begin{pmatrix} 1\,2\,3\,4\,5 \\ 1\,2\,3\,4\,5 \end{pmatrix}, \begin{pmatrix} 1\,2\,3\,4\,5 \\ 2\,3\,4\,5\,1 \end{pmatrix}, \begin{pmatrix} 1\,2\,3\,4\,5 \\ 3\,4\,5\,1\,2 \end{pmatrix}, \begin{pmatrix} 1\,2\,3\,4\,5 \\ 4\,5\,1\,2\,3 \end{pmatrix}, \begin{pmatrix} 1\,2\,3\,4\,5 \\ 5\,1\,2\,3\,4 \end{pmatrix} \right\}.$$

11.4 Fields

Recall from Chapter 1 that a system $(F, +, \times)$ is a *field* if and only
if it possesses the following properties:

*F*1. If a and b are any elements of F, then $a + b$ is a unique element
     of F (*closure property for addition*).

*F*2. If a, b, and c are any elements of F, then $(a + b) + c = a$
     $+ (b + c)$ (*associative property for addition*).

*F*3. There exists a unique element 0 of F such that $a + 0 = a$ for
     any element of F (*identity property for addition*).

*F*4. If a is any element of F, then there exists a unique element ${}^-a$ of
     of F such that $a + {}^-a = 0$ (*inverse property for addition*).

*F*5. If a and b are any elements of F, then $a + b = b + a$ (*com-
     mutative property for addition*).

*F*6. If a and b are any elements of F, then $a \times b$ is a unique element
     of F (*closure property for multiplication*).

*F*7. If a, b, and c are any elements of F, then $(a \times b) \times c = a$
     $\times (b \times c)$ (*associative property for multiplication*).

*F*8. There exists a unique element 1 of F such that $a \times 1 = a$ for
     any element a of F (*identity property for multiplication*).

*F*9. If a is any nonzero element of F, then there exists a unique element
     $\frac{1}{a}$ of F such that $a \times \frac{1}{a} = 1$ (*inverse property for multiplication*).

*F*10. If a and b are any elements of F, then $a \times b = b \times a$ (*com-
     mutative property for multiplication*).

*F*11. If a, b, and c are any elements of F, then $a(b + c) = ab + ac$
     (*distributive property*).

We have already learned that the rational number system, the real number system, the complex number system, and the modular number system modulo any prime are fields. Notice that we required that the identity elements 0 and 1 be unique, that each element have a unique additive inverse, and that each element *except 0* have a unique multiplicative inverse. The following definition of field is less restrictive than the above definition.

DEFINITION 5. A system $(F, +, \times)$ is called a *field* if and only if it possesses all of the following properties:

F1.   If a and b are any elements of F, then $a + b$ is a unique element of F (*closure property for addition*).

F2.   If a, b, and c are any elements of F, then $(a + b) + c = a + (b + c)$ (*associative property for addition*).

F3.   There exists an element 0 of F such that $a + 0 = a$ for any element of F (*identity property for addition*).

F4.   If a is any element of F, then there exists an element ^-a of F such that $a + {}^-a = 0$ (*inverse property for addition*).

F5.   If a and b are any elements of F, then $a + b = b + a$ (*commutative property for addition*).

F6.   If a and b are any elements of F, then $a \times b$ is a unique element of F (*closure property for multiplication*).

F7.   If a, b, and c are any elements of F, then $(a \times b) \times c = a \times (b \times c)$ (*associative property for multiplication*).

F8.   There exists an element 1 of F such that $a \times 1 = a$ for any element a of F (*identity property for multiplication*).

F9.   If a is any nonzero element of F, then there exists an element $\frac{1}{a}$ of F such that $a \times \frac{1}{a} = 1$ (*inverse property for multiplication*).

F10. If a and b are any elements of F, then $a \times b = b \times a$ (*commutative property for multiplication*).

F11. If a, b, and c are any elements of F, then $a(b + c) = ab + ac$ (*distributive property*).

Observe the difference between Definition 5 and the previous definition of field: in Definition 5 there is no requirement of *uniqueness* of identities and inverses. In fact, according to Definition 5, it appears possible that a field may have more than one additive (or multiplicative) identity and that an element may have more than one additive (or multiplicative) inverse. If this is actually the case, then Definition 5 does not agree with the original definition of field. Before we prove that the original definition of field is equivalent to Definition 5, we make the following observations:

1. Properties $F1$ through $F5$ are precisely the properties of Definition 1 with F replacing G and $+$ replacing $\odot$;
2. Properties $F6$ through $F10$ are precisely the properties of Definition 1 with F replacing G and $\times$ replacing $\odot$, except that 0 is not required to have an inverse;
3. Property $F11$ is a property involving both operations $+$ and $\times$.

Consequently, we can rewrite Definition 5 as follows.

A system $(F, +, \times)$ is a *field* if and only if it possesses all of the following properties:

(a) $(F, +)$ is a commutative group;
(b) $0 \times a = a \times 0 = 0$;
(c) $(F \setminus \{0\}, \times)$ is a commutative group;
(d) if a, b, and c are any elements of F, then $a(b + c) = ab + ac$.

Since $(F, +)$ is a commutative group, we know from Theorem 1 that the additive identity 0 is unique and from Theorem 2 that each element of F has a unique additive inverse. Similarly, since $(F \setminus \{0\}, \times)$ is a commutative group, we know from Theorem 1 and Theorem 2 that the multiplicative identity is unique and that each element of $F \setminus \{0\}$ has a unique multiplicative inverse. Thus *the original definition of field is a consequence of Definition 5*. Obviously *Definition 5 is a consequence of the original definition of field*. Hence the two definitions are *equivalent*.

This is an excellent illustration of the economy of abstraction. Having proved uniqueness in a group, we were able to prove uniqueness in a field. If the uniqueness of each identity and of inverses in a field had been available to us when we developed the rational numbers and the real numbers* our task would have been simplified.

We have already studied four systems which are fields. Now we shall reconsider some systems, studied previously, which are not fields. The counting number system $(C_0, +, \times)$ is not a field because $(C_0, +)$ is not a group. The reason $(C_0, +)$ is not a group is that 0 is the only element of C_0 which has an additive inverse in C_0. The system of integers $(I, +, \times)$ is not a field because $(I \setminus \{0\}, \times)$ is not a group. The reason $(I \setminus \{0\}, \times)$ is not a group is that 1 is the only element of $I \setminus \{0\}$ which has a multiplicative inverse in $I \setminus \{0\}$. If m is a composite number, the system $(I_m, +, \times)$ is not a field because some nonzero element of I_m does not have a multiplicative inverse in I_m. For example, 2_6 does not have a multiplicative inverse in I_6.

In pure mathematics, a mathematician formulates a basic set of un-

---

* Ohmer, Aucoin, and Cortez. *Elementary Contemporary Mathematics* (Massachusetts: Blaisdell Publishing Company, 1964).

defined terms, definitions, and postulates and builds an abstract mathematical system from these. In applied mathematics, a mathematician applies these general results to specific problems whose mathematical models can be formulated in the abstract system. For example, a mathematician known as an *algebraist* proves theorems about groups, fields, and other abstract systems. The primary interest of the pure mathematician is *creating* mathematics for its own beauty. He is especially interested in any theorem which *unifies* different branches of mathematics. Although our primary interest in this text has been the *algebraic structure of the common number systems*, in closing we mention that there are many other branches of pure mathematics; for example, *analysis, topology,* and *geometry.*

Exercise 11.4

I. Let $S = \{a + b\sqrt{3} : a \in R \land b \in R\}$.
   Prove that $(S, +, \times)$ is a field.

II. Let $K = \{a + b\sqrt{3} : a \in I \land b \in I\}$.
   Prove that $(K, +, \times)$ is *not* a field.

Answers to Problems

Chapter 1

Exercise 1.1

I. (1) Sentence   (17) Open sentence
   (3) Sentence   (19) Open sentence
   (5) Open sentence   (21) Neither
   (7) Sentence   (23) Open sentence
   (9) Neither   (25) Neither
  (11) Open sentence   (27) Neither
  (13) Open sentence   (29) Open sentence
  (15) Open sentence

II. (1) All   (9) All
   (3) Some (there exists)   (11) Some (there exists), no (none)
   (5) Some (there exists)   (13) All
   (7) All   (15) Some (there exists)

III. (1) No quantifier   (7) No quantifier
   (3) Implied   (9) No quantifier
   (5) No quantifier

IV. (3) All

V. (1) Sentence   (7) Sentence
   (3) Open sentence   (9) Sentence
   (5) Sentence

VI. (1) For all x, $x + x = 2x$ (true); for some x, $x + x = 2x$ (true); for no x, $x + x = 2x$ (false)

(3) For all t, $t + 5 = 5$ (false); for some t, $t + 5 = 5$ (true); for no t, $t + 5 = 5$ (false)

(5) For all y, $7 + y = y$ (false); for some y, $7 + y = y$ (false); for no y, $7 + y = y$ (true)

(7) For all t, $t + 6 = 6$ (false); for some t, $t + 6 = 6$ (true); for no t, $t + 6 = 6$ (false)

(9) For all a, $a + 7 = 3$ (false); for some a, $a + 7 = 3$ (false); for no a, $a + 7 = 3$ (true)

Exercise 1.2

III. (1) $0 \in A$, $0 \notin B$, $0 \notin C$, $0 \notin D$, $0 \notin E$, $0 \notin F$, $0 \in G$.

(3) $5 \notin A$, $5 \in B$, $5 \notin C$, $5 \in D$, $5 \notin E$, $5 \notin F$, $5 \in G$.

(5) $9 \notin A$, $9 \in B$, $9 \in C$, $9 \in D$, $9 \notin E$, $9 \in F$, $9 \notin G$.

(7) $\frac{5}{2} \notin A$, $\frac{5}{2} \notin B$, $\frac{5}{2} \notin C$, $\frac{5}{2} \notin D$, $\frac{5}{2} \notin E$, $\frac{5}{2} \notin F$, $\frac{5}{2} \notin G$.

(9) $24600000 \in A$, $24600000 \notin B$, $24600000 \in C$, $24600000 \notin D$, $24600000 \notin E$, $24600000 \notin F$, $24600000 \notin G$.

Exercise 1.3

I. $\{10\}$, $\{10, 12\}$, $\{10, 12, 14\}$.

V. (1) The set of all counting numbers greater than 100.

(3) The set of all numbers such that 5 times the number equals 10.

(5) The set of all odd numbers greater than 9.

Exercise 1.4

I. (1) $\begin{array}{cccc} 0 & 5 & 10 & 15 \\ \updownarrow & \updownarrow & \updownarrow & \updownarrow \\ a & b & x & y \end{array}$

(3) $w \leftrightarrow 11$

(5) $\begin{array}{ccccccc} 0 & 4 & 8 & 12 & 16 & \ldots & 4n & \ldots \\ \updownarrow & \updownarrow & \updownarrow & \updownarrow & \updownarrow & & \updownarrow & \\ 0 & 1 & 2 & 3 & 4 & \ldots & n & \ldots \end{array}$

III. (1) C, D, H

Exercise 1.5

I. (1) Subset of A

(3) An element of A

(5) An element of A

(7) Subset of A

(9) Subset of A

(11) Subset of A

(13) Subset of A

(15) Subset of A

III. (1) {2, 6, 10}   (7) { } or ∅
      (3) {0, 4, 6, 8}   (9) {2}
      (5) {2, 4, 6, 8, 10}

 V. (1) {x: x is a male}   (5) {x: x is a female}
     (3) {x: x is a single person}

Exercise 1.6

  I. (1) {2, 4, 6, 8, 9}   (5) {0, 1, 2, 3, . . .}
      (3) {0, 1, 2, 3, 4, 5}   (7) {0, 1, 2, 3, . . .}
      (9) {Jessie, May, Bea, Janice, Craig, Lisa, Inez}

III. (1) {0, 1, 2}, {0, 1}   (7) {1, 2, 3, 4, 5}, { }
      (3) {1, 2, 3, 4, 5, 6}, { } or ∅ (9) {0, 1, 2, 3, . . .}, {100}
      (5) {1, 2, 3, 4, . . .}, ∅   (11) {0, 1, 2, 3, . . .}, { }.

 V. $A \cap B = B \cap A$.

Exercise 1.7

 V. (1) The set of all students of mathematics or chemistry.
     (3) The set of all students of mathematics and chemistry.
     (5) The set of all students of chemistry or speech.
     (7) The set of all students of mathematics, and chemistry, and
         speech.

Exercise 1.8

  I. (1) {0, 1, 2, 4, 6, 8}   (19) ∅
      (3) {4, 6}   (21) {0, 2, 3, 4, 5, 6, 7, 9}
      (5) {1}   (23) {0, 1, 2, 3, 5, 7, 8, 9}
      (7) {0, 1, 2, 4, 6, 8}   (25) U
      (9) {1}   (27) ∅
     (11) {1, 4, 6, 8}   (29) {7}
     (13) {4, 6}   (31) {0, 1, 2, 4, 6, 7, 8}
     (15) {0, 1, 2, 3, 4, 5, 6, 8, 9} (33) U
     (17) ∅   (35) {4, 6}

 V. (1) {0, 6, 12, 18, . . .}
     (3) { }
     (5) {0, 2, 4, . . . , 98}
     (7) {0, 2, 4, . . .} or {x: x is even}
     (9) B
    (11) D

(13) $\{1, 3, 5, \ldots, 99, 105, 111, \ldots\}$
(15) $\{101, 103, 105, \ldots\}$
(17) $\{0, 2, 4, \ldots, 98\}$
(19) $\{0, 2, 4, 6, \ldots\}$

Exercise 1.9

I.   (1) $\{(2, 0)\}$
    (3) $\{(2, 1), (2, 2)\}$
    (5) $\{(0, 1), (0, 2), (0, 3), (1, 1), (1, 2), (1, 3)\}$
    (7) $\{(0, 0), (0, 1), (0, 2), (0, 3)\}$
    (9) $\{(10, 1), (10, 2), (10, 3), (10, 4), \ldots$
          $(11, 1), (11, 2), (11, 3), (11, 4), \ldots$
          $(12, 1), (12, 2), (12, 3), (12, 4), \ldots\}$

V.   (1) $A = \{1, 5\}, B = \{1, 2, 3\}$
    (3) $A = \{0\}, B = \{0, 1, 2\}$

Exercise 1.10

I.   (1) Equivalence relation
    (3) Equivalence relation
    (5) Equivalence relation
    (7) Equivalence relation
    (9) Equivalence relation

Chapter 2

Exercise 2.1

I.   (5) $F1, F2, F5$
    (7) $F6, F7, F8, F9, F10$

Exercise 2.2

I.   (1) Yes; 5   (3) No   (5) No   (7) Yes; 2   (9) No   (11) No
    (13) Yes; 3   (15) No   (17) No   (19) No

III.   (1) Yes; 5   (3) Yes; 0   (5) Yes; $^-1$ (7) Yes; 2   (9) No
    (11) No   (13) Yes; 3   (15) No   (17) No   (19) No

V.   (1) Yes; 5   (3) Yes; 0   (5) Yes; $^-1$ (7) Yes; 2   (9) Yes; $\frac{-1}{3}$

(11) Yes; $\frac{7}{5}$ (13) Yes; 3   (15) Yes; $\frac{\sqrt{5}}{3}$ and $\frac{-\sqrt{5}}{3}$
(17) Yes; $\sqrt{3}$ (19) No

Exercise 2.3

I. (1) 3   (3) $\frac{3}{2}$ (5) $\frac{7}{2}$ (7) $\frac{7}{6}$ (9) 5

III. (1) ⁻10   (3) ⁻6   (5) 8   (7) 160   (9) 24

V. (1) 2   (3) ⁻2   (5) 10   (7) 6   (9) 0   (11) ⁻8   (13) ⁻1.4
(15) 1.4   (17) 8π (19) $^-7\sqrt{2}\pi$

VII. (1) $\{1\}$ (3) $\{0\}$ (5) $\varnothing$ (7) $\{^-2, 2\}$ (9) $\left\{\frac{1}{3}\right\}$

Exercise 2.4

I. (1) 2, 3, 5, 7, 11, 13, 17, 19, 23, 29, 31, 37, 41, 43, 47, 53, 59, 61, 67, 71, 73, 79, 83, 89, 97.
(3) 15, 21, 25, 27, 33, 35, 39, 45, 49, 51, 55, 57, 63, 65, 69, 75, 77, 81.

III. (1) 1   (3) 3   (5) 42   (7) 42   (9) 11

V. (1) 3   (3) 1   (5) 1   (7) 1   (9) 50

VII. (1) $\frac{119}{660}$ (3) $\frac{545}{924}$ (5) $\frac{894}{5929}$ (7) $\frac{179}{180}$ (9) $\frac{-13}{1000}$

Exercise 2.5

I. (1) 5^4 (3) $\frac{1}{(2 \times 3^2)}$ (5) $\frac{6}{5}$ (7) $2^5\pi^5(\sqrt{2})^3$ (9) $\frac{1}{ac^4}$

III. (1) 2   (3) ⁻2   (5) $5a\sqrt{5}$ (7) $7b$ (9) 1

V. (1) $\frac{1}{2^3}$ (3) $\frac{1}{4^2}$ (5) $\frac{2}{a^3}$ (7) $\frac{1}{(2a)^3}$ (9) $\frac{1}{(2 + a)^2}$

Exercise 2.7

I. (1) 0   (3) 17   (5) 2

III. (1) The smallest element of B is 7
(3) The largest element of A is ⁻5
(5) No, because $A \cup B \neq R$

V. (1) 5   (3) 0   (5) $\sqrt{3} - 2$ (7) $\frac{2}{7}$ (9) 10   (11) 5

Chapter 3

Exercise 3.1

I. (1) 3   (3) $\sqrt{2}$ (5) 17   (7) 3   (9) $\left(\frac{-2}{3} + 4\right)$

III. (1) Multinomial   (3) Monomial   (5) Monomial
    (7) Multinomial   (9) Multinomial

V. (1) Equation   (3) Equation   (5) Not an equation
   (7) Not an equation   (9) Equation   (11) Equation
  (13) Not an equation   (15) Equation   (17) Equation
  (19) Equation

VII. (1) $\{1\}$,   (3) $\{0\}$,   (5) $\varnothing$,   (7) $\{^-2, 2\}$,   (9) $\{\frac{1}{3}\}$

Exercise 3.2

III. (1) ^-30x (3) $^-20 + 130x - 60x^2$ (5) $22x + 20$ (7) $10x + 5$
   (9) $24x + 6$ (11) 0   (13) $90x^2 + 54x + 6$ (15) $^-x - 9$
  (17) $^-11x + 6$ (19) $^-3$ (21) $30x^2 - 27x - 27$
  (23) $30x^2 - 45x - 3$ (25) $11x$ (27) $3x^2 + xy - 10y^2$
  (29) $6x^2 + 2y^2 + 8xy + 6xz + 2yz + 4x + 4y + 4z$
  (31) $x^2 + 4xy + 4y^2 + 6xz + 12yz + 9z^2$
  (33) $a^3 + 3a^2x + 3ax^2 + x^3$
  (35) $x^2 - 4a^2$ (37) $x^3 + 8$ (39) $x^3 - 3xy^2 + 2y^3$

Exercise 3.3

I. (1) $\{^-6\}$ (3) $\{1\}$ (5) $\{\frac{5}{2}\}$ (7) $\{\frac{-1}{2}\}$ (9) $\{\frac{88}{225}\}$

Exercise 3.4

I. (1) 34, 35, 36   (3) 45, 47, 49   (5) None
  (7) 35 nickels, 42 pennies   (9) 14 pennies, 19 nickels, 9 quarters
  (11) Elaine is 10 and her father is 30
  (13) Joseph is 15 and his father is 35   (15) 7:00 PM   (17) 9:00 AM
  (19) Width, 60 ft. and length, 90 ft.   (21) 142, 143, 144
  (23) $^-1, 0, 1$ (25) Yvonne, 8 mph and Sylvia, 12 mph

Exercise 3.5

I. (1) Yes   (3) Yes   (5) Yes   (7) No   (9) Yes
    (11) Yes (13) No   (15) Yes (17) Yes (19) Yes

Exercise 3.6

I. (1) $\{x:x \leq 1\}$ (3) $\{x: \frac{-1}{2} \leq x\}$ (5) U (7) $\varnothing$
    (9) $\{x: {}^-1 \leq x \leq 1\}$ (11) $\varnothing$ (13) $\{x: {}^-5 \leq x \leq 5\}$
    (15) $\{x: x \leq 5 \vee 7 \leq x\}$ (17) $\{x: 3 < x \leq 5\}$ (19) U
    (21) $\{8, 10\}$ (23) $\{x: 2 \leq x < 5\}$
    (25) $\{x: (x < 5) \vee (15 < x)\}$ (27) $\{x: 7 \leq x \vee x \leq {}^-7\}$
    (29) $\{x: \frac{3}{5} \leq x \vee x \leq {}^-1\}$
    (31) U (33) $\{x: 0 \leq x \leq 1\}$ (35) $\{x: {}^-1 < x < \frac{9}{5}\}$

Exercise 3.7

I. (1) 20 marbles   (3) 6 miles   (5) $21,600 $\leq x \leq$ $28,800
    (7) $225   (9) 18,000 pounds per sq. inch.

Chapter 4

Exercise 4.1

I. (1) $\{(2,0)\}$ (3) $\{({}^-1, 1), ({}^-1, 2), (0, 1), (0, 2), (1, 1), (1, 2)\}$
    (5) $\{(0, 0), (0, 1), (1, 0), (1, 1), (2, 0), (2, 1), \ldots\}$
    (7) $\{(0, a): a \in R\}$ (9) $\{$(Tom, Mary), (Tom, Jane),
         (Dick, Mary), (Dick, Jane), (Harry, Mary), (Harry, Jane)$\}$

III. (1) $\varnothing$ (3) $\{1\}$ (5) B (7) A (9) $\varnothing$

Exercise 4.2

I. (1) Function   (3) Function   (5) Not a function   (7) Function
    (9) Function   (11) Not a function   (13) Function
    (15) Not a function   (17) Function   (19) Not a function

Exercise 4.3

I. (1) Reals   (3) Reals   (5) Reals   (7) Reals   (9) Reals

III. (1) ⁻4 (3) 9 (5) 14 (7) ⁻65 (9) 17

 V. (1) 0 (3) 1 (5) ⁻2 (7) ⁻1 (9) 1

VII. R $\setminus$ {0}

 IX. (1) $x + h$

     (3) ⁻$2(x + h) + 1$

     (5) $(x + h)^2 - 2$

     (7) $(x + h)^3 - 1$

     (9) $(x + h)^2 + 1$

Exercise 4.5

 I. (1) Linear (3) Linear (5) Not a linear function
    (7) Not a linear function (9) Not a linear function

III. (1) $y = \left(\frac{-2}{3}\right)x + \frac{7}{3}$, slope is $\frac{-2}{3}$ (3) $y = x - 3$, slope is $\frac{1}{1}$
    (5) $y = 10x - 2$, slope is $\frac{10}{1}$
    (7) $y = \frac{-1}{5}x$, slope is $\frac{-1}{5}$ (9) $y = 2x + \frac{5}{2}$, slope is $\frac{2}{1}$

VII. (1) {(0, 2)} (3) {(0, 5)} (5) {(0, 0)}

Exercise 4.6

 I. (1) Not a quadratic function (3) Not a quadratic function
    (5) Quadratic function (7) Not a quadratic function
    (9) Quadratic function

Chapter 5

Exercise 5.1

 I. (1) ⁻2, 5 (3) 2, 1 (5) 10, ⁻3 (7) {(x, y): x = 2y + 3}
    (9) {(x, y): 2x − 3y = 4}

III. (1) $\frac{3}{2}, \frac{1}{2}$ (3) $\frac{33}{2}, \frac{121}{10}$ (5) 2, 5
    (7) $\frac{5}{2}, \frac{-5}{2}$ (9) $\frac{16}{11}, \frac{-17}{11}$

Exercise 5.2

 I. (1) ⁻3, 2 (3) ∅ (5) {(x, y): x + 4y = 3} (7) ∅
    (9) {(x, y): 2x − 3y = 4} (11) $\frac{-20}{11}, \frac{-41}{11}$
    (13) 0, 0 (15) ∅

III. (1) $\frac{18}{5}$, $\frac{2}{5}$ (3) 1, $^-2$ (5) $\{(x, y): 7x - 5y = 0\}$
(7) $\varnothing$ (9) 3, 3

Exercise 5.3

I. (1) 42 pennies, 35 nickels (3) Dianne is 12 and her father is 36
(5) Vicky is 14 and her mother is 34 (7) 8 oz. of $12 per oz.
and 12 oz. of $7 per oz. (9) 36 qt. of 4% and 42 qts. of 30%
(11) 39 years old (13) 45 (15) 12 or 24 or 36 or 48
(17) 200 mph, 250 mph (19) air speed -90 mph, wind speed $-$
45 mph

Exercise 5.4

II. (1) 8, $^-8\frac{1}{4}$ (3) 26, $^-17\frac{3}{5}$ (5) 19, 1 (7) 6, 0

Exercise 5.5

I. 20 lathes from W_1 to Lafayette, 0 lathes from W_1 to Baton Rouge,
10 lathes from W_2 to Lafayette, 25 lathes from W_2 to Baton Rouge

III. M_1 should operate 30 hours and M_2 should not operate

V. 80 acres of crop A and 20 acres of crop B

Exercise 5.6

I. (1) (1, 2, 3) (3) $(^-1, 2, 0)$ (5) (0, 0, 1) (7) (1, 0, 0)
(9) $(^-1, 1, ^-1)$

III. $(1, 0, ^-1, 2)$

Chapter 6

Exercise 6.1

II. (1) (5, 0) and (2, 0) (3) (0, 0) and $(^-10, 0)$
(5) $(^-4, 0)$ and (3, 0) (7) $(^-6, 0)$ and $(^-2, 0)$
(9) (0, 0) and (5, 0)

Exercise 6.2

I. (1) $6x^2 - 6x + 21$ (3) $^-15ax^4 + ^-25x^3 + 35x^2 + 20x$
(5) $^-2x^2y + ^-6xy^2 + 2x^3y + 8x^2y^2 + ^-14xy$ (7) $9x^2 - 1$

(9) $9x^2 - 6x + 1$ (11) $9x^2 - 4$ (13) $25x^2 + 40x + 16$
(15) $1 - 49x^2$ (17) $16x^2 + 8x + 1$ (19) $x^2 + 7x + 6$
(21) $5x^2 - 13x + 6$ (23) $6x^2 + 7x - 49$ (25) $8x^2 + 35x - 25$
(27) $3x^2 + 5x - 12$ (29) $9x^2 - 6x + 18xy - 12y$

II. (1) $7(x^3 - 3x^2 + 2x + 4)$ (3) $11x(x^2 + 3x - 5)$
 (5) $(x + 5)(x - 5)$ (7) $(3x + 4y)(3x - 4y)$
 (9) $32(x + 2y)(x - 2y)$ (11) $(x + 2)(x + 2)$
 (13) $(5x + 1)(5x + 1)$ (15) $(x - 6)(x - 6)$
 (17) $(x + 3)(x + 1)$ (19) $(2x - 1)(x + 2)$
 (21) $(2x - 3)(2x - 3)$ (23) $(2x - 1)(2x - 9)$
 (25) $(4x + 1)(x + 9)$ (27) $(x + 1)(4x + 9)$
 (29) $2x(3x - 2)(x + 2)$

Exercise 6.3

I. (1) $\{5, {}^-5\}$ (3) $\left\{\frac{4}{3}, \frac{-4}{3}\right\}$ (5) $\{2, {}^-2\}$ (7) $\{{}^-2\}$ (9) $\left\{\frac{-1}{5}\right\}$
 (11) $\{6\}$ (13) $\{{}^-1, {}^-3\}$ (15) $\left\{\frac{3}{2}\right\}$ (17) $\left\{\frac{1}{2}, \frac{9}{2}\right\}$
 (19) $\left\{\frac{4}{9}, 1\right\}$

III. (1) 5 or $^-5$ (3) $\frac{4}{3}$ or $\frac{-4}{3}$ (5) 2 or $^-2$ (7) $^-2$ (9) $\frac{-1}{5}$
 (11) 6 (13) $^-1$ or $^-3$ (15) $\frac{3}{2}$ (17) $\frac{1}{2}$ or $\frac{9}{2}$ (19) $\frac{4}{9}$ or 1

V. (1) $\dfrac{2x - 3}{(x - 1)(3x - 2)}$ (3) $\dfrac{x + y}{2x - y}$ (5) $\dfrac{(x - 3y)(x - 3y)}{(x + y)(x + y)}$
 (7) $\dfrac{(x + 2y)(x + 2y)}{(2x - y)(2x - y)}$ (9) $\dfrac{(x + 4)(x - 3)(2x - 5)(2x + 3)}{(2x + 5)(2x - 3)(x - 4)(x + 3)}$

Exercise 6.4

I. (1) $\{\sqrt{5}, {}^-\sqrt{5}\}$ (3) $\{2 + \sqrt{6}, 2 - \sqrt{6}\}$ (5) $\{{}^-1 + \sqrt{6}, {}^-1 - \sqrt{6}\}$
 (7) $\left\{\frac{1}{2} + \frac{\sqrt{3}}{2}, \frac{1}{2} - \frac{\sqrt{3}}{2}\right\}$ (9) $\varnothing$

Exercise 6.5

I. (1) $\{3, 1\}$ (3) $\{{}^-1, 2\}$ (5) $\left\{\frac{1 + \sqrt{17}}{4}, \frac{1 - \sqrt{17}}{4}\right\}$
 (7) $\left\{\frac{1}{3}, {}^-2\right\}$ (9) $\varnothing$ (11) $\left\{\frac{3 + 3\sqrt{21}}{10}, \frac{3 - 3\sqrt{21}}{10}\right\}$
 (13) $\left\{\frac{-3}{2}, \frac{2}{3}\right\}$ (15) $\varnothing$ (17) $\varnothing$ (19) $\left\{\frac{5 + \sqrt{2}}{3}, \frac{5 - \sqrt{2}}{3}\right\}$

Exercise 6.6

I. (1) 9 yrs. old   (3) Donald has 6 pencils and Bud has 31 pencils
 (5) William's speed is 8 mph and Homer's speed is 3 mph

(7) 20 problems   (9) 29 miles the first day and 35 miles altogether
(11) Velma worked 10 and Laureen worked 4
(13) He might have been, but ⁻9 could also be the number
(15) 0 and 6   (17) Vertex is $\left(\frac{5}{16}, 101\frac{9}{16}\right)$ (19) 10   (21) 210

III.   (1) $\{x: {}^{-}1 < x < 3\}$ (3) $\{x: 0 < x < 5\}$

(5) $\{x: {}^{-}5 \le x \le 4\}$ (7) $\{x: (x < {}^{-}3) \lor (7 < x)\}$

(9) $\{x: (x \le 0) \lor (3 \le x)\}$

Exercise 6.7

I.   (1) 3, 1   (3) 0, 1   (5) 2   (7) 9   (9) 0

Exercise 6.8

I.   (1) $\{(3, 0), ({}^{-}2, {}^{-}5)\}$ (3) $\{(0, 1), ({}^{-}3, 49)\}$
(5) $\varnothing$ (7) $\{(5, 31), (1, 3)\}$ (9) $\{(1, 6), ({}^{-}3, 10)\}$

Exercise 6.9

I.   (1) $(y + a)(y^2 - y + a^2)$
(3) $(3a - 2b)(9a^2 + 6ab + 4b^2)$
(5) $2(2a + 3b^2)(4a^2 - 6ab^2 + 9b^4)$
(7) $(a^2 + 4b^2)(a^4 - 4a^2b^2 + 16b^4)$
(9) $[(x - 1) + 2y][(x - 1)^2 - 2y(x - 1) + 4y^2]$
(11) $(a - 2b)(a + 2b)(a^2 + 4b^2)$
(13) $(a^2 - 2b^2)(a^2 + 2b^2)$
(15) $(x^2 + 1 - y)(x^2 + 1 + y)$
(17) $(x^2 + 1 - y)[(x^2 + 1)^2 + y(x^2 + 1) + y^2]$
(19) $[(x + a - 2) - 3by][(x + a - 2) + 3by]$
(21) $(a + 2)(x + 2y)$
(23) $(x - y)(x + y + 5)$
(25) $(x - y)(x + y - 8)$
(27) $(x - y)(x^2 + xy + y^2 + 3)$
(29) $(3x + y)(9x^2 - 3xy + y^2 + 2)$

III.   (1) $\dfrac{x + y}{x}$
(3) $\dfrac{a^2 - 3a + 10}{2a^2 - 7a + 15}$
(5) $\dfrac{2x + 2y - 1}{y}$
(7) $\dfrac{2a - 1}{a^2 - 1}$
(9) $\dfrac{2x^3 - 2x^2 + x + 2}{x^3 + 1}$

Chapter 7

Exercise 7.1

I. (1) $a = {}^-7$, $d = 5$ (3) $c = {}^-6$, $d = {}^-3$ (5) $6 \neq 7$
   (7) $a = 10$, $b = 5$ (9) $a = \frac{-10}{3}$, $b = \frac{-11}{6}$

III. (1) $83 + 66i$ (3) $\left(\frac{35}{2}\right)i$ (5) 58 (7) -10 (9) $5 + 12i$

Exercise 7.2

I. (1) -5 (3) $\left(\frac{-6}{7}\right)i$ (5) $-1 + {}^-3i$ (7) $5 + {}^-3i$
   (9) $\frac{6}{5} + \left(\frac{2}{3}\right)i$ (11) $0 + 0i$

III. (1) $\frac{3}{25} + \left(\frac{4}{25}\right)i$ (3) $\frac{-7}{625} + \left(\frac{-24}{625}\right)i$

Exercise 7.3

I. (1) $-1 + 5i$ (3) $-6 + 10i$ (5) $-5 + i$ (7) $-4i$ (9) $3 + 6i$

Exercise 7.4

I. (1) $\frac{3}{4} + \left(\frac{\sqrt{7}}{4}\right)i$ or $\frac{3}{4} - \left(\frac{\sqrt{7}}{4}\right)i$ (3) $\frac{1}{2} + \left(\frac{\sqrt{23}}{2}\right)i$
   or $\frac{1}{2} - \left(\frac{\sqrt{23}}{2}\right)i$ (5) $\left(\frac{-7 + \sqrt{13}}{2}\right)$ or $\left(\frac{-7 - \sqrt{13}}{2}\right)$
   (7) $\frac{-5}{6} + \frac{\sqrt{13}}{6}$ or $\frac{-5}{6} - \frac{\sqrt{13}}{6}$ (9) 1 or -5
   (11) $\left(\frac{-3 + \sqrt{5}}{2}\right)$ or $\left(\frac{-3 - \sqrt{5}}{2}\right)$ (13) $\sqrt{2}\,i$ or $-\sqrt{2}\,i$
   (15) 0 or $\frac{7}{3}$ (17) $3i$ or $-3i$ (19) $3 + \sqrt{11}$ or $3 - \sqrt{11}$

Chapter 8

Exercise 8.1

I. (1) $a^{5/3}$ (3) $(2a)^{3/7}$ (5) $(3a)^{5/3}$ (7) $5^{7/6}$ (9) $2^{5/6}$

III. (1) $2\sqrt{2}$ (3) $5\sqrt{3}$ (5) $2a^2\sqrt[3]{2}$ (7) $8\sqrt{2b}$ (9) $\frac{2}{3}$

   (11) $\frac{2a}{3b^2}\sqrt[5]{b^4}$ (13) $\sqrt[5]{5}$ (15) $\sqrt{2}$ (17) $8a\sqrt{2a}$ (19) $5(a + b)$.

Exercise 8.2

I. (1) $7\sqrt{2}$ (3) $14\sqrt{3}$ (5) $\frac{-1}{6}\sqrt[3]{3}$ (7) $\sqrt[6]{2}\,(1 + \sqrt{2})$
   (9) $\sqrt[4]{3}\,(2 + |a|)$.

V.   (1) $a^9b^3c^5$ (3) $(1 + b)$ bc (5) ac^2 (7) $\frac{(x + y)^3}{xy}$ (9) $36xy^{12/5}$

Exercise 8.3

I.   (1) $x^7 + 7x^6y + 21x^5y^2 + 35x^4y^3 + 35x^3y^4 + 21x^2y^5 + 7xy^6$
$+ y^7$.
(5) $x^7 - 7x^6y + 21x^5y^2 - 35x^4y^3 + 35x^3y^4 - 21x^2y^5 + 7xy^6$
$- y^7$.
(9) $81x^8 + 108x^6 + 54x^4 + 12x^2 + 1$.
(13) $\frac{81a^4}{16} - \frac{27a^3}{2} + \frac{27a^2}{2} - 6a + 1$.
(17) $8a^6 + 12a^4x + 6a^2x^2 + x^3$.
III. (1) 1.040604   (3) 1.061520

Chapter 9

Exercise 9.1

I.   (1) Quotient: $x^3 + 2x + 5$
Remainder: $8x + 4$
(3) Quotient: $3x^4 + 10x^3 + 36x^2 + 126x + 440$
Remainder: 3087
(5) Quotient: $2x^5 - x^2 + 1$
Remainder: 3
(7) Quotient: $8x^5 + 23x^3 + 70x$
Remainder: $209x$

Exercise 9.2

I.   (1) Yes   (3) Yes   (5) No   (7) No

Exercise 9.3

I.   (1) 1, multiplicity 3; $^-2$, multiplicity 2; $^-3$, multiplicity 1.
(3) 3, multiplicity 4; $^-2$, multiplicity 3.
(5) 7, multiplicity 1; $^-2$, multiplicity 2; $^-1$ multiplicity 3;
0, multiplicity 2.
III. (1) 1, $^-1$, $^-2$ (3) $^-1$, $\frac{(7 + \sqrt{65})}{4}$, $\frac{(7 - \sqrt{65})}{4}$
(5) $^-1$, $\frac{3}{2}$, $\frac{(-1 + \sqrt{3}\,i)}{2}$, $\frac{(-1 - \sqrt{3}\,i)}{2}$ (7) 1, $^-2$, $2i$, ^-2i
(9) 0, 1, $\frac{(-7 + \sqrt{31}\,i)}{10}$, $\frac{(-7 - \sqrt{31}\,i)}{10}$
V.   (1) No   (3) No

Exercise 9.4

I. (1) One zero between $^-2$ and $^-1$.
   One zero between $^-1$ and 0.
   One zero between 2 and 3.
   (3) One zero at $^-1$.
   One zero between $^-1$ and 0.
   One zero between 1 and 2.
   (5) One zero at $^-1$.
   One zero between 0 and 1.
   One zero between 3 and 4.
   (7) One zero at $^-2$.
   (9) One zero between 0 and 1.

Exercise 9.5

I. 2.17
III. $^-1.29$
V. 1.35 and 4.06

Chapter 10

Exercise 10.4

I. (1) 2   (7) 6
   (3) 9   (9) 8
   (5) 7

Chapter 11

Exercise 11.1

III. (1) Commutative group   (3) Not a group
   (5) Commutative group

Exercise 11.2

III. (1) $\begin{pmatrix} 1\ 2\ 3\ 4 \\ 2\ 3\ 1\ 4 \end{pmatrix}$ (3) $\begin{pmatrix} 1\ 2\ 3\ 4\ 5 \\ 4\ 3\ 2\ 5\ 1 \end{pmatrix}$ (5) $\begin{pmatrix} 1\ 2\ 3\ 4\ 5\ 6 \\ 3\ 2\ 1\ 6\ 5\ 4 \end{pmatrix}$

Index